SIGRID ENGELBRECHT

DER KLEINE COACH

Lass los,
was deinem Glück
im Weg steht

Warum halten wir eigentlich fest?

Seite 16

Spieglein, Spieglein an der Wand

Seite 6

Loslassen, was nicht glücklich macht

Seite 42

Was tun, wenn ich feststecke?

Seite 108

Loslassen,
das sagt sich so leicht …

• • • wo es doch so einiges gibt, woran wir uns gerne festhalten: Ansprüche an uns selbst und an andere, Lebenserfahrungen, Vorurteile, Erwartungen, treue Gewohnheiten … und vieles, vieles mehr.

IN DIESEM BUCH GEHT ES DARUM, das loszulassen, was Ihnen nicht guttut und Ihre Weiterentwicklung behindert. Ist das überhaupt ein Problem? Wenn ich etwas loslassen will, schreite ich dann nicht sofort zur Tat nach dem Motto: Gefahr erkannt, Gefahr gebannt? Doch so einfach scheint es nicht zu sein, denn sonst hätte sich jeder von uns zügig von vielen Dingen befreit, die das Weiterkommen im Job, das Glück in der Partnerschaft oder ganz einfach die Lebensfreude blockieren. Manchmal sind die Zusammenhänge zwischen Festhalten und Scheitern auch gar nicht klar. So wundern wir uns nur, uns erneut in einer vertrauten Sackgasse wiederzufinden, obwohl wir diesmal »wirklich alles ganz anders« machen wollten oder sich die Situation völlig unterschiedlich von den bisher gemachten Erfahrungen darzustellen schien.

Doch es gibt Wege aus einem solchen Verharren im Status Quo. Dieses Buch zeigt Ihnen, wie Sie klassische Entwicklungsbremsen Schritt für Schritt entschärfen und alternative, bessere Wege einschlagen können.

Am Anfang steht das »Erkenne dich selbst«. Mit einem ausführlichen
Selbsttest ermitteln Sie zunächst Ihr aktuelles »Blockade-Profil«.
Im darauf folgenden Kapitel erfahren Sie mehr über mögliche Ursachen.
Was trägt dazu bei, dass wir häufig auf Nummer sicher gehen wollen?
Warum sträuben wir uns in bestimmten Bereichen gegen Veränderungen,
obgleich sie doch zum eigenen Besten wären? Ein Einblick in die ent-
sprechenden Zusammenhänge schafft Aha-Erlebnisse, hilft dabei,
sich selbst besser zu verstehen, stärkt das Selbstvertrauen und fördert die
Motivation zur Veränderung.
Und dann geht es richtig los: Was können Sie tun, um Blockaden aus dem
Weg zu räumen und beherzt neue Wege zu gehen? Zahlreiche Übungen
und Tipps für den Alltag ermuntern zum Ausprobieren und dazu,
das Richtige für Ihren individuellen Weg auszuwählen: das, was zu Ihnen
und Ihrem »Blockade«-Profil passt und Sie am effektivsten in Richtung
Loslassen führt. Manche der Übungen und Tipps sind speziell auf ein
bestimmtes Profil zugeschnitten, andere wiederum unterstützen jeden
Typ dabei, besser loslassen zu können. Entsprechende Hinweise dazu
finden Sie dann jeweils im Text.
Im Schlusskapitel erfahren Sie, wie Sie bei Rückfallgefahr am besten mit
Ihrem »inneren Schweinehund« umgehen und bei der Stange bleiben.
Jede tiefer gehende Veränderung braucht Zeit und Training, damit das
Neue zur Gewohnheit werden kann. Dabei will der »kleine Coach« Ihnen
als Begleiter zur Seite stehen – ich wünsche Ihnen viel Erfolg auf Ihrem
Weg zu neuen Erfahrungen!

Sigrid Engelbrecht

Spieglein, **Spieglein** an der Wand

Festhalten hat viele Facetten
... und wie sieht es bei Ihnen aus?

NATÜRLICH KENNEN SIE IHRE BAUSTELLEN ... ODER?
Sie wissen wahrscheinlich schon recht gut, welche Vorzüge Sie auszeichnen und was Ihre empfindlichen Bereiche sind. Jeder von uns hat – bei aller Selbsterkenntnis – jedoch immer auch »blinde Flecken«, also Denk- und Reaktionsmuster, die ganz unbewusst ablaufen, die aber deswegen nicht weniger intensiv das Verhalten prägen. Manche dieser Muster haben Sie vielleicht auch noch nie unter dem Gesichtspunkt »Festhalten oder Loslassen« betrachtet.

Im nachfolgenden Test lernen Sie das, woran Sie gewöhnlich festhalten, (noch) besser kennen. Hundertprozentige Typzuschreibungen sind dabei aber eher selten. Meist stehen nur zwei oder drei Aspekte im Vordergrund, während Sie mit anderen Dingen dann relativ wenig am Hut haben. Wichtig ist, die jeweiligen blockierenden Muster nicht mit Stumpf und Stiel ausrotten zu wollen, sondern sich zu vergegenwärtigen, dass darin auch Qualitäten beheimatet sind. Im Vordergrund steht, künftig neu entscheiden zu können, wo die »alten« Muster beibehalten werden sollten und in welchen anderen Situationen Sie diese zugunsten neuer Verhaltensweisen loslassen wollen.

✓ TEST   Erkennen Sie sich selbst

*Nehmen Sie zu **jeder** der folgenden Aussagen Stellung und entscheiden Sie, inwieweit diese auf Sie ganz persönlich zutrifft. Tragen Sie dazu jeweils eine Zahl zwischen 1 und 5 in das entsprechende Feld ein.*

5   Punkte: stimmt genau

4   Punkte: stimmt weitgehend

3   Punkte: stimmt ein bisschen

2   Punkte: stimmt eher nicht

1   Punkt: stimmt weitgehend nicht

0   Punkte: stimmt überhaupt nicht

Ich bemühe mich meistens, es anderen Menschen möglichst recht zu machen.   **D**

Ich denke häufig: Eigentlich habe ich Besseres verdient.   **N**

Wenn ich eine Aufgabe begonnen habe, halte ich bis zum Ende durch, auch wenn mir während der Arbeit Zweifel daran kommen.   **S**

Den meisten, die ich kenne, geht es besser als mir.   **V**

Wenn mir etwas an anderen nicht gefällt, kann ich meine Meinung nicht sagen und Kritik nur schwer äußern.   **D**

Wenn mir etwas misslingt, dann kann ich mir das ganz schlecht verzeihen.   **P**

Es fällt mir schwer, Wichtiges von Unwichtigem zu unterscheiden.   **S**

Ich fühle mich häufig verkannt.   **N**

Jemandem, der mir geschadet hat, werde ich das niemals vergeben.   **V**

Ich frage mich oft, was andere von mir denken.   **D**

Ich vergleiche mich eigentlich ständig mit anderen.   **P**

Größere Projekte wachsen mir manchmal über den Kopf, weil ich mich in Details verbeiße.   **P**

Weil ich Schreckliches erlebt habe, kann ich nicht glücklich sein.   **V**

Ich habe oft Angst, mich falsch
zu entscheiden. S

Die Anerkennung anderer ist
mir sehr wichtig. D

Ich bin selten richtig zufrieden
mit mir. P

Wenn ich unfair behandelt werde,
ist mir der ganze Tag verdorben. D

Wenn mich jemand gekränkt hat,
denke ich noch lange danach
häufig daran und würde es ihm
am liebsten heimzahlen. V

Ich bewege mich gerne in Kreisen,
zu denen nicht jeder Zutritt hat. N

Bei Schnäppchen muss ich zu-
greifen, auch wenn ich die Sachen
gar nicht wirklich brauche. S

Ich fühle mich häufig unter Druck. P

Es fällt mir schwer, eigene
Vorstellungen durchzusetzen. D

Wenn mir jemand ins Wort fällt,
fällt es mir schwer, ihn aufzufor-
dern, mich ausreden zu lassen. D

Ich mache am liebsten alles selbst,
denn dann weiß ich, dass es
ordentlich gemacht wird. P

Einen sicheren Arbeitsplatz würde
ich behalten, auch wenn mir die
Arbeit nicht gefällt. S

Es gibt wenig Menschen, die ich
wirklich gern um mich habe. N

Mir ist eine friedliche entspannte
Atmosphäre wichtiger, als kritisch
meine Meinung zu sagen. D

Es gibt Personen oder Situationen,
die ich meide, weil alte Erinnerungen
hochkommen würden. V

Ich habe oft Angst, mein Partner
könnte mich verlassen. S

Menschen, die ungenau arbeiten,
nerven mich. P

Ich leiste mir gerne Dinge, die aus-
gefallen sind und zu denen andere
keinen Zugang haben. N

Es fällt mir generell schwer, mich
von jemandem zu trennen. S

✓ TEST

Es fällt mir sehr schwer, Gewohnheiten aufzugeben, auch wenn ich weiß, dass sie mir schaden.   S

Ich fühle mich leicht missachtet, angegriffen oder abgelehnt.   V

Ich lege an alles, was ich tue, hohe Maßstäbe an.   P

Ich sorge mich sehr darum, wie ich auf andere wirke.   D

Ich empfinde mein bisheriges Leben rückblickend als deprimierend.   V

Ich träume oft von einem besseren Leben, das meinen Ansprüchen wirklich gerecht wird.   N

Ich ärgere mich häufig über mich selbst.   P

Ich habe oft Angst, ich könnte meinen Arbeitsplatz verlieren.   S

Nur mit dem idealen Partner gehe ich eine Beziehung ein.   N

Sich im Job eine Blöße zu geben ist eine Katastrophe.   P

Wenn das Leben mir nicht so übel mitgespielt hätte, könnte ich ein glücklicher Mensch sein.   V

Ich fühle mich den meisten Menschen, die ich kenne, insgeheim überlegen.   N

Statussymbole sind mir durchaus wichtig.   N

Ich fühle mich in unvertrauten Situationen unwohl.   S

Ich kann anderen nur schwer etwas abschlagen.   D

Ich habe oft Rachegedanken.   V

Bewundert zu werden, macht mich richtig glücklich.   N

Ich hatte eine schreckliche Kindheit, und so etwas prägt einen doch fürs ganze Leben.   V

Zählen Sie nun Ihre Punkte in den einzelnen Buchstaben-Kategorien zusammen:

| GESAMT | P Punkte | D Punkte | S Punkte | N Punkte | V Punkte |

Wie sieht Ihr Profil aus? Die Auswertung

Je höher Ihre Punktzahl in den einzelnen Kategorien ist, desto ausgeprägter ist das jeweilige Profil. Wie das im einzelnen aussieht, erfahren Sie auf den folgenden Seiten. Und dies ist die Bedeutung der Buchstaben:

P = Miss Perfect
D = Everybody's Darling
S = Die treue Seele
N = Die heimliche Prinzessin
V = Die chronische Vergangenheitsbewältigerin

Miss Perfect

Erfolg haben heißt für Sie: Perfektion. Als »Miss Perfect« stellen Sie sehr hohe Ansprüche an sich selbst. Sie haben eine genaue Vorstellung davon, wie Sie selbst zu sein und wie Sie sich zu verhalten haben und auch davon, wie Aufgaben zu erledigen sind. Daran messen Sie sich eigentlich ständig, und da Sie die Messlatte sehr hoch gehängt haben, sind Sie selten wirklich zufrieden. Meist haben Sie die Kritiker-Brille auf und bemerken sofort das sprichwörtliche Haar in der Suppe. Infolge des hohen Anspruchs sind Sie häufig angespannt und ärgern sich leicht über sich und andere. Sie sind sehr aktiv und tun sich schwer damit, Arbeit zu delegieren. Dies würde Ihnen nämlich auch die Kontrolle darüber entziehen, dass die Dinge in Ihrem Sinne erledigt werden. Gelegentlich stehen Sie sich mit Ihrem Anspruch selbst im Weg und verlieren zugunsten von Details das große Ganze aus dem Auge. Sie sind nie wirklich »fertig«, denn es gibt aus Ihrer kritischen Sicht heraus immer noch etwas, was getan werden könnte. Andere sollen nichts an Ihnen und Ihrer Leistung auszusetzen haben, Sie wollen sich keine Blöße geben. Ihr großes Plus: Sie sind gewissenhaft, geben sich nicht mit Halbheiten zufrieden und setzen sich aktiv für gute Ergebnisse ein.

Loslassen bedeutet für Sie:
Die generell hohe Messlatte überall dort niedriger hängen, wo nichts wirklich Wichtiges auf dem Spiel steht; sich selbst und andere wertschätzen lernen, auch mit den jeweiligen Schwächen. Humor entwickeln, öfter mal lockerlassen, persönliche Normen entrümpeln.

Everybody's Darling

Erfolg haben heißt für Sie: Anerkennung. Beliebt zu sein, gemocht und geschätzt zu werden als Person und in dem, was Sie tun, bedeutet Ihnen sehr viel, und dafür sind Sie bereit, sich mächtig ins Zeug zu legen. Sie möchten einen guten Eindruck machen und scheuen davor zurück, Kritik auf sich zu ziehen und auch, Ihrerseits andere zu kritisieren. Andere sollen Sie nett finden und Sie mögen. Oft vergewissern Sie sich, ob Sie alles so gemacht haben, wie es gefordert wird oder wie es die anderen gerne hätten. Während Sie bei Lob und Anerkennung aufblühen, leiden Sie unter einer missgünstigen Arbeitsatmosphäre ganz besonders. Sie sind bereit, viel für andere zu tun, und freuen sich über deren Wertschätzung. Wenn Sie die Wahl hätten, eigene Vorstellungen durchzusetzen oder sympathisch zu wirken, würden Sie sich auf jeden Fall für die Sympathie entscheiden. Ihr großes Plus: Sie sind aufmerksam gegenüber anderen Menschen und ihren Bedürfnissen und können sich gut in andere einfühlen.

Loslassen bedeutet für Sie:
Zu sich selbst finden, eigene Bedürfnisse erkennen, sie ernst nehmen und erfüllen. Sich unabhängiger machen von Vorstellungen anderer. Sich abgrenzen, eigene Prioritäten setzen.

Die treue Seele

Erfolg heißt für Sie, geordnet, übersichtlich und angstfrei zu leben. Am Bewährten hängen Sie in vielen Lebensbereichen. Das kann eine bestimmte Umgebung sein, eine Beziehung, Gewohnheiten oder auch Dinge. Sie sind gerne auf der sicheren Seite. Veränderungen verunsichern Sie, und Sie möchten möglichst rasch wissen, »woran Sie sind«. Sie schätzen die Verlässlichkeit gewohnter Beziehungen. Andere sollen Sie brauchen; für diesen Wunsch sind Sie bereit, vieles hinzunehmen. Manchmal harren Sie auch in Situationen aus, von denen Sie wissen, dass sie Ihnen nicht guttun, und vermeiden eine Trennung, denn Sie sind ungern allein. Entscheidungen zu treffen erleben Sie als anstrengend und oft auch als Angst machend, denn dies bedeutet ja in der Regel, zugunsten des einen auf etwas anderes zu verzichten. Auch Besitztümer haben eine lange Verweildauer unter Ihrem Dach. Was einmal angeschafft wurde, bleibt erhalten, denn »man könnte es ja irgendwann wieder brauchen.« – Egal ob das Geschenkbänder, Kleider, Bücher, Möbel, CDs oder Werkzeuge sind.

Ihr großes Plus: Sie sind zuverlässig und sorgen gut für sich und die Menschen, die Ihnen wichtig sind.

Loslassen bedeutet für Sie:
Sich von Überlebtem trennen lernen. Es gilt, das Gefühl für Ihren Wert und für eigene Grenzen zu stärken, Mut zu entwickeln und sich Ziele zu setzen. Ihre zentrale Herausforderung heißt: sich den Ängsten vor Veränderung zu stellen und bewusst – auch schmerzhafte – Entscheidungen zu treffen.

Die heimliche Prinzessin

Erfolg heißt für Sie: Bestätigung, dass Sie etwas ganz Besonderes sind. Das steht Ihnen doch zu, oder? Sie möchten herausragen aus dem Mittelmaß und umgeben sich gerne mit Statussymbolen und Ungewöhnlichem. Bei anderen Menschen sind Sie sehr anspruchsvoll und fühlen sich heimlich den meisten überlegen. Sie stehen gerne im Mittelpunkt und genießen Bewunderung.

Oft stellen Sie sich ein ideales Leben vor, in dem Sie in Ihrer Umgebung »wirklich wer sind«. Andere sollen Sie interessant finden. Irgendwann sollen Ihre Träume von Größe und Bedeutung Wirklichkeit werden – ohne dass Sie allzu viel dafür tun müssen. Sich in den Niederungen des Alltags abzumühen ist Ihre Sache nicht. Die Gegenwart sehen Sie stets nur als eine Vorstufe zu einer glorreichen Zukunft. Sie träumen gerne von all dem, was Ihnen eines Tages möglich sein wird. Manchmal wären Sie auch gerne jemand anders, und dann könnten Sie erst recht ganz andere Dinge tun … Doch allmählich reift die Einsicht, dass schon viel Zeit vergangen ist, ohne dass Sie Ihren Wünschen nähergekommen sind.

Ihr großes Plus: Sie sind von sich selbst überzeugt und haben ausgeprägte Vorlieben und Abneigungen; Sie können sich gut abgrenzen.

Loslassen bedeutet für Sie: Ihren Anspruch absoluter Außergewöhnlichkeit zu mildern, zu erkennen, dass andere Menschen auf ihre Art genauso einzigartig sind wie Sie und dass die Welt Ihnen nichts schuldet.

Die chronische Vergangenheitsbewältigerin

Erfolg heißt für Sie: endlich Genugtuung erfahren. Sie können auf ein großes Reservoir an erlittenem Unrecht, an Zurückweisungen und Kränkungen zurückgreifen – Dinge,

> *»Ich kann freilich nicht sagen, ob es besser wird, wenn es anders wird; aber so viel kann ich sagen, es muss anders werden, wenn es gut werden soll.«*
>
> Georg Christoph Lichtenberg

die Sie seit Jahren, zum Teil schon seit Jahrzehnten beschäftigen. Und immer wieder kommen neue hinzu. Sie wünschen sich, dass andere Anteil daran nehmen, was Ihnen widerfahren ist, und mit Ihnen fühlen. Bitterkeit und der Wunsch nach Vergeltung beherrschen oft, ohne dass Sie dies wirklich wollen, Ihre Gedanken. Sie träumen davon, dass all jene, die Ihnen geschadet haben, irgendwann die ausgleichende Gerechtigkeit ereilt. Doch leider geschieht dies nur selten und so müssen Sie oft mit ansehen, wie es genau den Menschen besonders gut zu gehen scheint, die es am wenigsten verdienen – was Ihre Stimmung natürlich nicht verbessert. Oft denken Sie darüber nach, wie anders Ihr Leben hätte verlaufen können, hätten Sie nur bessere Startbedingungen vorgefunden. Aber jetzt, so sind Sie überzeugt, sind die Weichen gestellt und es lässt sich kaum noch etwas ändern. Jede neue Kränkung ist Ihnen eine Bestätigung dafür.

Ihr großes Plus: Sie haben ein sensibles Gerechtigkeitsempfinden und scheuen nicht davor zurück, sich auch mit unangenehmen Themen und Gefühlen zu beschäftigen.

Loslassen bedeutet für Sie: Die Vergangenheit akzeptieren und Lehren aus ihr ziehen zugunsten von mehr Lebensgenuss im Hier und Jetzt; denen, die Sie einmal verletzt haben, vergeben können.

Haben Sie sich wiedergefunden?

Vermutlich haben Sie Ihre typischen Verhaltensweisen in mehr als einem Profil erkannt, denn schließlich ist niemand zum Beispiel nur perfektionistisch oder rein vergangenheitsorientiert. Die Herausforderungen, die sich Ihnen in Sachen Loslassen stellen, sind nun recht klar. Doch warum fällt es so schwer, das Erkannte umzusetzen? Warum wir so gerne festhalten, erfahren Sie im folgenden Kapitel.

Warum halten wir eigentlich fest?

Festhalten und Loslassen – einige *grundsätzliche* Überlegungen …

FESTHALTEN IST AN SICH NICHTS SCHLECHTES, was Ihnen jeder Bergsteiger gerne bestätigen wird. Doch auch beim Bergsteigen gilt, genauso wie im Alltagsleben: Festhalten und Loslassen sind in gleicher Weise wichtig. Wenn Sie am Berg stur festkleben und nicht loslassen, um weiterzuklettern, werden Sie Stunden an der gleichen Felsnase verbringen. Wenn Sie sich hingegen vorschnell lösen, noch bevor Sie sicheren Tritt gefasst haben, dann verlieren Sie die Balance und stürzen unweigerlich ab.

Festhalten ist also tatsächlich nichts an sich Schlechtes und Loslassen ist nicht automatisch etwas Gutes. Es kommt auf den Zusammenhang und auf die konkreten Umstände an, auf Ihre persönliche Einschätzung und vor allem auch auf Ihre Gefühle. Loslassen ist kein Selbstzweck. Weshalb sollten Sie nicht an den Dingen »festhalten« wollen, die sich bewährt haben, die Ihnen hilfreich sind, die Ihnen Freude machen? Wie Sie im Selbsttest ab Seite 8 gesehen haben, gibt es bei jedem typischen Verhaltensmuster genug Positives, das sich zu bewahren lohnt. Es geht also nur darum, sich langsam aber sicher von denjenigen Dingen und Umständen zu lösen, die Ihnen nicht guttun. Aber auch das ist kein Muss, sondern Ihre Entscheidung!

Was Loslassen bedeutet und was nicht

Beim Loslassen geht es also nicht darum, generell Verzicht üben zu müssen, sich jeglichen Genuss zu versagen, um künftig ein »edles«, karges, entbehrungsreiches Leben zu führen. Es geht auch nicht darum, einen Menschen, eine Sache oder ein Verhalten um jeden Preis aus dem eigenen Leben entfernen zu »sollen«, wenn Sie innerlich gar nicht bereit dazu sind. Eine Sache verbissen und mit der Einstellung »Ich muss das jetzt« aufgeben zu wollen, ist so wenig Erfolg versprechend, wie der Versuch, auf Kommando witzig zu sein. Sie müssen nichts loslassen. Sie dürfen alles festhalten. Sie dürfen sich Zeit nehmen, die Dinge reifen zu lassen. Sie selbst entscheiden, wo Sie auch künftig festhalten wollen und wo nicht mehr. Sie sind der Boss. Niemand hat Ihnen in Ihr Leben hineinzuregieren. Auch der »kleine Coach« will Ihnen hier nichts vorschreiben, sondern hat die Aufgabe, Ihnen als starker Rat- und Impulsgeber mit Ideen, Tipps und Angeboten zur Seite zu stehen.

Loslassen heißt aktiv werden

Um den Begriff des Loslassens ranken sich verschiedenste Vorstellungen, Interpretationen und auch Missverständnisse. Verglichen mit Qualitäten wie Erwerben, Kämpfen und Durchhalten haftet dem Loslassen oft etwas Defensives, fast schon Fatalistisches an. Viele Menschen, die eigentlich loslassen möchten, bringen damit Begriffe wie Abschied, Scheitern, Verzicht oder Verlust in Verbindung.
Das häufigste Missverständnis ist, Loslassen mit Resignation gleichzusetzen, damit, sich ergeben in sein Schicksal zu fügen (oder dem, was man dafür hält), garniert mit dem Stoßseufzer: »Es ist halt so wie es ist, da kann man eh nichts machen.«

Der Reigen der Abschiedsängste

- Angst vor dem Prozess des Loslassens selbst, vor allem vor schmerzlichen Gefühlen, die damit verbunden sein könnten
- Angst, die falsche Entscheidung getroffen zu haben, und dies hinterher zu bereuen
- Angst, durch ungewohntes Verhalten angreifbar zu werden
- Angst vor der Leere danach
- Angst vor dem Neuen, mit dem man sich nach dem Loslassen vielleicht auseinandersetzen muss
- Angst, sich Kritik und Missbilligung auszusetzen
- Angst, mit einer Entscheidung ganz allein dazustehen
- Angst davor, dass die Situation eher schlimmer als besser wird
- Angst vor dem Scheitern, wenn der neu eingeschlagene Weg die Erwartungen nicht erfüllt
- Angst zu versagen
- Angst, infolge einer Entscheidung nicht mehr geliebt, gemocht, akzeptiert zu werden
- Angst vor Kontrollverlust
- Angst davor, Schuldgefühle und ein schlechtes Gewissen zu bekommen oder sich zu schämen
- Angst vor der Erkenntnis, dass das Problem gar nicht da lag, wo man es vermutet hatte
- Angst davor, sich täppisch, dumm und unbeholfen anzustellen, wenn man Neuland betritt

Doch so ist Loslassen nicht gemeint. Resignation lässt keine Offenheit, keine Kreativität, keine Neugier zu – und somit keine anderen Wege. Wer resigniert, kapituliert. Aufgeben birgt keine Entwicklungschancen, sondern verleitet dazu, sich als Opfer der Umstände zu sehen: Machtlos, wehrlos, chancenlos.

Sich auf Neues einlassen

Die Opferhaltung liegt dem Loslassen völlig fern. Es hat nichts mit Selbstmitleid, Selbstkasteiung oder Selbstverleugnung zu tun, ganz im Gegenteil: Man lässt etwas bewusst los, um Kopf und Hände frei zu haben für neue Wege und neue Erlebnisse. Dazu gehört die Offenheit, sich auf Unbekanntes einzulassen, die Neugier darauf, eine Erfahrung zu machen, die Kreativität, Ungewöhnliches für sich selbst in Betracht zu ziehen. Es ist ein spannender Weg, dem »Eigentlichen« immer näher zu kommen – analog der Michelangelo zugeschriebenen Metapher: »Die Statue ist bereits im Marmor verborgen – der Künstler bringt sie nur zum Vorschein« – nämlich, indem er alles herausmeißelt und abräumt, was nicht zur Form der Statue gehört.

Wer loslässt, hat Kopf und Hände frei

Sie befreien sich von Unnötigem und Überflüssigem, von Dingen, die nicht mehr wirklich zu Ihnen gehören und lassen gelebtes Leben hinter sich, um sich anderen Möglichkeiten zuzuwenden, die Ihnen ein Plus an innerem Frieden oder an Erfüllung und Zufriedenheit bringen. Loslassen heißt: sich bewusst lösen, sich öffnen und neugierig sein, was auf den kleinen oder großen Abschied folgt. Dies braucht natürlich auch Mut, denn Sie haben nur die Garantie, dass das, was dann kommt, eine andere Qualität hat, als das, wovon Sie sich verabschiedet haben – ein »Mehr« oder »Besser« kann Ihnen niemand versprechen.

Loslassen hat also viel mit Lebendigkeit und Leichtigkeit zu tun. Mit dem Ablegen überlebter oder einengender Vorstellungen über sich selbst, Ihre Mitmenschen oder das Leben generell befreien Sie sich auch von entsprechenden Gewohnheiten, Lebensumständen, Dingen usw., die vielleicht bislang Ihre Lebensqualität eingeschränkt hatten. Darin liegen viele Chancen. Wer nur in dem, was er kennt, verharrt, kann die Entwicklungsimpulse, die das Loslassen bietet, nicht wahrnehmen. Loslassen schafft Abstand und hat mit Aufbruch und Befreiung zu tun, einem entschiedenen »Nein!« zum Bisherigen zugunsten eines in die Zukunft gerichteten »Ja!«. Dabei trauen Sie sich zu, auch neue Wege zu gehen.

Beispiel: Beziehung

Nehmen wir einmal die Liebe: Loslassen kann heißen, sich zu trennen. Es kann aber auch bedeuten, die eigenen, festgefügten Vorstellungen darüber, wie eine Beziehung zu funktionieren hat, in Frage zu stellen, sich beraten zu lassen, möglicherweise auch ein professionelles Coaching ins Auge zu fassen. Loslassen kann auch heißen, sich mehr Zeit für sich selbst zu nehmen und nicht das ganze Leben allein auf die Partnerschaft auszurichten. Loslassen kann also viele Facetten haben. Immer entsteht aber dabei ein Freiraum für Veränderungen.

Loslassen als Teil des Lebensprinzips

Veränderung ist das Wesen jeglicher Entwicklung, wofür wir im Alltag viele Beispiele finden. Das Leben ist ständig in Bewegung, eine stetige Abfolge von Entstehen, Werden und Vergehen … gleichgültig, ob wir dabei den Wechsel der Jahreszeiten, die Wellen des Meeres oder den Apfelbaum im Garten im Blick haben: Es ist stets dasselbe Prinzip, das Lebensprinzip schlechthin. Ohne Veränderungen gäbe es keine

Entwicklung, wäre kein Fortschritt möglich und hätte es auch die Evolution nie geben können.

»Stirb und Werde«

So wie die Natur geprägt ist von vielfältigen Formen des Entstehens, Werdens und Vergehens, besteht auch unser Alltag aus vielen Ausprägungen des Erwerbens, Festhaltens und Loslassens – von Menschen, Dingen, Vorlieben, Vorstellungen, Erinnerungen… im Kleinen wie im Großen, immer wieder und stets neu. Nichts bleibt. Eigentlich wissen wir das. Insofern umfasst Festhalten immer nur die begrenzte Zeit zwischen dem Erwerben und der Trennung vom Erworbenen. Wir selbst können entscheiden, wie lang diese Zeitspanne ist, wie lange wir eine bestimmte Gewohnheit pflegen, einer bestimmten Arbeit nachgehen, ein bestimmtes Auto fahren usw. – auch wenn uns das durch die Macht der Gewohnheit meist gar nicht mehr bewusst ist. Wir sind von Geburt an unser ganzes Leben lang bis hin zum Tod gefordert, verschiedenste Herausforderungen im Leben zu bewältigen: Wir werden geboren, lernen krabbeln, laufen und sprechen, machen Erfahrungen in Kindergarten, Schule, Lehre oder Studium und im Berufsleben. Wir verlieben uns, heiraten, bekommen Kinder – oder nicht –, wir trennen uns vom Partner oder bleiben mit ihm zusammen. Wir altern, müssen uns verstärkt mit Krankheiten und dem Tod von Freunden und Angehörigen auseinandersetzen.

> *»Und so lang du das nicht hast, dieses ›Stirb und werde!‹ bist du nur ein trüber Gast auf der dunklen Erde.«* Johann Wolfgang v. Goethe

Es geht ständig um die Bewältigung von Herausforderungen, um Erwerben, Festhalten und Loslassen. Daran wachsen wir und erfahren uns selbst als lebendig.

Einige dieser Veränderungsprozesse fallen uns leicht, mit anderen können wir uns nur schwer anfreunden. Manches wollen wir vielleicht gar nicht wahrhaben. Wir tun uns vor allem schwer damit, zu akzeptieren, dass Verluste, Krankheiten, Schicksalsschläge und auch der Tod zum Leben gehören, dass geliebte Menschen uns verlassen, und dass auch wir eines Tages sterben werden.

Wenn die Balance gestört ist

Die Prinzipien Erwerben und Festhalten können ebenso Schwierigkeiten bereiten wie das Loslassen. Es gibt durchaus Menschen, die es nicht verstehen, zu erwerben und festzuhalten: Der eine schreckt vor Bindungen jeglicher Art zurück, dem anderen zerrinnt das Geld zwischen den Fingern, dem dritten fehlt es an Beharrlichkeit, ein einmal angefangenes Projekt zu Ende zu bringen; stattdessen gibt er es schon beim geringsten Gegenwind auf usw. Festhalten können ist also durchaus eine Qualität!

Wenn Festhalten zur Last wird

Zu viel davon verwandelt diese Qualität jedoch in eine lähmende Last. Wer sich nicht von im Lauf der Zeit angehäuften Sachen trennen kann, hat bald Papiertürme im Büro, einen zugestopften Kleiderschrank im Schlafzimmer und eine Wohnung, die aussieht wie eine Kreuzung aus Möbellager und Museum. Und wer in Gewohnheiten und Abläufen festhängt, steht generell unter dem Druck, auch als irrig Erkanntes weiterführen zu müssen und hat möglicherweise auch so ungesunde Angewohnheiten wie Rauchen, zu viel Essen oder zu viel Alkohol als Dauergäste im Verhaltensrepertoire. Wer sich schwer damit tut, »nein« zu sagen, und sich schlecht von Menschen trennen kann, ist oft dazu verurteilt, seine Lebenszeit gerade mit jenen zu verbringen, die ihm am wenigsten guttun.

Probleme mit zu viel Festhalten sind häufiger als solche mit zu viel Loslassen. Weshalb fällt uns Festhalten – oft auch wider besseres Wissen – so viel leichter als Loslassen?

Festhalten geschieht ganz instinktiv

Sicherheit ist ein menschliches Grundbedürfnis. Wir wollen uns orientieren können und wissen, womit wir es zu tun haben, um möglichen Gefahren ausweichen oder ihnen die Stirn bieten zu können. Dies ist Teil unserer »Überlebensstrategie«. Jedes Neugeborene, das auf die Welt kommt, hat diese Sicherheit auch bitter nötig, denn es ist nicht in der Lage, für sich selbst zu sorgen. So braucht es Schutz, Halt und Hilfe durch andere, durch erwachsene Menschen.

Wichtige Sicherheitsreflexe

Schon bei Neugeborenen lassen sich zwei instinktive Formen des Festhaltens beobachten: der »Saugreflex« und der »Klammerreflex«. Wenn man die Lippen eines Babys berührt, spitzt es sie ganz unwillkürlich, weil es die Brustwarze umschließen will, von der die Muttermilch kommt. Mithilfe des Klammerreflexes schließt das Baby seine kleinen Händchen mit erstaunlicher Kraft um einen Finger oder einen Gegenstand, den man ihm entgegenhält. Dieses instinktive Festhalten des Babys dient dem Schutz gegen das Fallen.

Bleibende Grundbedürfnisse

Alle Babys sind auf die Mutter, den Vater – oder eine andere nahe Bezugsperson – angewiesen. Menschen sind Rudeltiere. Sie orientieren sich an anderen »Rudelgenossen«. So hat das Baby neben dem Bestreben, körperlich versorgt, vor allem satt und sauber sowie sicher vor möglichen Gefahren zu sein, noch weitere, soziale Bedürfnisse. Liebevoll im Arm gehalten werden, Nähe und menschliche Wärme erfahren, gestreichelt werden, kuscheln, Hautkontakt – dies ist notwendig zur Entwicklung seiner Kommunikations- und Empathiefähigkeit.

Unsere Grundbedürfnisse bleiben ein Leben lang erhalten. Das Gefühl für die eigene Identität entsteht früh durch Kontakt und Kommunikation mit wichtigen Bezugspersonen. Dazu braucht der junge Mensch ein Gegenüber, das durch Liebe, Anerkennung, aber auch das Setzen von Grenzen die Entwicklung eines stabilen Selbst-Gefühls unterstützt.

Auch als Erwachsener kann sich niemand der Abhängigkeit von anderen und dem Wunsch nach Anerkennung gänzlich entziehen. Doch ist dies – je nachdem, was wir in der Kindheit fürs Leben mitbekommen haben – stärker oder schwächer ausgeprägt (siehe auch ab Seite 29).

Wichtig: Wertschätzung und Zuverlässigkeit erleben

Auch als Erwachsene wollen wir gesehen werden und Wertschätzung erfahren, wollen, dass jemand Anteil nimmt, wenn es uns schlecht geht und mit uns jubelt, wenn es etwas zum Freuen gibt. Wir wollen, dass unser Partner, unsere Familie und unsere Freunde zuverlässig sind. Gerade wer vielleicht als Kind erlebt hat, dass geliebte Personen plötzlich gehen und nicht mehr wiederkommen, neigt dazu, sich hinsichtlich der Verlässlichkeit seiner Freunde und Partner immer wieder rückzuversichern und sich besonders »festzuhalten«.

Zuwendung, Bestätigung und Anteilnahme von anderen erleben wir immer als wohltuend. Fehlen sie, so kann dies stark verunsichern. Sicherheit führt zur Entspannung, Unsicherheit und die damit unwillkürlich verbundene Wachsamkeit rufen Anspannung hervor. Wir sind dann sozusagen »ständig auf dem Sprung«, also in Alarmbereitschaft.

Tief verwurzelt: unser Sicherheitsgefühl

Immer wichtiger für das Sicherheitsgefühl wird, schon beim Baby und beim Kleinkind, auch die Strukturierung der Zeit: Die rhythmische Wiederkehr von Vertrautem gibt ein Gefühl von Überschaubarkeit. Wir können voraussehen, wann was kommen wird, wir kennen uns aus. Auch dies unterstützt unser Sicherheitsgefühl. Abläufe, die uns vertraut sind, die wir einschätzen können, denen wir immer wieder begegnen, und die wir wiedererkennen, schaffen Orientierung.

Rhythmus schafft Struktur

Die Regelmäßigkeit von Abläufen ist sozusagen eine Vorform späterer (Erziehungs-)Regeln, die Kinder leichter erlernen können, wenn sie von Geburt an solche Regelmäßigkeiten gewöhnt sind. Es gibt eine Zeit zum Essen, zur Körperpflege, zum Schlafen, zum Spielen … verschiedene Rhythmen und Rituale gliedern den Tag, die Woche und die Jahreszeiten. Gerade kleine Kinder lieben die Wiederholung.

Auch als Erwachsene möchten wir, dass unsere Tage, Monate, Jahre einer Struktur folgen, dass es Abschnitte in der Zeit gibt, die unsere verschiedenen Aktivitäten »ordnen« oder besondere Akzente setzen – Arbeitszeit, Feierabend, Wochenende, Weihnachten, Silvester, Familienfeste, der Jahresurlaub usw. Rhythmen geben Halt. So erleben manche Menschen den ersehnten Urlaub plötzlich als problematisch, weil keine Struktur vorgegeben ist und die Tage »einfach so« vor ihnen liegen. Sie versuchen dann dem aufkeimenden Unbehagen vorzubeugen, indem sie sich auch am Urlaubsort ein »volles Programm« schaffen – so kommt es, dass die freie Zeit bei so manchem ebenso straff organisiert und vollgepackt wird wie der Arbeitsalltag. Das ist zwar sehr anstrengend, schafft aber Übersicht und Sicherheit.

> »*Unsere Sehnsüchte sind unsere Möglichkeiten.*« Robert Browning

Wer sich sicher fühlt, kann Neugier zeigen

Das Baby entdeckt seine Welt und hat Spaß an all dem, was es zu sehen, zu hören, zu riechen und zu schmecken gibt. Es will alles anfassen und nach Möglichkeit auch gleich in den Mund nehmen. Schon früh erfährt es: Wenn man Vertrautes loslässt, kann man etwas Neues anpacken – eine Überraschung, ein Abenteuer, etwas ganz Erstaunliches. Da es aber noch wenig Erfahrung mitbringt, wie dieses Neue einzuschätzen ist, entstehen leicht auch Ängste und Unsicherheiten. Wenn dann die Lage allzu unübersichtlich wird, schiebt sich das Sicherheitsbedürfnis wieder massiv in den Vordergrund, und das Kind tritt den Rückzug an.

Auch als Erwachsene suchen wir Anregung, wollen Neues lernen, uns ausprobieren. Wir schätzen Unterhaltung, die Spannung erzeugt oder uns zum Lachen bringt. Neues und Unbekanntes fasziniert – doch nur solange es nicht wirklich bedrohlich für uns wird.

Dabei hat jeder sein individuelles Level, bei dem sich automatisch das Sicherheitsprogramm einschaltet. Manche Menschen lieben etwa die extreme Spannung eines Horrorfilms, anderen müsste man ein Schmerzensgeld zahlen, damit sie überhaupt zuschauen – und dann würden sie mit Herzklopfen vor dem Bildschirm sitzen und bei den schauerlichsten Szenen die Augen schließen. Manche brauchen auch den realen Nervenkitzel, den sie sich durch Extremklettern oder Fallschirmspringen holen, während es anderen schon beim bloßen Gedanken an solche Herausforderungen schlecht wird.

Wann gibt es Entwarnung?

Nur wenn wir Neues einschätzen können und es für ungefährlich halten oder uns selbst der Herausforderung gewachsen fühlen, gibt unser Sicherheitsprogramm Entwarnung. Wenn wir nachts im Bett feststellen, dass der Lärm draußen nur vom Balzen eines Katers herrührt, wenn wir nach einer Präsentation beifälliges Gemurmel hören, dann entspannen wir uns und fühlen uns wieder sicher. Dieses unwillkürliche Abscannen der Umgebung nach möglichen Gefahren läuft im Hintergrund und ist als Frühwarnsystem eine wichtige Orientierungshilfe. Tut es aber zu viel des Guten, leben wir ständig in Alarmbereitschaft und sind auf Abwehr programmiert, auch wenn gar nichts Bedrohliches in Sicht ist.

Wie Muster wirken

Dieses Alarmprogramm ist eine der Grundlagen unserer Wahrnehmungs-, Denk- und Handlungsmuster, die uns ein Optimum an Sicherheit und Freiheit von Angst garantieren sollen. In den ersten fünf Lebensjahren bestehen besonders günstige neurobiologische Bedingungen dafür, diese Muster herauszubilden. Das Prinzip ist einfach: Jede Handlung ruft eine Reaktion hervor. Immer wenn unsere Bezugspersonen positiv auf unser Verhalten reagierten, wurde es wahrscheinlicher, dass wir es beim nächsten Mal genauso machten. Erhielten wir eine negative Resonanz – Schmerz, Spott, Ignoriertwerden, Ausgrenzung … – haben wir höchstwahrscheinlich versucht, das Verhalten künftig zu vermeiden.

Der Sinn von Mustern

Muster sind nichts prinzipiell Schlechtes. Einigen davon verdanken Sie vermutlich viele Ihrer sozialen und beruflichen Erfolge. Beispielsweise konnten Sie eine wichtige Prüfung nur bestehen, weil Sie im Vorfeld diszipliniert und konzentriert gelernt haben.

Vielleicht haben Sie als Kind erlebt, wie ärgerlich Ihre Mutter werden konnte, wenn Sie mit einem Loch in der Hose und von oben bis unten verschmutzt vom Spielplatz kamen. Dann haben Sie Ihre Abenteuerlust gebremst und künftig auf Ihre Kleidung geachtet.

Die Anpassungshaltung

Sobald Sie als Kind den Zusammenhang zwischen »Bravsein«, Lob und Süßigkeiten erkannt hatten, haben Sie sicher öfter versucht, brav zu sein. Die Botschaft hinter solchen Verhaltenssteuerungen ist ebenso simpel wie nachhaltig: »Sei so, wie ich mir vorstelle, dass du sein sollst, dann wird es dir gut gehen.« Viele verharren noch als Erwachsene allzu oft in einer Anpassungshaltung: bedroht von der Angst, etwas falsch zu machen oder zu versagen, und darauf ausgerichtet, sich das Wohlwollen wichtiger Mitmenschen zu erhalten.

Wenn wir als Kinder gelernt haben, dass braves Sich-Anpassen Lob und Zuwendung bringt – und damit gute Gefühle – werden wir dieses Verhalten wahrscheinlich immer wieder zeigen. Je nachdem wie stark die Zuwendung für die Anpassung, vor allem aber die Ablehnung als Reaktion auf unangepasstes Verhalten ausfiel, ist der Drang, es anderen auf Kosten eigener Bedürfnisse recht zu machen, schwächer oder stärker. Bei starker Ausprägung werden wir uns auch selbst als brav und gefügig erleben. Schließlich glauben wir, wir »seien einfach so« und denken über uns selbst: »Für mich ist es am besten, wenn ich mich unterordne.« Das Verhalten erfolgt irgendwann ganz unwillkürlich, ohne dass wir weiteres Nachdenken oder alternative Verhaltensweisen erwägen. Mit solchen Mechanismen treiben wir uns selbst zu einem bestimmten Verhalten an – eben so, wie wir es vor langer Zeit erlernt haben.

Die inneren Antreiber

Es ärgert uns heute natürlich, dass wir an solchen Mustern festhalten –

Hitliste der inneren Antreiber

- »Sei perfekt«
- »Streng dich an«
- »Sei stark«

- »Mach schneller«
- »Mach es allen recht«
- »Reiß dich zusammen«

umso mehr, wenn wir spüren, dass wir uns damit eher schaden. Diese »inneren Antreiber« erzeugen viel Druck. Beispiele hierfür sind:»Alle sollen mich mögen«,»Ich muss Zeit sparen« oder»Schwächen darf man nicht zeigen«. Natürlich haben solche Maximen auch positive Aspekte und helfen dabei, den Alltag zu bewältigen, Aufgaben zu erfüllen und ein sozial verträglicher Mensch zu sein. Doch ist es ungut, wenn sie über die persönliche Entscheidungsfreiheit dominieren. Ein Zuviel davon führt dazu, unflexibel zu werden, sich den Weg zu neuen, kreativen und guten Entscheidungen zu verbauen und stattdessen aus inneren Zwängen heraus zu handeln. Wer als Kind stark gemaßregelt

wurde, verinnerlicht oft einen ganzen Wald von Regeln, anstatt ein solides Selbstvertrauen zu entwickeln. Neurologen stellten fest, dass häufig auftretendes gleichartiges Verhalten im Gehirn für immer stabilere Verschaltungen zwischen den beteiligten Nervenzellen sorgt. Reaktionen, die aus der Kindheit stammen, graben sich so als Muster ein. Je öfter wir einen Gedanken oder eine Tat ausführen, desto fester wird es. Im Extremfall ist es im Erwachsenenalter so automatisiert, dass wir auch daran festhalten, wenn es zu unserem Nachteil ist. Statt danach zu suchen, was uns selbst begeistert und entspricht, fühlen wir uns anerzogenen Normen und einem Ideal verpflichtet.

Vor- und Nachteile

Wer sich anpasst, vermeidet Angst, Verunsicherung, Konflikte und Zuwendungsverlust. Die Nachteile, die einem erst mit der Zeit bewusst werden, sind Unselbstständigkeit, Unsicherheit und eine dumpfe Unzufriedenheit, die sich scheinbar nicht richtig fassen lässt.

So halten wir, je nach Prägung, an verschiedenen haltgebenden Dingen, Umständen und Riten fest und entwickeln feste Handlungsmuster. Diese bestimmen dann, was wir denken, welchen Idealen und Leitbildern wir gehorchen, worüber wir sprechen und worüber nicht, wo es uns hinzieht, was wir ablehnen, wie wir Gefühle ausdrücken usw.

So kann es sein, dass »Miss Perfect« keine Probleme hat, sich von jemandem zu trennen, sich aber außerstande sieht, mit dem Putzen im Bad aufzuhören, ehe das letzte Schmutzpartikelchen entfernt ist. Miss Perfect will eine »perfekt geordnete« Welt und hat alles in ihrer Umgebung gern voll im Griff. Erst dann fühlt sie sich beruhigt. Die heimliche Prinzessin reagiert gekränkt oder aggressiv, wenn jemand ihren – gefühlten – Sonderstatus in Frage stellt. Denn sie glaubt, dass sie nur Anerkennung und Zuwendung bekommt, wenn sie etwas Besonderes ist. Im Extremfall: dass sie sonst überhaupt keine Existenzberechtigung hat. Ein Sonderstatus stellt für die treue Seele überhaupt nichts Erstrebens- oder Behaltenswertes dar, aber wenn ihr Freund sie verlassen will, kann sie mit depressiver Verstimmung bis hin zu Herzbeschwerden reagieren.

Sicherheitsdenken in den Hintergrund schieben

Die Erscheinungsformen des Festhaltens am Status quo sind bei allen Profilen unterschiedlich, doch der Mechanismus ist stets derselbe: Wenn Angst auftritt, greifen wir nach dem, von dem wir gelernt haben, dass es scheinbar gut funktioniert, einfach, um uns wieder sicher fühlen zu können – bewusst

10 falsche Vorstellungen vom Festhalten

1 Je reicher ich bin, je mehr ich besitze, desto angesehener, sicherer und glücklicher werde ich sein.

2 Je mehr ich mich für andere einsetze, desto mehr werden andere mich mögen und schätzen.

3 Wenn ich die Wünsche meines Partners über meine eigenen stelle, wird er mich mehr lieben und wird mich nicht verlassen.

4 Erst wenn ich das Vergangene vollständig bewältigt habe, kann ich ein freies und glückliches Leben führen.

5 Nur wenn ich alles perfekt erledige, darf ich mit mir zufrieden sein.

6 Wenn ich viel in eine Sache investiert habe, kann ich sie nicht einfach wegwerfen oder sein lassen.

7 Was ich einmal angeschafft habe, muss ich behalten, denn ich könnte es irgendwann einmal brauchen.

8 Wenn ich mich nicht mehr als totales Unikat betrachten könnte, würde mir mein Leben keinen Spaß mehr machen.

9 Ein Leben ohne meine »Lieblingsdroge« (Alkohol, Rauchen, Fernsehen …) fühlt sich unvollständig und langweilig an.

10 Nur wenn die anderen mich mögen, anerkennen und etwas von mir halten, kann ich mich wertvoll fühlen.

oder unbewusst. Je stärker diese reflexhafte Sicherheitsorientierung ausgeprägt ist, desto zurückhaltender und abwehrender reagieren wir auf Überraschendes und Unvorhergesehenes. Bevor wir Altes loslassen und Lust an der Veränderung entwickeln können, müssen wir das

stark einschränkende Sicherheits-
denken etwas in den Hintergrund
verlagern, denn dieses Denken
richtet die eigenen Gedanken und
Gefühle immer wieder auf die
Wahrnehmung von Bedrohung aus
– auch dort, wo gar keine existiert.

Sie haben die Wahl

Loslassen ermöglicht Freiheit von
einschränkenden Mustern, auch
wenn Sie dafür Unsicherheit,
Unwägbarkeiten und vielleicht
auch Ängste in Kauf zu nehmen
haben. Den eigenen Weg zu finden
im Spannungsfeld zwischen Festhalten und Loslassen, ist eine span-
nende Angelegenheit. Auch wenn
Sie durch das Loslassen eingefah-
rener Muster vielleicht nur ein
kleines Stück individueller Freiheit
dazugewinnen: Auf jeden Fall entdecken Sie dabei, dass Sie die Wahl
haben, wie Sie Ihr Leben und Ihren
Alltag gestalten, und fühlen sich
nicht länger als das Opfer der Umstände oder eigener schematischer
Handlungszwänge.

Ideales und tatsächliches Selbst

Überlegen Sie, was alles Sie als
Kind tun mussten, um sich die ge-
wünschte, für Ihr Selbstwertgefühl
notwendige Anerkennung und
Wertschätzung zu verschaffen.
Waren die Erwartungen Ihrer
Eltern sehr hoch? War die Messlatte
manchmal kaum zu erreichen?
Dann werden Sie wahrscheinlich
auch den Gradmesser für Ihre
Zufriedenheit so hoch angesetzt
haben, dass Sie praktisch ständig
»auf Zehenspitzen stehen«. Oder
Sie haben sich in die Totalverweige-
rung geflüchtet und müssen nun
dauernd mit einem unterschwelli-
gen schlechten Gewissen kämpfen,
weil Sie die »böse«, nicht funktio-
nierende Tochter sind.
Waren die Erwartungen Ihrer
Eltern hingegen zu niedrig, sei es
aus mangelnder Wertschätzung
oder gar aus Desinteresse heraus,
dann erwarten Sie auch nichts
Besonderes von sich selbst.

Der Grundstock für Ihr Selbst

In beiden Fällen fühlten Sie sich schon als Kind ungenügend, und dieses Gefühl haben Sie bis ins Erwachsenenalter bewahrt. Die Versuche, den Erwartungen und den Maßstäben Ihrer Eltern zu entsprechen, bilden den Grundstock dafür, wie Sie sich selbst einschätzen, Ihr Selbst, Ihre Identität.

Vielleicht keimt bei den vielen Verweisen auf den elterlichen Einfluss langsam Wut in Ihnen auf – »Hätte ich doch mehr Anerkennung von meinen Eltern erfahren, hätten sie mich einfach um meiner selbst willen geliebt, was hätte aus mir werden können« – durchaus nahe liegende Gedanken, die besonders der chronischen Vergangenheitsbewältigerin vertraut sein müssten. Es geht aber nicht darum, anzuklagen oder einen Sündenbock zu finden, sondern darum, Zusammenhänge besser zu verstehen, um etwas am Status quo ändern zu können. Anklagen bringen nur Kummer und Schmerz – sonst nichts. Vertrauen Sie darauf, dass Ihre Eltern Sie so gut erzogen haben, wie es ihnen eben möglich war, und dass sie versucht haben, ihr Bestes zu geben – auch wenn daraus einige spezielle Herausforderungen und Entwicklungsaufgaben für Sie entstanden.

Die Fähigkeit zur Selbstreflexion

Ein wesentlicher Grund für das Festhalten an Gewohnheiten und Mustern ist die Diskrepanz zwi-

> »Den Schlüssel zum Erfolg kenne ich nicht. Der **Schlüssel zum Scheitern** ist der Versuch, es allen recht zu machen.« Bill Cosby

schen dem »idealen« und dem »wirklichen« Selbst. Sehr früh schon entwickeln wir – im Unterschied zu den Tieren – die Fähigkeit zur Selbstreflexion, das heißt, uns selbst anzusehen und zu beurteilen, wie wir andere Menschen und Dinge betrachten können. So können wir uns ein Bild von uns selbst machen. Dabei gibt es einerseits ein realistisches Selbstbild, so wie man sich selbst sieht und fühlt (actual self) und zum anderen ein ideales Selbstbild, so wie man gerne wäre oder wie man meint, sein zu sollen (ideal self).

Bei allem was Sie tun, findet zwischen diesen beiden Aspekten Ihres Selbst ein steter Abgleich statt – »Ist mir das gut gelungen oder könnte es besser sein?« – »Sehe ich in diesem Kostüm attraktiv aus oder bin ich zu dick dafür?«

Wenn actual self und ideal self übereinstimmen, fühlen Sie sich wohl und machen einfach weiter wie gehabt. Gibt es Widersprüche, dann fühlen Sie sich wahrscheinlich unbehaglich und versuchen, diese zu beseitigen.

Das geschieht entweder durch Angleichen Ihres Verhaltens an das Idealbild (»… da muss ich mich halt noch mehr anstrengen!«) oder indem Sie versuchen, sich der Situation oder dem auslösenden Reiz zu entziehen (»… dann sage ich lieber gar nichts mehr, bevor ich mich von den anderen blöd anschauen lasse.«). Wenn die heimliche Prinzessin also zum Beispiel bei einer Party nicht die Aufmerksamkeit genießt, die sie aufgrund ihrer internen Erwartungen voraussetzt, versucht sie zunächst, sich so zu verhalten, dass sie doch noch in den Mittelpunkt des Interesses kommt. Klappt dies nicht, so findet sie einen Grund, die Party zu verlassen (»Langweilig hier«, »Muss noch wo hin« usw.).

Der Unterschied zwischen Wollen und Sein

Die Vorstellungen davon, »wie man sein sollte«, sind natürlich das Produkt unterschiedlicher Einflüsse – da spielen wieder die Erwartungen des Elternhauses eine Rolle, später auch die Werte wichtiger Peergroups, also Gruppen von Gleichaltrigen, denen man sich zugehörig fühlt, bis hin zu scheinbar »idealen« Frauen- und Männerbildern in den Medien.

Große Differenzen zwischen dem »idealen« und dem »aktuellen« Selbst führen vor allem dann zu dauerhafter Unzufriedenheit, wenn die Vorstellungen, die mit dem »idealen« Selbst verbunden sind, sehr hochgeschraubt oder außerhalb der Reichweite sind. Jemand mit einem kräftigen Körperbau wird auch mit der strengsten Diät keine Elfe. Jemand über vierzig wird auch mithilfe sämtlicher kosmetischer Korrekturen nicht mehr aussehen wie zwanzig. Es spricht überhaupt nichts dagegen, eine Idealvorstellung von sich selbst zu haben – wenn diese aber zum Maß aller Dinge wird, ist Unglücklichsein vorprogrammiert.

Die Macht von Schuld- und Schamgefühlen

Wenn man schon als Kind wegen seines Aussehens, seiner Fähigkeiten oder seines Verhaltens ständig als unzureichend bewertet wurde, ist die Chance groß, dass man diese Vorstellungen übernimmt und sich schließlich selbst für seine (scheinbaren) Unzulänglichkeiten verurteilt. Dieses negative Selbsturteil führt dazu, dass man sich schlecht fühlt und sich wenig zutraut. Driften Ideal und Wirklichkeit also stark auseinander, wird dies zum Nährboden für dauerhafte Schuld- und Schamgefühle. Solche Gefühle machen gefügig gegenüber Ansprüchen und Forderungen anderer, in der Partnerschaft, genauso wie im Beruf. »Wie konntest du nur …!«, »Warum hast du nur nicht …«, »Das hätte dir niemals passieren dürfen«, »Wenn du gescheit wärst, hättest du …«. Wem solche Vorwürfe von früher vertraut sind, der spricht höchstwahrscheinlich irgendwann so streng und unbarmherzig mit sich selbst, sobald das actual self den Ansprüchen des ideal self nicht genügt.

Das Fatale an Selbstvorwürfen
Jeder Tag bietet Gelegenheit, das Muster immer wieder zu bedienen, sich selbst zu kritisieren und sich niederzumachen. Besonders Miss Perfect mit den hohen Ansprüchen ihres ideal self ist dafür sehr anfällig. Selbstvorwürfe und die damit verbundenen Scham- und Schuldgefühle führen aber nicht dazu, dass die Dinge künftig besser laufen – dann hätte dieser unfreundliche Umgangsstil mit sich selbst ja wenigstens noch einen Nutzen. Selbstvorwürfe bewirken vielmehr, sich weniger statt mehr zuzutrauen und

bestimmten Dingen, Menschen, Situationen ganz aus dem Weg zu gehen, um die befürchteten Scham- und Schuldgefühle zu vermeiden.

Scheitern bedroht das »ideal self«

Das Festhalten an erlernten Mustern kann also sehr kontraproduktiv sein und sogar gefährlich werden. Im Wirtschaftsleben gibt es dafür den Begriff der »Eskalation des Engagements«. Dies bezeichnet den Punkt, an dem man eigentlich erkannt hat, dass man lieber loslassen als weiter festhalten sollte, jedoch nicht zugeben will, dass man sich geirrt hat und den Folgen dieser Erkenntnis nicht ins Auge sehen möchte. Stattdessen verstärkt man

»*Die **Freiheit** des Menschen liegt nicht darin, dass er tun kann, was er will, sondern dass er **nicht tun muss**, was er nicht will.*«

Jean-Jacques Rousseau

die Anstrengungen, macht noch mehr von demselben in der Hoffnung, so letztlich doch zu anderen Ergebnissen zu kommen. So würde etwa die treue Seele ignorieren, dass der Partner offensichtlich schon wieder eine Affäre hat – in der Hoffnung, die Sache würde sich totlaufen, weil seine früheren Affären auch irgendwann zu Ende gingen. Sie spricht es einfach nicht an, sondern bangt, wartet, hofft und scheut sich, der Wahrheit ins Auge zu sehen: dass an der Beziehung etwas grundsätzlich nicht in Ordnung ist und sie selbst gefordert ist, zu entscheiden – entweder den Partner zur Rede zu stellen, auch mit dem Risiko, dass dieser dann seine Koffer packt, oder sich zu fragen, ob sie diese ständigen Seitensprünge nicht satt hat und selbst die Trennung zu vollziehen. Wenn wir schon viel investiert haben, sei es Zeit, Geld oder Gefühle, dann kommt uns Loslassen in der Tat oft wie ein gravierendes Versagen vor. Wir klammern uns

an die einmal gehegten Hoffnungen und Vorstellungen, auch wenn wir intuitiv spüren, wie aussichtslos dies ist. »Wenn du auf einem toten Pferd sitzt, dann steig ab«, sagt ein indianisches Sprichwort – doch die Schwierigkeit scheint eben darin zu bestehen, zu erkennen, wann »das Pferd tatsächlich tot ist« – wann der Punkt gekommen ist, sich von etwas zu verabschieden. Manche Menschen neigen dazu, lieber auszubrennen oder krank zu werden, als sich einzugestehen, dass sie sich zu viel zumuten oder unrealistischen Vorstellungen nachjagen. Doch auch Niederlagen und Scheitern gilt es zu verarbeiten und damit innerlich loszulassen.

Willkommen bei den Jägern und Sammlern

Besonders deutlich zeigt sich Festhalten in der Gewohnheit des Sammelns und Anhäufens. Zwar ist der Drang zum Jagen und Sammeln als Teil unserer Entwicklungsgeschichte in jedem von uns mehr oder weniger stark ausgeprägt, doch kann er in Form chronischer Schnäppchenjagd und dem Horten aller möglicher Sammelsurien auch ziemlich entgleisen. Sammeln hat eine lange Tradition.

Die Sammelfreude liegt in unseren Genen

Der Urmensch als Jäger und Sammler galt als umso erfolgreicher, je mehr er erbeutete. Sammeln, Bewahren und das Anlegen von Vorräten war gerade in unseren Breiten lebensnotwendig, um den harten Winter zu überstehen.

Schon beim kleinen Kind stärkt das Erobern begehrter Gegenstände – vorübergehend – sein Selbstwertgefühl. Mit dem Sammeln und Ordnen folgt es eigenen Vorlieben und fühlt sich als Herr oder Herrin eines Königreichs kleiner Schätze. Als aktivste Phase kindlicher Sammelleidenschaft wird die Zeit zwischen dem 7. und 12. Lebensjahr betrachtet. Doch kann dieser Hang auch fortbestehen. Noch als Erwachsene »jagen« und sammeln wir unterschiedlichste Gegenstände – nicht um zu überleben, sondern weil wir uns daran erfreuen oder der Besitz die eigene Bedeutung zu erhöhen scheint – »Guck mal, was ich da habe«. Wir sammeln Schmuck, kluge Sprüche und seltene Münzen, Steine, Postkarten und Bücher, Büroklammern, Schuhe und CDs, Zeitschriften, Kochrezepte und Geschenkpapier.

Von Hormonen gesteuert

Wir sammeln, weil in uns immer noch die gleichen Hormone ausgeschüttet werden, wie seinerzeit beim Cro-Magnon-Menschen, als er sich mit Nüssen, Beeren und Heilpflanzen auf den Weg zurück in seine Höhle machte. Beim Ergattern eines »Schnäppchens« belohnen uns die Wohlfühlhormone Dopamin und Serotonin mit Hochstimmung, Endorphine vermitteln

> *»Was es alles gibt,*
> *was ich nicht brauche!«*   Aristoteles

ein euphorisches Glücksgefühl und der Botenstoff Oxytocin, das »Kuschelhormon«, sorgt für eine enge Bindung zwischen uns und unserem ergatterten Objekt. Dieser Hormoncocktail regte früher den Urmenschen dazu an, immer noch weiter zu sammeln. Und, wie man sieht, funktioniert dies auch heute noch bestens.

Mit verantwortlich dafür ist auch der Kick, den der Zugriff auf die »Beute« auslöst. Während des Kaufens werden Adrenalin und Noradrenalin ausgeschüttet. Der Blutdruck steigt, das Herz schlägt schneller – positiver Stress setzt ein. Doch hält der Kick nicht lange an. Kaum ist die »Beute« erlegt, sinken die Hormonspiegel wieder. Was bleibt, ist Ernüchterung: Wozu brauche ich eigentlich das vierte Paar braune Pumps? Nichtsdestotrotz erwacht bald wieder der

Wunsch, auf »Beutezug« zu gehen. Inzwischen sammeln sich in der häuslichen Höhle allerhand nützliche und unnütze Dinge an, eben alles, was wir meinten, unbedingt haben zu müssen und wovon wir uns jetzt ganz schlecht trennen können. Schließlich hat es ja sauer verdientes Geld gekostet. Dazu kommt all das, was ungebeten ins Haus flattert, wie Werbesendungen, Warenproben, Prospekte, Gratis-Zeitungen, E-Mails …

Wenn Gewohnheit sich verselbstständigt

Ähnlich wie beim Jagen, Häufen und Horten lösen auch andere Gewohnheiten, Zwänge und Süchte entsprechende Glückshormonausschüttungen im Gehirn aus und machen es schwer, kontrolliert mit ihnen umzugehen: Schon ist man in Gefahr, vom entsprechenden »Kick« abhängig zu werden. »Abhängigkeit« – dieses Wort verbinden viele vor allem mit Süchten. Doch nicht nur Alkohol, Zigaretten, Medikamente oder Drogen können in die Abhängigkeit führen, sondern auch vielerlei anderes kann dazu verführen, festzuhalten und nicht mehr loszulassen: Statussymbole, Geld, Erinnerungen, Anerkennung, Aufmerksamkeit und vieles mehr. Gefährlich wird es immer dann, wenn als lustvoll erlebte Erfahrungen uns beherrschen und wir uns »ohne« unwohl oder unvollständig fühlen.

Abhängigkeiten beginnen im Kopf. Schöne Momente endlos »verlängern« zu wollen, sich nicht davon lösen können, noch ein Bier, noch eine Zigarette, noch länger bleiben, es ist doch gerade so schön … und am nächsten Morgen dann der dicke Kopf und die Reue über alles, was da gesagt und getan wurde … Wie bei den meisten Dingen des Lebens, sei es nun Wein, Sex, Einkaufen, Sport, Genuss oder Arbeit, geht es nicht um Askese, sondern um das richtige Maß, um die Balance zwischen Festhalten und Loslassen.

Zurückfinden zur Balance

Wer nicht loslassen kann, schleppt viel mit sich herum. Dies gilt im materiellen wie im ideellen Sinne. Einen Mantel, der einem nicht steht, jahrelang im Kleiderschrank hängen zu lassen – nur weil er so teuer gewesen ist? Die 35. Diät machen und hoffen, dass dann für alle Zeiten Größe 38 angesagt ist? Auch wenn die meisten Festhalte-Gewohnheiten keineswegs lebensbedrohlich sind, so zehren sie doch an Laune und Lebenskraft. Zeit, dass sich etwas ändert! Es ist nie zu spät, das, was sich überlebt hat oder einfach nicht zu einem passen will, loszulassen. Selbst wenn Sie keinen Beifall von anderen dafür erhalten – es ist ungeheuer befriedigend, sich nicht mehr von Gewohnheitsdiktaten lähmen zu lassen!

Loslassen, was **nicht glücklich** macht

Der »kleine Coach« kann viel für Sie tun,
*damit Sie Veränderungen **nicht nur zulassen,***
*sondern auch **aktiv angehen.***

COACHING IST EINE WIRKSAME METHODE, um Probleme und Konflikte zu klären und Impulse für eine Neuorientierung zu geben. Dabei regt der Coach Veränderungen in Einstellung und Verhalten an und gibt Werkzeuge an die Hand, um diese Veränderungen gezielt zu trainieren. Dasselbe möchte ich Ihnen mit dem »kleinen Coach« bieten. Er unterstützt Sie dabei, Ihren persönlichen Klärungs- und Veränderungsprozess effektiv zu gestalten. Er stellt Gewohnheiten, Überzeugungen, und bestehende Verhaltensweisen in Frage, um Veränderung und Weiterentwicklung zu ermöglichen.

Ähnlich wie beim Sport gibt es auch im Coachingprozess klare Ziele, konkrete Aufgabenstellungen, Korrektur- und Handlungshilfen und auch immer wieder ein »Controlling«, einen Soll-Ist-Vergleich, ob die angestrebten Veränderungen erreicht werden. In diesem Kapitel lernen Sie die vier Phasen des Loslassens kennen, die Sie Schritt für Schritt zu Ihrem Ziel führen werden.

Sie bringen nur die Bereitschaft mit, vertraute Denk- und Verhaltensmuster zu hinterfragen und sich auf Neues einzulassen – und natürlich einen möglichst stark ausgeprägten Wunsch, tatsächlich etwas verändern zu wollen …!

PRAXIS

Phase 1: Einen Rahmen schaffen und Bilanz ziehen

In dieser ersten Phase geht es darum, sich der eigenen Denk- und Handlungsmuster stärker als bisher bewusst zu werden. Außerdem eine Bilanz der bisherigen Entwicklung zu ziehen und sich so die Entstehung gewisser Einstellungen und Reaktionsweisen zu vergegenwärtigen. Was führte zu was? Loslassen ist ein Prozess – und funktioniert nicht auf Knopfdruck. Gewohnheiten und Abhängigkeiten haben sich in teilweise jahrzehntelanger Prägung eingespurt. Viel Zeit und Energie sind nötig, um sich von ungünstigen Mustern zu lösen und förderliche Denk- und Verhaltensstrukturen aufzubauen.

Der äußere Rahmen

Als Erstes sollten Sie sich einen passenden äußeren Rahmen für Ihren Veränderungsprozess schaffen.

Legen Sie die Zeit fest

Feste Zeiten schaffen Verbindlichkeit – so können Sie Ihre Fähigkeit zum Herausbilden und Festhalten von Gewohnheiten ideal nutzen. Ein gutes Maß ist, sich zweimal wöchentlich eine Stunde Zeit für sich selbst zu nehmen, um sich ganz auf das Thema »Loslassen« in den Aspekten Erfahren, Experimentieren und Üben zu konzentrieren. Natürlich können Sie sich auch häufiger Ihrer »Eigen«-Zeit widmen. Es kann gut sein, dass Sie mit zweimal pro Woche starten und dann so viel Gefallen daran finden, dass es Sie förmlich drängt, Ihrer Selbstentwicklung mehr Zeit zu widmen!

Bestimmen Sie den Ort

Wählen Sie einen Ort, den Sie mögen und an dem Sie ungestört sind: ein Raum, dessen angenehme Atmosphäre Sie bei Ihrem Termin mit sich selbst unterstützt. Vielleicht finden Sie irgendetwas, das für Sie das Thema »Loslassen« verbildlicht (eine Feder, ein Foto von fließendem Wasser …). Stellen Sie Ihr kleines Symbol so auf, dass Sie einen guten Blick darauf haben. Vielleicht hören Sie während Ihrer Übungszeit Musik im Hintergrund, vielleicht haben Sie es auch lieber ganz still. Probieren Sie einfach aus, was besser passt.

Ein Projektbuch anlegen

Ihr Projektbuch ist ausschließlich dem Thema »Loslassen« und dem Finden und Verwirklichen Ihrer Wünsche und Träume gewidmet. Der »kleine Coach« lädt Sie immer wieder dazu ein, konkrete Erfahrungen zu machen. Sie finden auf den folgenden Seiten viele Anregungen, Neues zu erproben, zu üben und Ihre Ergebnisse schriftlich zu dokumentieren. **In Ihrem Projektbuch sammeln Sie alle Ihre Beobachtungen, Erkenntnisse und Erfahrungen** und haben jederzeit einen Überblick darüber, wo Sie gerade stehen. Arbeiten Sie auch mit Symbolen, Collagen, Zeichnungen – allem, was sich eignet, Ihre Gedanken und Gefühle darzustellen. Dabei gibt es kein »richtig« oder »falsch« – was Ihr »Bauchgefühl« als wichtig erkennt, ist es wert, hier dokumentiert zu werden. Das Projektbuch kann ein richtiges »Buch« zum Anfassen sein, aber auch ein Ordner, in den Sie einzelne Blätter abheften, oder ein virtueller Ordner mit entsprechenden Dateien – wählen Sie die für Sie passende Form.

Der innere Rahmen

Es geht nicht darum, sich selbst als Mängelwesen anzusehen, an dem es »Verbesserungen« vorzunehmen und »Defizite« auszugleichen gilt. In dem Glauben, Sie müssten besser, schneller, schöner oder perfekter werden, um endlich die Liebe und die Wertschätzung zu bekommen, nach der Sie sich sehnen, haben Sie Ihr Leben lang viel, viel Energie aufgewendet. Sie kennen das zur Genüge. Nein, Sie sind okay so, wie Sie sind, mit allem Drum und Dran. Sie müssen gar nichts verän-

> »*Der größte **Feind** der Ruhe ist der **Druck**, unter den wir uns **selbst setzen**.*« Anselm Grün

dern, wenn Sie dies nicht wollen. Loslassen bedeutet, sich von dem zu befreien, was Sie bislang daran hinderte, Erfüllung in Ihrem Leben zu finden und immer mehr zu dem vorzudringen, was Ihre Persönlichkeit, Ihre gefühlte Bestimmung ist. Das heißt auch, zu akzeptieren, dass Sie nicht bekommen haben, was Sie sich gewünscht hatten. Und dass Sie sich bewusst entschließen, nicht weiter danach zu streben, sondern stattdessen einen neuen Weg einzuschlagen. Sehen Sie sich selbst mit liebevoller Distanz – so, wie Sie jemanden betrachten würden, an dem Ihnen sehr gelegen ist – offen und mit großem Wohlwollen.

Lernen Sie zu akzeptieren

Der erste Schritt hin zur Veränderung ist stets, den bestehenden Zustand zu akzeptieren. »Akzeptieren« bedeutet dabei keineswegs »gutheißen«, sondern nur, sich selbst etwas zu sagen wie: »Es gibt Verschiedenes an mir selbst oder in meinem Leben, das ich mir ganz anders wünschen würde. Doch es ist eben so, wie es ist. Ich nehme dies wahr, und ich lehne es ab, mich deswegen unter Druck zu setzen, mich zu verurteilen oder mich schlecht zu fühlen.«

Wenn Sie zulassen können, dass Ihr Leben genauso ist, wie es ist, und nicht anders, und wenn Sie fühlen können, dass trotz aller Unvollkommenheiten nichts falsch an Ihnen ist – dann geschieht bereits eine Art »Mini-Loslassen«, obgleich Sie Ihren Loslass-Prozess noch gar nicht gestartet haben. Das beständige Hadern mit Ihrer Situation lässt Sie Hilflosigkeit oder Ohnmacht spüren – Gefühle, die zum Festhalten führen, an dem »Was sein sollte« und vor allem dem »Wie Sie sein sollten«. Dieses Festhalten hat ein Ende, wenn Sie einfach nur wahrnehmen, was ist. Gleichzeitig ist dieses vorbehaltlose »Annehmen was ist«, die Voraussetzung dafür, dass Sie die mit dem Loslösen verbundenen Gefühle zulassen können.

Gefühle wahrnehmen

Es ist traurig, wenn eine Erwartung nicht erfüllt wird, es tut weh, sich von einem lang verfolgten Plan zu verabschieden. Solange wir hadern, stellen wir uns den Gefühlen des Schmerzes nicht, die der Abschied von einem Traum mit sich bringt. All das können wir erst fühlen, nachdem wir diesen ersten Schritt getan haben: annehmen was ist. Kein »Ich muss«, Ich sollte«, »Ach, hätte ich doch«, »Ach, wäre doch« sondern: Es ist, wie es ist. Wenn wir die Realität ohne Verurteilung und ohne Schönfärberei akzeptieren, entsteht Offenheit und die Bereitschaft aus dem, was geschehen ist, wirklich zu lernen.

Was immer bei diesem vor Ihnen liegenden Prozess des Loslassens zutage kommt: Es ist, wie es ist, und Sie sind in Ordnung mit all Ihren Stärken und Schwächen, mit Ihren einmaligen Vorzügen und Eigenheiten und mit Ihren Grenzen.

So tun als ob

Wahrscheinlich fällt Ihnen das »Akzeptieren, wie es ist« nicht leicht, vor allem wenn Sie
- akzeptieren mit kapitulieren gleichsetzen,
- glauben, ein verbesserungsbedürftiges Mängelwesen zu sein,
- gewohnheitsmäßig im Nörgelton mit sich selbst reden,
- meinen, zwei Stunden pro Woche »nur für Ihre Selbstentwicklung« stünden Ihnen nicht zu,
- sehr stark an Ihrer Fähigkeit, loszulassen, zweifeln.

Grübeln Sie nicht nach, weshalb Sie sich schwer damit tun, sondern pflegen Sie gleich zum Einstieg in Ihre Übungsstunde die Haltung des »so tun als ob«. Sie tun einfach für

PRAXIS

47

die Dauer Ihrer Übungszeit so, als wären diese Akzeptanzprobleme gar nicht Ihr Ding. Gehen Sie fest davon aus, dass es möglich, »erlaubt« und wirksam ist, das Gegebene einfach zu akzeptieren.

Der Sinn dieses »So tun als ob« liegt darin, Ihre alten Muster zu durchbrechen und sich neu auszurichten. Wenn Sie für eine gewisse Zeitspanne eine neue innere Haltung einnehmen, erweitert das Ihr Vorstellungsvermögen über das, was Sie für sich für möglich halten – und langsam ändert sich dann wirklich Ihr Selbstverständnis. Es ist sozusagen eine »Veränderung durch die Hintertür«.

Bevor Sie sich nun an Ihre Übungsstunde machen, sagen Sie sich laut die folgenden Sätze vor, um Ihre innere Haltung zu stärken:

- Ich bin völlig in Ordnung, so wie ich bin.
- Ich gehe mit mir um, als wäre ich selbst meine beste Freundin.
- Ich vertraue darauf, loslassen zu können.
- Ich bin bereit, offen und unvoreingenommen wahrzunehmen, was ist, und zu akzeptieren, was ist.
- Ich heiße jede Erkenntnis willkommen, auch jede schmerzliche.

Üben Sie, sich selbst zu akzeptieren

Jegliches Festhalten soll Unsicherheit und Angst vermeiden. Dieses Grundproblem haben wir alle gemeinsam – von Miss Perfect bis zur Vergangenheitsbewältigerin (siehe auch Seite 31), nur die Auswirkungen sind bei jeder anders. Miss Perfect fühlt sich (halbwegs) beruhigt, wenn sie alles hundertprozentig auf die Reihe gekriegt hat. Everybody's Darling fühlt sich (halbwegs) beruhigt, wenn sie glaubt, dass alle sie mögen und niemand ihr Übles will. Die treue Seele fühlt sich (halbwegs) beruhigt, wenn alles beim Alten bleibt. Die heimliche Prinzessin fühlt sich (halbwegs) beruhigt, wenn sie unbestritten der Star des Abends ist. Die chronische Vergangenheitsbewältigerin fühlt sich (halbwegs) beruhigt, wenn sie sich den Herausforderungen des Hier und Jetzt nicht wirklich stellen muss. Doch stetige Angstabwehr strengt an und schwächt. Wie viel Energie müssen wir dafür aufbringen, den eigenen strengen Ansprüchen zu genügen? Was kostet es zum Beispiel Miss Perfect an Kraft, die lauernde Angst abzuwehren, einmal etwas übersehen zu haben und dann als unzulänglich oder unfähig dazustehen? Wie viel Aufwand muss Everybody's Darling betreiben, darüber zu grübeln, was ein scheeler Seitenblick einer Person nun bedeutet …? »What you resist persists« – »Das, wogegen du dich wehrst, bleibt dir erhalten«. Je öfter Sie sich schlecht fühlen, weil Sie Ihrem Idealbild nicht gerecht werden und sich selbst sagen: »Ich sollte mich nie wieder so verhalten« oder »Künftig muss ich darauf achten, dass ich nie mehr …«, desto mehr stärken Sie diese als Schwäche oder Fehler empfundenen Charakterzüge oder Verhaltensweisen.

Der Weg zu innerem Frieden

Natürlich möchten Sie – wie jeder andere Mensch auch – gut über sich und Ihr Leben denken und sich mit sich selbst wohlfühlen. Dieser ganz natürliche Wunsch verleitet jedoch oft dazu, als negativ empfundene Eigenschaften und Verhaltensweisen zu bekämpfen oder sich dafür zu genieren. Selbstbejahung und ein stabiles Selbstwertgefühl können sich jedoch nur entwickeln, wenn Sie auch die eigenen Unvollkommenheiten wohlwollend betrachten. Wenn Sie darauf bestehen, die Vorstellung davon, wie Sie sein »sollten«, mit Ihrem Selbstwert zu verknüpfen, werden Sie weiter unter ständiger Anspannung stehen. Sie werden sich nicht selbst, so wie Sie sind, annehmen und lieben können. Und es wird Ihnen nicht möglich sein, Ihr Dasein einfach zu genießen, ohne ständig irgendetwas anders haben zu wollen. In dem Maße, wie Sie sich selbst und alles, was hier und jetzt Ihre Situation ausmacht – inklusive aller ungelösten Probleme, Konflikte, Fehler und Unvollkommenheiten – akzeptieren lernen, wachsen Selbstachtung, Gelassenheit und innerer Friede.

Ihr »Päckchen« akzeptieren

Die Lebenserfahrung lässt sich mit einem Päckchen vergleichen, das man als Ausrüstung auf dem Rücken durchs Leben trägt; in diesem Päckchen sind nicht nur schöne Erfahrungen verstaut, sondern auch alle Verletzungen, die Ihnen bisher zugefügt wurden.

Es ist vieles darin, was gut und nützlich ist, aber auch etliches, was nur unnütz zusätzliches Gewicht schafft. Auch die harten »Marschbefehle«, die die Richtung im Leben vorgeben, sind da mit eingepackt sowie eine mehr oder weniger große Anzahl von ehernen Regeln, die bestimmen, was man wann zu tun und wie man sich wem gegenüber zu verhalten hat. Natürlich können in dieser Nachbarschaft Sorgen, Ängste und Grübeleien aller Art gut gedeihen.

Je mehr Kränkungen, deprimierende Erfahrungen, Sorgen, verinnerlichte Befehle und Regeln es in Ihrem Leben gibt, desto schwerer ist auch das Päckchen, das Sie zu tragen haben. Doch es verliert an Gewicht, sobald Sie beherzt anerkennen, dass es da ist und es nicht einfach aufhört zu existieren, wenn Sie es aus Ihrer Wahrnehmung ausblenden. Ja, Sie haben, wie jede andere auch, »Ihr Päckchen zu tragen«. Es ist ein Teil Ihres gelebten Lebens und daran ist nichts verkehrt. Es gehört zu Ihnen und will, wie alles an und in Ihnen, gesehen, akzeptiert und gewürdigt werden. Und in Ihrem Prozess des Loslassens darf das Päckchen natürlich auch immer leichter werden…

So wird es konkret

Atmen Sie jetzt einfach einmal tief durch! Dann weihen Sie Ihr Projektbuch mit der Übung auf der nächsten Seite ein. Sie wird Ihnen dabei helfen, sich besser akzeptieren zu lernen.

Übung: Das Selbst-Manifest

1 Legen Sie in Ihrem Projektbuch eine »Mecker- und Moserliste« an, in der Sie alles auflisten, was Sie an sich selbst ablehnen, was Sie kritisieren, wo Sie sich als unzulänglich empfinden, beispielsweise »Ich bin zu langsam«, »Ich kann mich schlecht ausdrücken«, »Meine Beine sind zu dick«, »Ich grüble zu viel« usw. Schreiben Sie einfach frisch von der Leber weg, bis Ihnen nichts mehr einfällt, egal, ob es letztendlich drei Zeilen oder drei Seiten werden.

2 Ziehen Sie, wenn Sie alles Störende beieinander haben, einen dicken Strich unter Ihre Mecker- und Moser-Liste und schreiben Sie dann – möglichst groß – etwas wie:

»Ich bin ich. Ich bin so wie ich bin. Ich verzeihe mir selbst meine Fehler und Unzulänglichkeiten und sage Ja dazu, dass ich so bin, wie ich bin.
Es gibt kein Gesetz und keine Verordnung, die besagen, dass ich nur aus guten Eigenschaften zu bestehen habe oder dass mein Verhalten stets mustergültig sein muss.
Ich bin völlig in Ordnung, so wie ich bin. Ich darf auch ohne irgendwelchen Anforderungen gerecht zu werden, froh und glücklich sein. **Ich bin wie ich bin, und ich bin gut so.«**

Vielleicht übernehmen Sie die Sätze so, wie Sie dastehen – vielleicht aber formulieren Sie ein eigenes Manifest, das ausdrückt, dass Sie sich entschlossen haben, sich so zu akzeptieren, wie Sie sind. Lesen Sie Ihr Selbst-Manifest vor jeder Ihrer Übungsstunden. Sie können es auch stets bei sich tragen. Wann immer Sie ein paar Minuten Zeit haben, lesen Sie es durch und vergegenwärtigen sich auf diese Weise Ihren Entschluss.

Selbstakzeptanz vertiefen

Ihre Selbstakzeptanz lässt sich mit der folgenden Übung vertiefen. Es braucht Zeit, bis Ihnen dies zur Gewohnheit geworden ist – doch wenn Sie konsequent trainieren, werden Sie eines Tages nicht mehr verstehen, warum Sie früher in überkritischer und herabsetzender Weise über sich geurteilt haben. Wenn Sie diese Übung zum ersten Mal machen, wehrt sich vielleicht alles in Ihnen dagegen. Sie denken etwa: »Nein, nein, ich werde niemals hinnehmen, zu dick zu sein. Ich werde mich immer dafür hassen.« Lassen Sie dann den Einwand einfach stehen und wiederholen Sie Ihren Satz: »Obwohl ich zu dick bin, liebe und akzeptiere ich mich.«

 ## Übung: Versöhnungsformel

Alte Muster sind zählebig. Wenn Sie sich dabei ertappen, sich selbst zu verurteilen oder herabzusetzen, dann sprechen Sie (auch wiederholt) innerlich, oder wenn Sie allein sind, auch laut, eine Versöhnungsformel, die Sie entsprechend Ihrem gefühlten Manko ergänzen: »**Obwohl ich …** (hier nennen Sie das, was Sie belastet, etwa ›zu dick bin‹ … ›mich so doof verhalten habe‹ … ›dieses Problem nicht gelöst habe‹ … ›es nicht schaffe, mich von diesem alten Krempel endlich zu trennen‹ usw., usw.) … **liebe und akzeptiere ich mich voll und ganz.«**

Wann immer Ihnen dies möglich ist, sprechen Sie Ihre Versöhnungsformel laut aus; dies verstärkt die Wirkung.

Geben Sie sich Mühe, Ihren neuen Satz mit Leben zu erfüllen, ihn zumindest zu 5 Prozent für wahr zu halten. Wenn Sie beharrlich weiter üben, dann halten Sie den Satz irgendwann schon zu 20 Prozent für wahr, dann zu 40 Prozent, schließlich zu 70 Prozent …

Üben Sie auch, sich selbst wie Ihre beste Freundin zu behandeln. Wäre Übergewicht ein Grund, sie nicht mehr zu mögen? Doch wohl kaum. Betrachten Sie die Menschen in Ihrem Umkreis: Oft empfinden Sie deren »Fehler« als liebenswert oder besonders charakteristisch. Je mehr Sie sich selbst akzeptieren, Ja zu sich sagen und sich nicht nur berechtigt fühlen, so wie Sie sind, auf der Welt zu sein, sondern auch in ihr etwas zu bewegen, desto einfacher wird es, Belastendes loszulassen und neue Wege zu gehen.

Loslassen – fast wie von selbst

Aber, werden Sie vielleicht einwenden, wenn ich das alles, was ich an mir nicht leiden kann, und Verhaltensweisen, die ich mir übel nehme, jetzt einfach akzeptiere – geht dann nicht jegliche Motivation dahin, etwas ändern zu wollen?

Nein, wenn Sie sich selbst akzeptieren, können Sie endlich mit den Selbstverurteilungen aufhören, die Sie überhaupt nicht weitergebracht haben, und Sie beginnen von selbst mit dem Loslassen. Wenn Sie die Versöhnungsformel regelmäßig üben, wird der Drang, sich selbst und alles, was Sie in die Hand nehmen, perfekt machen zu wollen, abnehmen, Ihr Wunsch, anderen unbedingt gefallen oder gefällig sein zu wollen, ebenfalls. Wenn Sie bisher eher in der Vergangenheit als in der Gegenwart zu Hause waren, wird die Versöhnungsformel Ihnen dabei helfen, Frieden mit dem Gestern zu schließen. Und vielleicht gelingt Ihnen Ihr Vorhaben, etwa abzunehmen, nun viel leichter, weil Sie den Druck herausnehmen – schon in dem Moment, wo Sie sich sagen »Trotz alledem liebe und akzeptiere ich mich«, und sich in

Ihnen ein Gefühl von Frieden und Versöhnung ausbreitet, haben Sie bereits ein Stück losgelassen – noch bevor Sie ein spezielles Thema zum Üben des Loslassens in Angriff genommen haben. Die »Versöhnungsformel« nur einmal zu praktizieren und das dann »abzuhaken«, ist allerdings relativ nutzlos. Die Formel ist umso wirksamer, je konsequenter und direkter Sie sie nach einer Selbstabwertung einsetzen.

Was genau ist Ihr Thema?

Jetzt geht es richtig zur Sache! Werden Sie sich klar darüber, worum es Ihnen beim Loslassen geht. Loslassen kann sich ebenso auf Menschen wie auf Besitz beziehen, auf eine berufliche oder gesellschaftliche Position oder auch auf tief liegende innere Überzeugungen. Wo haben Sie den Eindruck, durch Festhalten am Status quo in einer Sackgasse zu sein? Oder in einer Art Endlosschleife? Was quält Sie, nervt Sie, macht Sie mürbe? Welche Ihrer Reaktionsmuster erleben Sie zunehmend als belastend? In welchen Bereichen haben Sie den Eindruck, Sie seien immer wieder in die gleichen Konflikte mit Vorgesetzten, Partnern, Familienmitgliedern oder Freunden verwickelt? Was sind die Themen dieser Auseinandersetzungen? An welchen alten, eigentlich längst ausgedienten Denk- und Verhaltensmustern klammern Sie sich dabei gerne fest? Was hätten Sie liebend gern los und warum?

Um das zu klären, schlagen Sie Ihr Projektbuch auf und machen die Übung auf der nächsten Seite. Vielleicht lesen Sie sich vorher als kleine Hilfe noch einmal Ihr Profil oder gleich alle Merkmale nacheinander durch (siehe ab Seite 8), wenn Sie – wie viele Menschen – mehrere Aspekte bei sich erkannt haben.

Von Anforderungen frei werden

Die typische heimliche Prinzessin würde vielleicht gerne Muster los-

Übung: Meine Mühlsteine

Schreiben Sie diejenigen Dinge, Situationen, Gefühle, Gedanken und Überzeugungen auf, unter denen Sie häufig leiden. Listen Sie auf:

- was und wer Sie ärgert
- wodurch Sie sich deprimiert fühlen
- womit Sie sich selbst nerven
- was Sie abschaffen wollen
- wer womit Druck auf Sie ausübt

Überlegen Sie beim Anfertigen der Liste, welchen Personen oder welchen verinnerlichten Ansprüchen, Maßstäben und Regeln Sie bisher Macht über sich selbst, Ihre Entscheidungen und die Gestaltung Ihres Lebens gegeben haben.

Notieren Sie alles, wovon Sie sich beeinträchtigt fühlen, so anschaulich wie möglich. Schreiben Sie, malen Sie, fügen Sie Bilder oder Symbole ein – es ist Ihr persönliches Projektbuch, worin alles stehen darf, was Ihnen wichtig erscheint.

lassen, die dafür sorgen, dass sie sich in bestimmten Situationen klein, übersehen oder schlecht behandelt fühlt. Die treue Seele und auch Miss Perfect könnten sich von starren Gewohnheiten trennen wollen, an denen sie wider besseres Wissen festhalten; oder auch von Maßstäben und Regeln, die sie von ihren Eltern oder anderen Personen übernommen bzw. irgendwann einmal für sich selbst festgelegt haben. Die chronische Vergangenheitsbewältigerin möchte vielleicht damit aufhören, erlittene Kränkungen, Zorn oder Groll, enttäuschte Hoffnungen und zerstörte Träume festzuhalten. Everybody's Darlings Herausforderung ist, Gefühle von Abhängigkeit, Ohnmacht und Entmutigung aufzugeben. Allen Profilen gemeinsam ist vielleicht der Wunsch, Ersatzbefriedigungen wie zu viel Einkaufen, Essen, Rauchen … loszulassen (und durch Handlungen zu ersetzen, die nicht über ein Problem hinwegtrösten, sondern etwas daran ändern).

Weitere innere Muster entdecken

Ergänzen Sie Ihre Bestandsaufnahme bei Ihren nächsten Terminen mit sich selbst um die beiden Übungen »Liste der Ladenhüter« und die »Ich-häng-so-dran-Liste«, die weitere Muster aufdecken helfen. Sie beziehen sich auf feste Gewohnheiten und Verhaltensweisen in Ihrem Leben. Viele davon sind gut und sinnvoll. Sie erleichtern Ihnen das Leben an sich und Ihr Zusammenleben mit anderen. Dazu gehören beispielsweise achtsame Körperpflege, gute Umgangsformen, gesunde Ernährung, effektive Arbeitstechniken und ethische Werte wie Ehrlichkeit, Hilfsbereitschaft usw. Es gibt aber auch Regeln und Gewohnheiten, an denen Sie festhalten, obgleich sie längst überholt oder kontraproduktiv sind. Irgendwann haben diese Regeln wirklich »Ihren Laden gehütet«, oder das »Daran-Hängen« hat Ihnen gute Gefühle beschert. Mittlerweile stimmt das aber nicht mehr. Um solchen nicht mehr situationsgerechten inneren Regeln und Gewohnheiten auf die Spur zu kommen, betrachten Sie einen typischen Tagesablauf, häufig vorkommende Kommunikationssituationen, Ihren Arbeitsstil, Ihr Verhalten bei Termindruck, bei Ärger, bei Unvorhergesehenem. Registrieren Sie dabei besonders zwiespältige Empfindungen, also »durchwachsene« Gefühle:

> »Was wir **nicht schaffen,** müssen wir loslassen, sonst **schafft es uns.**   Ernst Ferstl

Nehmen Sie Ihr Projektbuch zur Hand und schreiben Sie auf, an welchen überholten Regeln Sie bisher festgehalten haben. Beispiele können sein: immer aufzuessen, was auf dem Teller liegt, niemandem eine Bitte ausschlagen dürfen, keine Ansprüche äußern, jemanden, der Sie gekränkt hat, für immer links liegen lassen, das Horten von Dingen und so weiter.

Meine überholten Regeln sind:
- Ich muss (immer) . . . .
- Ich darf nicht/nie . . . .
- Nur wenn ich . . . . ,
  dann darf ich . . . .
- Gut für mich ist . . . .
- Schlecht für mich ist . . . .

- Sie »sollten« und wollen eigentlich gar nicht.
- Sie würden gerne anders handeln, fühlen sich aber irgendwie »verpflichtet«, so wie bisher weiterzumachen.
- Sie trödeln und schieben Dinge vor sich her … welche?
- Sie haben Angst vor …

Zu den Regeln gehören auch Vorstellungen, wie Sie zu sein hätten, um sich überhaupt als halbwegs anständiger Mensch fühlen zu dürfen und Befehle, die Sie sich selbst vielleicht geben, wie »Reiß dich zusammen!«, »Nur wenn du …, dann darfst du …« usw. (siehe auch »die inneren Antreiber«, Seite 30). Wohlgemerkt: Es geht nur um jene Regeln und Gewohnheiten, die Sie als einengend und überholt empfinden, um ausgediente Muster, an die Sie sich festklammern, obwohl sie Ihnen nicht guttun.

Selbst entscheiden können

Wenn Sie bei der Ladenhüter-Übung bei Ihren »überholten

PRAXIS

Übung: Die »Ich-häng-so-dran«-Liste

Nehmen Sie sich wieder Ihr Projektbuch vor und gehen Sie der Reihe nach auf die folgenden Punkte ein:

1 Wovon fühlen Sie sich abhängig?

2 Wovon wollten Sie sich schon x-mal befreien, was bisher aber nicht geklappt hat?

3 Wovon wissen Sie, dass es nicht gut für Sie ist, tun es aber trotzdem immer wieder?
Ein typisches Beispiel kann etwa die Gewohnheit sein, sich in harten Zeiten mit Süßigkeiten zu »trösten« oder »Ja« zu sagen, wenn einem jemand etwas aufbürdet.

Regeln« zum Beispiel geschrieben haben »Ich muss immer nett zu anderen Menschen sein«, dann überlegen Sie, was dahinter stecken könnte. Was denken und erwarten Sie wohl von sich selbst? Vermutlich etwas wie: »Andere sind wichtiger als ich«, »Wenn ich nicht nett bin, zieht das Schlimmes nach sich« oder Ähnliches. Nun, Sie sollen sich jetzt nicht von einem freundlichen und umgänglichen Zeitgenossen in eine Nervensäge verwandeln; es geht nur darum, wie absolut dieser Anspruch ist und inwieweit Sie ihm als Everybody's Darling oder treue Seele fast reflexhaft gehorchen.

Es ist ein großer Unterschied, ob Sie sich dafür entscheiden, in einer bestimmten Situation nett zu sein – oder ob Sie sich gezwungen fühlen, unter allen Umständen gute Miene zum bösen Spiel zu machen. Genau darum geht es aber: die eigene Entscheidungsfreiheit zurückzugewinnen und damit auch Souveränität und Gelassenheit zu stärken. Gelassen ist, wer losgelassen hat.

Ganz wichtig: Indem alle diese Notizen in Ihrem persönlichen

Buch stehen, entwickelt sich kein Zwang zur Veränderung, sondern es entstehen Ideen und neue Vorstellungen.

Bleiben Sie dran

Fragen Sie sich bei Ihren Terminen mit sich selbst von Zeit zu Zeit, was dafür und was dagegen sprechen könnte, alles beim Alten zu lassen. Woran meinen Sie festhalten zu müssen? In welchen Bereichen möchten Sie das Diktat des »Ich muss…« lockern und wo würden Sie es gerne ganz außer Kraft setzen? Sie können Ihre Mühlstein-, Ladenhüter- und Ich-häng-so-dran-Listen ergänzen, wann immer Ihnen etwas Neues dazu einfällt. Spielen Sie damit. Unterstreichen Sie, verwenden Sie Symbole – Sie sind der Boss.

Wenn Sie mit der Zeit den Eindruck haben, dass Ihre Listen nun alle wesentlichen Aspekte enthalten, die Ursache dafür sind, dass Sie sich bedrückt, bedrängt, umzingelt, ausgenutzt oder ausgepowert fühlen, dann beginnen Sie mit der nächsten Übung.

 ## Übung: Was ist wichtig und was nicht?

Stufen Sie alles, was in Ihren drei Listen steht, Punkt für Punkt auf einer Skala von 0 bis 10 nach der Wichtigkeit für Ihr tägliches Leben ein.

Die Einstufung erfolgt möglichst intuitiv und spontan, dabei ist
0 = völlig unwichtig
10 = äußerst wichtig

Mithilfe dieser Gewichtung erfassen Sie klar, wo Sie am meisten unter Abhängigkeiten, eigenen Ansprüchen und Erwartungen anderer leiden. In der Regel sind die hohen Punktzahlen auch dort, wo viel Angst und Unlust vorhanden sind und bisher eine Änderung blockiert haben.

Erste Schritte in die richtige Richtung machen

Mithilfe der letzten Übung haben Sie herausgefunden, unter welchen »Altlasten« Sie besonders stark leiden und welche Sie weniger belasten. Schätzen Sie nun in der Übung unten ein, wie leicht oder schwer Ihnen das Loslassen bei den einzelnen Punkten auf Ihren Listen fällt. Je mehr Sie sich Ihrer persönlichen Sichtweise im Ist-Zustand bewusst werden, desto mehr fangen Sie unwillkürlich damit an, manches nicht mehr als gegeben hinzunehmen, sondern sich zu überlegen, welche anderen Möglichkeiten es geben könnte. Es geschieht also eine »Auflockerung«. Mit dem In-Frage-Stellen vertrauter Reaktionsmuster machen Sie einen Schritt hin zur Entscheidung: Festhalten oder Loslassen.

Es geht also nicht darum, ein Verhalten auszurotten oder quälende Erinnerungen für alle Zeiten ausradieren zu wollen, sondern darum, die eigene Entscheidungsfreiheit wiederzugewinnen und flexibler einzuschätzen, in welcher Situation welches Verhalten zu guten Ergebnissen für Sie führt.

 ## Übung: Was ist einfach und was nicht?

Ordnen Sie nun die Punkte auf Ihren Listen neu zu – wieder auf einer Skala von 0 bis 10, dabei bedeuten 0 = leicht loszulassen und 10 = äußerst schwer loszulassen. Schauen Sie sich jetzt beide Einstufungen an und meditieren Sie ein wenig darüber:

- Was ist relativ unwichtig und leicht loszulassen?
- Was ist wichtig und doch relativ leicht loszulassen?
- Was ist relativ unwichtig und trotzdem schwer loszulassen?
- Was ist wichtig und zudem schwer loszulassen?

Übung: Festhalten oder Loslassen?

Klären Sie nun mithilfe Ihres Projektbuchs folgende Fagen:

- Wo, in welchen Situationen möchte ich auf das Festhalten am alten Verhalten nicht oder noch nicht verzichten?
- In welchen Situationen ist es gut und sinnvoll? In welchen Situationen ist es bedrückend?
- Wo genau will ich loslassen? Diese Übung hilft Ihnen dabei, die einzelnen Punkte, die Sie bei der vorhergehenden Übung gefunden haben, zu reflektieren, vielleicht manches zu relativieren, neue Aspekte zu entdecken und schließlich Ihr Verhalten neu zu bewerten.

Loslassen und Entspannen unterstützen sich gegenseitig

Übermäßiges Festhalten fesselt nicht nur die Gedanken, sondern führt auch auf der körperlichen Ebene zu chronischen Anspannungen. Diese können sich in Form von Kopf-, Nacken- oder Rückenschmerzen bemerkbar machen, aber auch als Schlaf- und Verdauungsstörungen. Außerdem lassen sie den Blutdruck ansteigen.

So wie Festhalten und Anspannung Hand in Hand gehen, sind auch Loslassen und Entspannen eng miteinander verknüpft. Daher ist es sinnvoll, Ihre Sitzungen mit sich selbst mit gezielter Entspannung abzurunden. Entspannungsübungen, die Sie regelmäßig durchführen, helfen Ihnen dabei, innere Sicherheit, Gelassenheit und Zuversicht zu entwickeln und zugleich Ihre Gesundheit und Ihr Immunsystem zu stärken. Schließen Sie daher Ihre Sitzungen mit sich selbst jeweils mit der nachfolgenden Übung auf Seite 62 ab. Sie benötigen für einen Durchgang jeweils etwa 8 bis 10 Minuten Zeit.

PRAXIS

Übung: Entspannen, Loslassen und neue Energie schöpfen

1 Setzen Sie sich aufrecht mit geradem Rücken so hin, dass Ihr Atem frei fließen kann. Schließen Sie die Augen.

2 Denken Sie an das, was Sie loslassen wollen und an etwas, was Sie gerne anstelle dessen als neue Qualität hätten.

3 Atmen Sie ein und wieder aus. Spüren Sie, wie der Atem ein- und wieder ausströmt. Forcieren Sie nichts, lassen Sie ihn kommen und gehen, wieder und wieder.

4 Beim Ausatmen stellen Sie sich vor, dass das, was Sie loslassen wollen, mit dem Atem wegströmt. Sie können das mit einem gedanklichen »Looos« begleiten.

5 Bei jedem Einatmen stellen Sie sich vor, wie neue Energie in Sie einströmt. Auch dies können Sie gedanklich mit einem »Eeeinn« oder mit einem »Jaaa« unterstreichen.

6 Sobald Sie sich im Zuge von Phase 2 für ein neues Ziel oder für eine Qualität entschieden haben, die Sie verstärken wollen, können Sie auch variieren und sich beim Einatmen vorstellen, wie sich die Kraft für Ihr Ziel in Ihnen ausbreitet, bis alle Zellen davon durchdrungen sind.

7 Vielleicht finden Sie auch ein geeignetes Wort, das Ihr Ziel oder Ihre Qualität näher beschreibt. Lassen Sie dann Ihren Atem einfach weiter fließen und wiederholen Sie gedanklich bei jedem Einatmen dieses Wort.

8 Schließen Sie die Übung mit einem Dank ab – an Gott, an das Universum, an die Natur – was für Sie passend ist.

Phase 2: Entwickeln Sie Ihre Zielvorstellung

In dieser Phase bündeln Sie Ihre Kraft und geben Ihrem Handeln eine Ausrichtung. Natürlich könnten Sie sagen: »Ich will einfach nur loslassen lernen, was soll ich mich um Visionen kümmern?« Doch erst, indem Sie eine Zielvorstellung entwickeln, sorgen Sie dafür, dass das, was Sie tun, Richtung und Sinn bekommt – weg von dem, was Sie nicht mehr wollen und hin zu dem, was Sie wollen. Das ist etwas anderes als einfach nur nach der Devise zu handeln: »Ich lass jetzt mal los und schau, was dann wird.« Nehmen Sie nun Ihr Projektbuch zur Hand und schauen Sie sich noch einmal die Mühlstein-, Ladenhüter- und Ich-häng-so-dran-Listen an (siehe ab Seite 55). Darin steht, was Sie nicht mehr wollen und auch, was Ihnen davon wichtig erscheint und was weniger wichtig sowie was Ihnen schwer oder weniger schwer fällt. Sie wissen also, was Sie nicht mehr wollen – doch was wollen Sie stattdessen? Finden Sie es mithilfe der folgenden Übung heraus.

 Übung: »Weg-von« in »Hin-zu« verwandeln

1 Legen Sie in Ihrem Projektbuch eine zweispaltige Tabelle an und übertragen Sie in die linke Seite all Ihre Punkte aus den Mühlstein-, Ladenhüter- und Ich-häng-so-dran-Notizen.
2 Kehren Sie im zweiten Übungsschritt alle Aussagen um!

Links steht, was Sie nicht mehr wollen, rechts schreiben Sie auf, was Sie anstelle dessen wollen.

Auf der nächsten Seite sehen Sie in einem Beispiel, wie so etwas für die einzelnen Profile aussehen kann.

Beispiele für eine Weg-von–Hin-zu-Liste

Was ich nicht mehr will	Was ich stattdessen will
Mich immerzu und für alles zuständig fühlen. (Miss Perfect)	Meinen Arbeitsbereich und meine Arbeitszeit klar abgrenzen können, diese Grenzen freundlich und souverän aufzeigen können.
Mich überrumpeln und voreilig zu Gefälligkeiten überreden lassen. (Treue Seele und Darling)	Freundlich, aber bestimmt »Nein« sagen können, wenn man mir etwas zusätzlich aufladen will.
Alles bis zum letzten Komma perfekt machen müssen – auch wenn dabei ein Teil meiner Freizeit draufgeht. (Miss Perfect)	Mich bei alltäglichen, weniger wichtigen Aufgaben mit 80 Prozent Perfektion begnügen und mein Plus an freier Zeit genießen.
Immer wieder den Schmerz alter Kränkungen spüren. (Chronische Vergangenheitsbewältigerin)	Wieder vertrauen können, mich auf Neues einlassen, inneren Frieden fühlen, ganz bei mir sein.
Mich nur dann gut fühlen, wenn mich alle bewundern. (Heimliche Prinzessin)	Mich selbst auch dann akzeptieren und mich wohlfühlen können, wenn ich »durchschnittlich« bin.
Bei Frust und Stress Süßigkeiten in mich hineinzustopfen. (Sich trösten wollen betrifft alle Typen, am meisten die treue Seele und Everybody's Darling.)	Eine andere – gesündere – Form der Aufmunterung und Entspannung ausprobieren (spazieren gehen, mit einem lieben Menschen telefonieren, eine Tasse süßen Tee trinken…).
Schnell beleidigt sein, wenn nicht alles nach meinen Wünschen läuft. (Heimliche Prinzessin)	Freundlich und unbefangen nachfragen können, warum der andere »nein« gesagt hat.

Versuchen Sie die Punkte auf der rechten Seite so anschaulich und positiv wie möglich zu formulieren. Wenn Sie sie dann konzentriert durchlesen, erkennen Sie, wo Ihre Bedürfnisse, Wünsche und Sehnsüchte liegen. Vielleicht hatten Sie aber auch Schwierigkeiten, die Aussagen in der ersten Spalte so konkret umzudrehen bzw. Ihre Ziele derartig klar zu formulieren wie in unserem Beispiel. Versuchen Sie es in diesem Fall mit der folgenden Übung.

 ## Übung: Ihrer Vision auf der Spur

Versuchen Sie sich zu entspannen und in die Zukunft zu träumen. Stellen Sie sich dabei vor, dass Sie Ihre Mühlsteine, veralteten Regeln und Ladenhüter bereits losgelassen haben, dass Sie frei von all dem sind, was Ihnen lange Zeit das Gefühl gegeben hat, innerlich angekettet, in einer Tretmühle oder einer Sackgasse gelandet zu sein ... frei davon, ganz frei. Wie fühlt sich das an? Was sehen Sie und was hören Sie, wenn Sie sich in diesen Zustand des Gelöstseins und der Freiheit versetzen? Wo zieht es Sie hin? Was möchten Sie verwirklichen?

Lassen Sie einfach aufsteigen, was von selbst kommt. Lassen Sie sich ruhig Zeit beim Hineinspüren. Achten Sie auf das, was Sie stark bewegt und wo Sehnsucht aufkommt, so etwas wie »Ja, genau, so soll es sein, da möchte ich hin«.
Fühlen Sie sich nun befreit, erleichtert und stark zu Ihrer Zukunftsvision hingezogen? **Wenn Sie jetzt aus vollem Herzen »JA« sagen können, dann ist Ihre Vision auch wirklich Ihre Vision,** und die Ziele, die Sie sich später setzen, werden auch wirklich Ihre Ziele sein.

Vorsicht vor neuen Ansprüchen an sich selbst

Wenn Sie Ihre Ziele bei der letzten Übung deutlich gespürt haben, versuchen Sie es noch einmal mit der zweiten Spalte Ihrer Tabelle und der Formulierung Ihrer Vorhaben. Wenn Sie bei der Vorstellung aber eher Druck empfunden haben bzw. die Vorstellung merkwürdig blass und ohne nennenswerte innere Anteilnahme blieb, dann hat sich wahrscheinlich in Ihre Vorstellungswelt ein neues »sollte« eingeschlichen: sozusagen ein Anspruch, »was Sie eigentlich wollen sollten«. Haben Sie in diesem Fall Geduld mit sich.

Alle Punkte, die bei der Zielvorstellung wenig Gefühl aufkommen lassen, sind so noch keine wirklichen Loslass-Kandidaten. Sie können nun mit anderen Formulierungen zu der Frage »Was will ich anstelle dessen?« experimentieren. Ihr Gradmesser ist stets das Gefühl. Eine gute Möglichkeit, den eigenen Gefühlen und Bedürfnissen auf die Schliche zu kommen, ist die nächste Übung, die sogenannte »Wunderfrage«.

 ## Übung: Die Wunderfrage

Stellen Sie sich vor, über Nacht wäre ein Wunder geschehen. Eine gute Fee hätte Sie besucht. Während Sie schliefen, hätte sie das, was Sie nicht mehr haben wollen, einfach weggezaubert.
Woran würden Sie die Änderung merken? Was wäre anders?

Die Antwort auf diese Fragen – die Sie natürlich am besten schriftlich in Ihrem Projektbuch aufzeichnen – führt Sie direkt hin zu denjenigen Wünschen, Bedürfnissen und Träumen, die Ihnen bisher vielleicht nicht so bewusst waren.

Ihr Gefühl ist wichtig

Sowohl die Vorstellung, das loszulassen, was Sie so nicht mehr wollen, als auch die Vorstellung, was stattdessen sein soll, braucht also Ihre emotionale Beteiligung, um tragfähig zu sein.

Vielleicht wollen Sie das Rauchen loslassen, doch Ihre Zielvorstellung, rauchfrei zu sein, enthält keinerlei positive Gefühle als Ansporn, sondern nur Verstandesargumente wie »Gesundheit« und »Geld sparen«. Sogar bei der Beantwortung der Wunderfrage sehen Sie sich nur neidisch auf alle Noch-Raucher schielen – in diesem Fall wird es recht anstrengend werden, Ihren Wunsch in die Tat umzusetzen. Haben Sie jedoch ein Bild vor sich, wie Sie topfit einen Berg hochwandern, tief die würzige sauerstoffreiche Waldluft einatmen und dann von oben einen sagenhaften Panoramablick genießen, dann lockt das schon mehr, oder? Je anschaulicher, beschwingter und optimistischer Ihre Vision ist, desto leichter wird

es sein, sich in dieser Richtung in Bewegung zu setzen.

Was aber tun, wenn sich beim einen oder anderen Punkt in der Umkehrung statt Erleichterung eher Beklemmung breitmacht? Angenommen, Sie wollen alte Kränkungen loslassen und deshalb Ihrem Exfreund verzeihen, dass er Sie betrogen und verlassen hat. Und nun haben Sie trotz aller Vorstellungs- und Formulierungskünste ein mulmiges Gefühl, wenn Sie das lesen. In diesem Fall lassen Sie den problematischen Punkt einfach vorläufig als Option stehen und setzen Sie ein Sternchen oder ein Fragezeichen dahinter. Es wird dann fürs erste (noch) nicht weiter bearbeitet.

Haben Sie Geduld mit sich

Beim Loslassen ist es wie mit Obst: Ein Apfel fällt erst dann vom Baum, wenn er richtig reif ist. Loslassen wollen, ohne wirklich bereit zu sein, hieße, sich etwas abzunötigen und es sich richtig schwer zu machen. Der »kleine Coach« möchte

> *»Wer glücklich reisen will,*
> *reise mit leichtem Gepäck.«* Antoine de Saint-Exupéry

Sie aber zu mehr Leichtigkeit in Ihrem Leben verlocken. Bürden gibt es ja schon mehr als genug!

Stellen Sie die sperrigen Punkte einfach in die Warteschleife (sie laufen Ihnen sicher nicht weg) und halten sich dafür an jene Punkte, wo Sie ganz klar fühlen: »Das will ich loslassen – künftig will ich lieber …!«

Gehen Sie Ihre Liste daraufhin noch einmal durch und achten Sie dabei besonders auf Ihre Gefühle.

Wählen Sie etwas Einfaches

Wählen Sie nun einen der Punkte auf der Liste aus und machen Sie ihn zu Ihrem ersten Loslass-Projekt. Wählen Sie einen Punkt aus, der

● Ihnen vom Gefühl her sehr wichtig ist; bei dem sowohl das »Ich will das nicht mehr« als auch die Vorstellung von dem, was Sie erreichen wollen, von starken Gefühlen begleitet sind.

● nicht gerade in die Kategorie »sehr schwierig« fällt, sondern eher ein Punkt ist, von dem Sie spontan etwas sagen würden wie: »Ja, das ist zu schaffen!« oder: »Ich bin überzeugt, dass ich daran etwas verändern kann.«

Wenn Sie, um das letzte Beispiel wieder aufzugreifen, das Thema »Alte Kränkungen loslassen« bearbeiten wollen, könnte so ein einfach zu bearbeitender Punkt sein: »Mich immer schweigend gekränkt zurückziehen, wenn jemand einen Vorschlag von mir ablehnt.«

Schreiben Sie diesen Punkt noch einmal in Ihr Projektbuch und setzen Sie dahinter: »Das will ich loslassen!«

Dann notieren Sie groß und dick Ihre Zukunftsvorstellung zu diesem Punkt (beispielsweise: »Inneren Frieden fühlen.)« und schreiben dahinter: »Das will ich!«

Verbindlichkeit schaffen

Es macht einen Unterschied, ob das Anliegen, worum es Ihnen geht, nur im Kopf als rein theoretischer Gedanke da ist oder ob Sie es konkret auf Papier bringen. Indem Sie Ihre Vision aufschreiben, verdeutlichen Sie, dass Sie es ernst meinen und nicht nur vor sich hinträumen.

Gleichzeitig haben Sie eine kleine Loslass-Übung schon ganz nebenbei praktiziert: Indem Sie sich für ein Projekt entschieden haben, auf das Sie sich konzentrieren wollen, haben Sie bereits alles andere erst einmal losgelassen.

Mit den nachfolgenden beiden Übungen können Sie nun Ihre Motivation weiter stärken.

 Übung: Motivation zum Loslassen stärken

Notieren Sie in Ihr Projektbuch die Antwort auf folgende Fragen:

1 Was will ich loslassen?

2 Welchen Preis habe ich bisher für das Festhalten bezahlt, dafür, dass ich nach dieser Regel oder Überzeugung lebe und welchen Preis werde ich wohl zahlen, wenn ich das auch weiterhin tue?

3 Welchen Schmerz oder Stress erzeugt das Festhalten an dieser Gewohnheit, Regel, Überzeugung oder Abhängigkeit in meinem Leben?

4 Welchen negativen Einfluss hat dieses Festhalten auf mein Selbstwertgefühl und mein Selbstvertrauen?

5 Was bewirkt das Festhalten in meinem Umfeld? Wer profitiert davon, wer leidet darunter?

6 Welchen Preis werde ich in fünf Jahren zahlen müssen?

7 Wie sieht es in zehn Jahren aus? Was hat mich das Festhalten am Status quo bis dahin psychisch, körperlich und finanziell gekostet?

Was Festhalten kosten kann

Für das Festhalten an alten Kränkungen zahlen Sie beispielsweise mit immer wieder aufwallendem Zorn und schließlich mit Verbitterung. Sie zahlen damit, Misstrauen zu verallgemeinern (könnte ja schließlich wieder passieren!) und sich zukünftige schöne Erfahrungen bereits im Vorfeld zu vermasseln. Diese immer wiederkehrenden Gedanken an vergangenes Leid schmerzen und deprimieren gehörig. Irgendwann kann das auch seinen Niederschlag auf körperlicher Ebene finden. Typische Beispiele sind Erschöpfung, Muskelverspannungen, Kopf- oder Magenschmerzen, Schlafstörungen und andere Beschwerden. Ihr Selbstwertgefühl und Selbstvertrauen werden unterminiert, Sie fühlen sich oft als hilfloses Opfer. Wer profitiert davon? Eigentlich haben nur Menschen, die Ihnen nicht gut gesinnt sind, etwas davon, wenn Sie sich selbst schwächen. Ihre Freunde aber leiden wahrscheinlich darunter, dass Sie sich so quälen. Die Vorstellung, dass dies so weitergehen könnte und Ihnen das Leben immer weiter vermiest, müsste Ihnen eigentlich ganz spontan ein »Um Himmels willen, bloß nicht!« entlocken …

Was ist in fünf Jahren?

Was immer Sie loslassen wollen, nehmen Sie dazu stets die 5-Jahres-Perspektive ein und Sie sehen klarer, welche Folgen ein »Weiter so« haben könnte. Dies zeigt Ihnen vor allem, welchen Preis Sie für das Festhalten zahlen, und ist ein **Gradmesser dafür, wie ernst Sie es mit dem Loslassen meinen.** Wenn Ihnen der Gedanke daran, dass Sie in fünf Jahren immer noch ohne neuen Partner sind, sich 20 Jahre älter fühlen, als Sie sind, und mit Ihrer Bitterkeit sämtliche liierten Freundinnen vergrault haben, nur ein Achselzucken entlockt, dann werden Sie sich nicht die Mühe machen, sich allmählich auf Neues einzulassen.

Die folgende Übung hilft Ihnen, Ihre Motivation weiter zu stärken.

Übung: Zielmotivation stärken

Nehmen Sie Ihr Projektbuch und beantworten Sie diese Fragen:
1 Was will ich künftig?
2 Welche positiven Auswirkungen hat das auf mein Leben? Was wird dadurch anders sein als bisher?
3 Welchen Einfluss auf mein Selbstwertgefühl und mein Selbstvertrauen wird es haben, wenn ich dieses Ziel erreiche?
4 Was werde ich langfristig betrachtet dadurch gewinnen?

Malen Sie sich alles so anschaulich wie möglich aus, damit es Sie regelrecht zum Aufbruch drängt.

Nicht übertreiben

Vielleicht würde es Sie reizen, gleich jetzt vieles auf einmal loszulassen – wo Sie doch gerade so schön in Aufbruchstimmung sind! Dagegen ist nichts einzuwenden – mit einer Einschränkung: Es dürfen gerne mehrere Sachen aus der Kategorie »Fällt mir leicht« sein (beispielsweise sich von bestimmten Sachen trennen, an denen Ihr Herz ohnehin wenig hängt), denn dies beschert Ihnen rasch Erfolgserlebnisse. Jedoch: Verzetteln Sie sich nicht! Es sollte nur ein einziges anspruchsvolleres Projekt darunter sein, bei dem Sie mit größeren inneren und/oder äußeren Widerständen zu rechnen haben. Gerade wenn Sie einige Wesenszüge von »Miss Perfect« an sich bemerkt haben, geraten Sie immer wieder in Versuchung, zu viel auf einmal erreichen zu wollen und sich dadurch zu verzetteln.

Es ist besser, kleine Schritte zu machen und Erfolg zu haben, als gleich die Sieben-Meilen-Stiefel anzuziehen und sich damit vielleicht entmutigt im Dickicht wiederzufinden. Starten Sie also nicht mit drastischen Aktionen, sondern richten Sie zunächst den Blick auf das, was Sie ohne allzu viel Aufwand künftig anders machen wollen und können.

Loslassen als Prozess erfahren

Schritt um Schritt geschehen dann kleine Veränderungen, die Sie weiterbringen. Sie lockern eingefahrene Verhaltensweisen und schaffen damit Raum für Neues. Jedes erfolgreiche Lassen wird Sie erleichtern und gleichzeitig auch zu weiteren Veränderungen anspornen. Setzen Sie sich dabei nicht selbst unter Druck. Lassen Sie geschehen. Wenn es nicht vorangehen will, machen Sie die Schritte kleiner. Zeigen Sie Geduld mit sich, wenn sich nicht gleich alles nach Ihren Wünschen entwickelt, Stagnation und Rückschritte sind völlig normal (siehe auch ab Seite 108). Schließlich lassen sich alte Denk- und Verhaltensgewohnheiten nicht mit einem einfachen Entschluss in Luft auflösen. Dokumentieren Sie Ihre Erfahrungen in Ihrem Projektbuch, die Erfolge ebenso wie die schwierigen Phasen.

Ein Schritt nach dem anderen

Erst wenn Sie mit Ihrem ausgewählten Projekt auf einem Verwirklichungsstand sind, von dem Sie aus vollem Herzen sagen: »Ja, das ist jetzt okay so, damit komme ich jetzt gut klar«, dann wählen Sie das nächste Loslass-Projekt auf Ihrer Liste aus. Arbeiten Sie sich zum Mittelfeld Ihrer Liste und dann zu den schwierigeren Projekten vor. Je mehr Erfahrungen Sie mit dem Loslassen gewinnen, desto leichter wird es Ihnen schließlich fallen.

> »*Man muss es so einrichten, dass einem das Ziel entgegenkommt.*« Theodor Fontane

Phase 3: Abschied nehmen und loslassen

Sie wissen nun konkret, was Sie an Ballast und alten Zöpfen über Bord werfen wollen, und Sie haben eine deutliche Vorstellung davon entwickelt, wohin die Reise gehen soll. Beglückwünschen Sie sich selbst zum bis hierher schon zurückgelegten Weg!

Nun gehen Sie es praktisch an und lassen das, was Sie zunehmend als Belastung erleben, hinter sich.

Orientieren Sie sich neu

Auf den nächsten Seiten unterstützt Sie der »kleine Coach« bei diesem Vorhaben mit Rat und Tat. Sie finden Anregungen, konkrete Tipps und Übungen zu den Aspekten, die den meisten Menschen die größten Schwierigkeiten beim Loslassen bereiten. Je nachdem, wie viele Anteile Sie von welchem Profil haben, halten Sie normalerweise an einem der folgenden Punkte fest.

Das gilt es loszulassen:

- Perfektionsdrang (Miss Perfect)
- Ansprüche an die eigene Persönlichkeit (Miss Perfect und heimliche Prinzessin)
- Angst vor Ablehnung (Everybody's Darling)
- erzwungene Verpflichtungen und Verfügbarkeit (Everybody's Darling und treue Seele)
- unnütz Gewordenes (alle Profile, am meisten aber Everybody's Darling und treue Seele)
- Verletzungen und Groll (Vergangenheitsbewältigerin)
- Bindungen, die nicht guttun (treue Seele).

Gut sind Sie besser als perfekt

Natürlich gibt es Tätigkeiten, bei denen Fehler richtig gefährlich werden können: das Steuern eines Fahrzeugs, die Verabreichung von Medikamenten usw. Ganz klar: Das Steuer Ihres Autos ist nicht das richtige Feld, um sich im Loslassen

PRAXIS

zu üben. Doch gibt es vergleichsweise wenige Situationen im Alltag, in denen es auf perfekte Konzentration und Genauigkeit ankommt. Und dennoch werden Sie, besonders wenn Sie viele Anteile von Miss Perfect haben, gute Argumente dafür finden, alles hundertprozentig tun zu wollen. Beispielsweise könnten Sie denken, dass Sie Ihre Leistungsfähigkeit und Ihren Erfolg nur Ihrem Perfektionsdrang zu verdanken haben oder dass andere Sie nur akzeptieren, wenn Sie sich und Ihre Arbeit ohne Fehler präsentieren können. Doch das stimmt nicht.

Perfektion garantiert keine Zuwendung

Anerkennung und Zuneigung werden von verschiedenen Menschen aus ganz unterschiedlichen Gründen gewährt – oder auch nicht. In Kommunikationstrainings wird häufig betont, wie wichtig es ist, Sachebene von Beziehungsebene zu trennen. Übertragen Sie dieses Prinzip auf sich selbst und Ihre Leistung. **Trennen Sie Ihre Leistung und deren Bewertung von Ihrem Wert als Person.**

Blättern Sie in Ihrem Projektbuch noch einmal in die Abteilung »Innere Haltung«, zum Selbstmanifest und zur Versöhnungsformel zurück (im Buch ab Seite 51), wo Sie sich anerkennen, jenseits von Wenn und Aber. Wenn Sie stark zum Perfektionismus neigen, ist es wichtig, diese Übungen nicht nur als Einleitung für Ihre Verabredung mit sich selbst, sondern auch »zwischendurch« im Alltag möglichst häufig durchzuführen.

Gleich bleibende Perfektion ist eine Illusion

Sie sind ein Mensch mit ganz unterschiedlichen Stimmungen und Gefühlen – kein Computer und keine Maschine. Von daher wird es immer Schwankungen in Ihrer Tagesform und Ihrer Leistungsfähigkeit geben – wenn Sie beispielsweise müde, hungrig und traurig sind, können Ihre Leistungen nachlassen. Wenn Sie ausgeschlafen, fit und gut gelaunt sind, leisten Sie mehr. Gestehen Sie sich Leistungsschwankungen zu. Erwarten Sie nicht von sich selbst, wie ein Uhrwerk zu funktionieren und haben Sie vor allem an den leistungsschwächeren Tagen Verständnis für sich.

Perfektionsstreben verhindert spielerische Neugier

Menschen mit starkem Perfektionsanspruch haben so viel Angst davor, Fehler zu machen, dass sie sich oft davor scheuen, überhaupt etwas Neues auszuprobieren. Die Vorstellung, als »Anfänger« zwangsläufig Dinge falsch zu machen oder sich ungeschickt anzustellen, lähmt sie. Ganz neu in irgendetwas einzusteigen, sei es eine Sprache, eine Sportart oder ein Gesellschaftstanz, kostet natürlich Mut – aber wie wollen Sie den aufbringen, wenn Sie sich selbst als schlimmste Kritikerin im Nacken sitzen?

Vergleiche fördern den Tunnelblick

Überprüfen Sie einfach mal, inwieweit Ihnen die Bewertung von Leistungen in »perfekt« oder »nicht perfekt« schon so in Fleisch und Blut übergegangen ist, dass Sie Ihre extrem hohen Ansprüche an sich selbst auch auf Ihre Mitmenschen übertragen.

Wenn Sie andere aufgrund einzelner Fehler oder Makel »aussortieren«, nehmen Sie sich selbst die Chance, deren Stärken und liebenswerten Eigenschaften zu entdecken.

»Wir sind gegen keine *Fehler an anderen* intoleranter, als welche die *Karikatur* unserer eigenen sind.«

Franz Grillparzer

Perfektion – oder lieber: Mut zur Lücke?

Eine alltägliche Situation: Sie wollen eine Präsentation vorbereiten und sehen, dass sich auf Ihrem Schreibtisch mehrere Stapel unterschiedlichster Papiere angesammelt haben – Unterlagen für verschiedene Projekte, Briefe, Notizen …

1 Perfektionistische Reaktion: Sie seufzen: »Eigentlich müsste ich meinen Schreibtisch gründlich aufräumen und auch die Regale, damit das alles richtig eingeordnet werden kann. Ich bräuchte neue Ordner, ich müsste im Regal Platz schaffen …« Dann lassen Sie die Stapel aber liegen, denn Sie erkennen, dass Sie keine Chance haben, die Ordnungsvorstellung zu verwirklichen, die Sie vor Augen haben. Mit dieser »Ganz-oder-gar-nicht-Vorstellung« im Kopf lassen Sie es dann lieber ganz sein und schlagen sich anschließend mit einem schlechten Gewissen und Ihrer Unzufriedenheit herum.

2 Mut-zur-Lücke-Reaktion: Sie wollen jetzt den Tisch frei haben, verstauen deshalb nur die Unterlagen, die sich zuordnen lassen, um das Chaos zu mindern, die restlichen schichten Sie zu einem Stapel.

Natürlich wäre es vernünftig, grundlegend Ordnung zu schaffen. Doch ist es wirklich das Wichtigste, was Sie momentan zu tun haben? Geht es nicht darum, so viel Platz zu schaffen, dass Sie Ihre Präsentation auf den Weg bringen können? Indem Sie nicht in Alles-oder-nichts-Kategorien, sondern ganz pragmatisch denken, schaffen Sie zum einen eine kleine Abhilfe für das Ordnungsproblem, widmen sich dann aber mit voller Kraft Ihrer anstehenden aktuellen Aufgabe.

»Viel hilft viel« stimmt nicht

Mühsam Erarbeitetes scheint oft wertvoller als leicht Erreichtes. Dahinter steht meist ein verinnerlichtes »Streng dich an!«. Jedoch lässt sich mit weniger Mühe oft genauso viel oder mehr erreichen. Wenn Sie etwa einen Bericht geschrieben und schon genau auf Fehler geprüft haben, lassen Sie es spätestens dann gut sein. Eine zweite, dritte, vierte Runde, um vielleicht doch noch den letzten Kommafehler zu finden, ist ineffektiv. Die Zeit, die Sie darauf verwenden, können Sie für andere Aufgaben besser einsetzen.

Wann lohnt sich Perfektionismus, wann nicht?

Wenn Sie viel von »Miss Perfect« in sich haben, was heißt dann »Loslassen« für Sie? In erster Linie: differenzieren lernen. Differenzieren Sie zwischen wichtigen und unbedeutenden Unvollkommenheiten. Auch Sportler teilen sich ihre Kraft überlegt ein und unterscheiden zwischen Trainings- und Wettkampftagen. Für Ihren Alltag heißt das: **Arbeiten Sie nicht ständig mit hundertprozentigem Einsatz.** Idealerweise kommen Sie an normalen Tagen mit 60 bis 80 Pro-

 ## Übung: Aufgaben neu einteilen

Legen Sie in Ihrem Projektbuch mit den unten genannten Punkten eine Tabelle an. Tragen Sie darin ein, wie perfekt Sie Tätigkeiten in Zukunft erledigen wollen. Wo wollen Sie ab jetzt Abstriche bei Ihrem Anspruch an sich selbst machen? Welche Aufgaben wollen Sie künftig noch mit ganzer Perfektion erledigen? Wo reichen 80 Prozent? Wo 60 und weniger? Was können Sie an andere delegieren (= ganz loslassen)?

Perfektion 100 %	Perfektion 80 %	Perfektion 60 %	Perfektion nicht erforderlich	Delegieren

zent aus. Mehr Perfektion streben Sie dann an, wenn es wirklich um etwas geht: bei einer Bewerbung oder Präsentation, bei einem wichtigen Kundengespräch usw.

Das 80/20-Prinzip

Lassen Sie sich vom »Pareto-Prinzip« leiten. Es besagt, dass Sie 80 Prozent Ihrer Ergebnisse in 20 Prozent Ihrer Zeit erzielen. 80 Prozent der Zeit brauchen Sie dann, um die verbleibenden 20 Prozent des Ergebnisses zu erreichen. Dieses 80/20-Verhältnis können Sie auf viele Bereiche übertragen: Beim Aufräumen eines Raumes schaffen Sie 80 Prozent des Eindrucks von Ordnung in nur 20 Prozent der gesamt eingesetzten Zeit. Freiberufler erwirtschaften 80 Prozent ihres Ertrages mit 20 Prozent ihrer Klienten, usw. Geben Sie sich also in 80 Prozent der Fälle mit guten und befriedigenden Leistungen zufrieden. Die eingesparte Zeit und Energie haben Sie dann für die wirklich wichtigen Aufgaben und Ziele zur Verfügung.

Ein bisschen »schludern« ist erlaubt

Natürlich wird Sie, wenn Sie in das praktische Üben von Nicht-Perfektionismus einsteigen, anfangs ein mulmiges Gefühl beschleichen, so in der Richtung: »Darf ich das überhaupt? Muss ich nicht wirklich bei allem, was ich tue, mein Bestes geben?« Solche Anflüge von schlechtem Gewissen gehören zur Veränderung mit dazu.

> »Es ist **besser, unvollkommene** Entscheidungen durchzuführen, als beständig nach vollkommenen Entscheidungen zu suchen, die es niemals geben wird.«
>
> Charles de Gaulle

Suchen Sie bewusst Gelegenheiten, bei denen Sie gezielt unperfekt handeln, bei denen es nicht wirklich um etwas geht, wie beispielsweise das an sich harmlose wöchentliche Meeting mit den Kollegen, bei dem Sie ausnahmsweise mal nicht jedes Detail parat haben. Vielleicht legen Sie sogar einmal einen gänzlich unperfekten Tag ein – ohne Pläne und Tagesagenda, an dem Sie einfach alles so nehmen, wie es kommt.

Den inneren Kritiker stoppen

Achten Sie dabei auf Ihren inneren Dialog. Wer perfektionistische Ambitionen hat, hat in der Regel auch einen recht strengen inneren Kritiker. Sie werden feststellen, dass dieser sehr beunruhigt ist, wenn Sie anfangen, Ihre Perfektionsansprüche loszulassen. Halten Sie inne, wenn Sie merken, dass Sie Ihre üblichen »Du-solltest-aber-eigentlich-Sätze« denken. Sagen Sie sich dann nachdrücklich etwas wie: »Mein Einsatz dafür reicht völlig aus.« Je häufiger Sie auf diese neue Art handeln, umso leichter wird es Ihnen schließlich auch fallen. Es geht nicht darum, Perfektion künftig um jeden Preis zu vermeiden, sozusagen »perfekt unperfekt« sein zu wollen. **Es geht darum, die Entscheidungsfreiheit wiederzugewinnen: Ja zur Perfektion, wo sie tatsächlich unabdingbar ist und Nein zur Perfektion, wo Sie damit nur Ihrem gewohnten Schema folgen** oder wo sie zu Stress und Selbstquälerei führt.

Sagen Sie Ja zu sich

»Wenn ich nur schöner, schlanker, reicher, intelligenter, kreativer (oder sonst wie anders) wäre, dann wäre ich auch glücklicher.« Ein Irrglaube, der viele Menschen chronisch unzufrieden, gestresst und unglücklich macht, der viel Energie bindet und der besonders die heimliche Prinzessin beeinflusst. Lassen Sie Ihre Ansprüche an die eigene Persönlichkeit los und sagen Sie Ja zu sich, mit allem Drum und Dran.

Sie wiegen vielleicht ein paar Kilo zu viel, aber Sie haben dichtes, glänzendes Haar und tanzen großartig. Sie sind vielleicht kein Genie im logischen Kombinieren, haben aber einen herrlich trockenen Humor …

Achten Sie auf Ihre Stärken

Beten Sie sich nicht Ihre Schwächen vor, sondern genießen Sie Ihre Stärken. Sie müssen nicht die attraktivste, klügste, gebildetste, originellste Person der Welt sein, um eine Existenzberechtigung zu haben. Sie dürfen genau so sein, wie Sie sind. Akzeptieren Sie Ihr Ich mit all dem, was Sie als unvollkommen empfinden. Das ist gut für Ihre Ausstrahlung und Ihren Seelenfrieden. Lächeln Sie sich öfter mal im Spiegel an und **sagen Sie zu Ihrem Spiegelbild: »Ich mag dich. Du bist völlig okay, so wie du bist.«** Und werfen Sie sich dann eine Kusshand zu.

Tun, was guttut

Beziehen Sie Ihren Körper und Ihre Gefühle stärker in Ihre Lebensgestaltung ein. Ein enges Pflichtenkorsett kann einem regelrecht die Luft abdrücken. Fragen Sie sich im Alltag häufiger mal, wie Sie sich fühlen, was Sie jetzt im Moment brauchen und wonach Ihrem Körper gerade ist. Nach Bewegung? Nach Dehnen, Strecken oder nach Entspannung? Gestehen Sie sich Ihre Bedürfnisse zu und sofern es irgendwie geht, setzen Sie sie um. Entrümpeln Sie Ihren Regelkatalog. Nehmen Sie sich bewusst Zeit für Dinge, die nicht direkt zielgerichtet sind, die kein Geld oder Prestige bringen und nichts mit Konkurrenz zu tun haben. Dinge, die Ihnen einfach nur Spaß machen und Entspannung bringen: Gehen Sie ins Wellnessbad, machen Sie lange Spaziergänge oder hören Sie einfach nur mal wieder Ihre alten Platten und CDs an.

Geben Sie dem inneren Kritiker öfter mal frei. Fragen Sie sich weniger, wie Sie auf andere wirken, sondern worüber Sie selbst sich freuen und was Sie genießen können.

»Alle Liebe dieser Welt ist auf Eigenliebe gebaut.«

Meister Eckhart

Sie dürfen Sie selbst sein

Die Angst davor, abgelehnt zu werden oder bei anderen in Ungnade zu fallen, kennen sowohl Everybody's Darling als auch die treue Seele sehr gut. Das Diktat dieser Angst drängt, ja verpflichtet sie fast schon, das zu tun, was andere erwarten – oder was sie meinen, dass sie erwarten. Sie glauben zudem, dass bereitwillige Anpassung und Verzicht auf Widerspruch oder das Formulieren eigener Wünsche durch Wohlwollen »belohnt« werden.

Doch ist es unmöglich, von allen gemocht zu werden, und im Prinzip wissen Sie das auch. Sich weiterhin der Angst vor Ablehnung zu beugen, heißt auch weiter »Ja« sagen, wo Sie »Nein« meinen, heißt, sich weiterhin vor Kritik zu fürchten und peinlich genau darauf zu achten, nur ja niemanden zu kränken – sogar dann, wenn Sie sich in einer Gruppe nicht ernst genommen fühlen und sämtliche Frotzeleien auf Ihre Kosten gehen. So ertragen Sie auch lammfromm einen Vielschwätzer und trauen sich vielleicht nicht, in einer Diskussion eine abweichende Meinung zu äußern. Es liegt auf der Hand, dass Ihnen das nicht guttut.

Selbstschutz verändern

Je stärker Sie sich vor Ablehnung fürchten, desto mehr wollen Sie sich schützen, vor allem um die hinter der Angst lauernden Gefühle der Unzulänglichkeit abzuwehren. Die Schlussfolgerung, die Ihrer Angst zugrunde liegt, ist: »Wenn andere mich ablehnen, bin ich nichts wert.«

Vielleicht ging es früher einmal darum, sich durch Wohlverhalten die Zuneigung der Eltern zu sichern, denn als Kind empfindet man Ablehnung als Im-Stich-Gelassen- oder Verstoßen-Werden. Obgleich diese Zeit längst vorbei ist, funktioniert das »Programm« aber immer noch, so wie auch andere, einmal erlernte Einstellungs- und Verhaltensweisen weiter funktionieren, ohne dass sie noch Sinn machen – bis Sie Stopp sagen und damit beginnen, etwas zu verändern.

Fehler machen schmälert nicht den Selbstwert

Um die Angst vor Ablehnung loslassen zu können, müssen Sie sich selbst davon überzeugen, dass Sie absolut in Ordnung sind. Solange Sie glauben, dass andere Sie für genauso unattraktiv oder einfältig halten wie Sie sich selbst, blockiert Sie das im Kontakt mit Ihren Mitmenschen, weil Sie automatisch davon ausgehen, dass Ihr Gegenüber Sie nicht akzeptieren wird. Praktizieren Sie das Selbstmanifest und die Versöhnungsformel (siehe Seite 51) im Alltag so oft wie möglich, bis sie Ihnen sozusagen nicht nur zur zweiten, sondern zur ersten Natur geworden sind.

Je stärker Sie sich überzeugen, dass Fehler und Mängel Ihren Wert als Mensch nicht schmälern, desto weniger kümmert Sie das, was andere vielleicht über diese Schwächen denken könnten. Und desto weniger können Kritik oder Ablehnung Ihnen als Person etwas anhaben. Sie werden das auch körperlich spüren. Je mehr Sie in sich selbst zuhause sind, desto leichter fällt es Ihnen, sich zu entspannen. Chronische Muskelanspannungen lassen nach und Ihre Atmung vertieft sich.

Der eigenen Wahrnehmung und Urteilskraft vertrauen

Ein weiterer Schritt zur Unabhängigkeit vom »Gemochtwerden« ist, Vertrauen in die eigene Wahrnehmung und Urteilskraft zu entwickeln. Fragen Sie sich öfter, was Sie sich wünschen, was Sie gut finden und was nicht und was Ihre persönlichen Gründe dafür sind. Bilden Sie sich Ihr eigenes Urteil und stehen Sie dazu. So werden Sie unabhängiger von Meinungen anderer und erleben Ablehnung nicht mehr als Vernichtungsschlag. Ihre eigene Wahrnehmung und Wertung ist gleichrangig mit der anderer, nicht besser und nicht schlechter.

Um Ihr Wahrnehmungs- und Urteilsvermögen zu trainieren, beziehen Sie zunächst bei kleineren Streitfragen Stellung. Mit der Zeit fällt es Ihnen immer leichter, eigene Standpunkte zu vertreten, und damit auch, Ihren eigenen Weg zu gehen. Die Angst, die Sie dazu veranlasste, den einfacheren Weg des reflexhaften Nachgebens zu wählen, weicht zugunsten selbstständigen Denkens und Handelns. Das heißt nicht, sich guten Vorschlägen anderer zu verschließen, sondern sich bewusst zu entscheiden, ob Sie sich einer Meinung anschließen oder eine Gegenposition beziehen.

Das Bewusstsein ändern
Besonders Everybody's Darling und die treue Seele sind darauf abonniert, ungünstige Rahmen-

 ## Übung: Die eigenen Bedürfnisse wahrnehmen

Wenn Sie mit einer Situation unzufrieden sind, so fragen Sie sich:
- Was genau stört mich?
- Was sind meine Wahlmöglichkeiten, um in dieser Situation etwas zu verändern?

Schreiben Sie sich diese Fragen auf einen kleinen Zettel, stecken Sie ihn in Ihre Brieftasche und tragen Sie ihn immer bei sich. Immer wenn Sie mit einer Situation unzufrieden sind, schauen Sie auf den Zettel und beantworten sich die Fragen. So erkennen Sie sehr schnell, wo es sich lohnt, Energie aufzuwenden, und wo nicht.

bedingungen einfach hinzunehmen und sich anzupassen. Mithilfe des Zettels aus der eben vorgestellten Übung schaffen Sie es, Ansprüche an andere zu stellen und dies zu üben. **Es geht dabei um eine Bewusstseinsänderung:**
1. Sie brauchen Ihre eigenen Bedürfnisse nicht mehr automatisch hintanzustellen, weil sie gleichrangig mit denen anderer sind.
2. Sie dürfen Ihre Wünsche und Ansprüche äußern.

Befürchtungen benennen und entkräften

Stellen Sie sich vor, Sie geben nicht klein bei, sondern formulieren Ihre eigenen Wünsche und Vorstellungen. Welche Befürchtungen tauchen da auf? Wenn Sie diese besser kennen, verschwindet das diffus-mulmige Gefühl im Bauch. Sie sehen klar, worauf sich die Ängste, die Sie hegen, beziehen, und können sich gezielt Gedanken über mögliche Abhilfe machen, anstatt wie bisher einfach unbewusst dem inneren Programm »Ich muss Ablehnung vermeiden!« zu gehorchen. Befürchten Sie,

- dass der andere Sie dann nicht mehr mag?
- dass der andere beleidigt ist, und Sie das fühlen lässt?
- dass Sie sich schuldig fühlen würden, wenn der andere enttäuscht, verärgert oder verletzt ist, und Sie dies nicht ertragen?
- dass der andere Sie herzlos und egoistisch findet?
- dass der andere aggressiv wird und Sie sich dann wehrlos fühlen?
- dass jemand, der Ihnen viel bedeutet, sich von Ihnen abwendet?

Und selbst wenn das so wäre? Wie hoch ist die Wahrscheinlichkeit, dass Ihre Befürchtungen eintreffen? Und: Welche langfristigen Auswirkungen hätte es demgegenüber, wenn Sie weitermachen wie bisher? Tipp: Wiederholen Sie noch einmal die Übung von Seite 69, in der Sie die 5-Jahres-Perspektive einnehmen, um diese Frage besser beantworten zu können.

Üben Sie das Formulieren eigener Einschätzungen und Bewertungen zunächst in harmlosen Zusammenhängen, etwa im Familien- oder Freundeskreis. Dies kann man durchaus mit Aufwärmübungen im Sport vergleichen. So wenig Sie bei einem Tausend-Meter-Lauf untrainiert einfach loslaufen, so wenig sollten Sie Ihr neues Verhalten ausgerechnet gegenüber der bissigen Kollegin oder dem autoritären Abteilungsleiter trainieren. Starten Sie mit kleinen Schritten und erwerben Sie sich Schritt für Schritt mehr Sicherheit (siehe auch ab Seite 96).

Verantwortung ja – aber in Maßen

Viele Frauen kennen das Problem, sich zu viel aufzubürden. Besonders bei Miss Perfect, bei der treuen Seele und bei Everybody's Darling ist der Glaube, immer verfügbar sein zu müssen, sehr ausgeprägt. Bei Ersterer, weil sie davon überzeugt ist, nicht anerkannt zu wer-

den, wenn sie nicht alles perfekt macht. Bei Letzteren, weil sie befürchten, abgelehnt zu werden, wenn sie einmal »Nein« sagen. Die anderen beiden Profile sind an diesem Punkt etwas egozentrischer und nicht so sehr bereit, sich jenseits der eigenen Probleme (Vergangenheitsbewältigerin) oder der eigenen Wunschvorstellungen (Prinzessin) viel aufbürden zu lassen.

Wo tun Sie zu viel?

Überprüfen Sie alle Tätigkeiten und Gefälligkeiten, die Sie anderen erweisen, daraufhin, ob es Ihnen Freude macht oder innere Befriedigung gibt, oder ob Sie es nur deswegen tun, weil sich kein anderer zur Verfügung gestellt hat. Wie oft denken Sie: »Wenn ich es nicht tue, bricht alles zusammen«? Wäre es wirklich so? Und wenn? Sind dann nicht alle anderen dafür genauso verantwortlich wie Sie selbst? Welche Dinge, die Ihnen eigentlich gar nichts bringen, übernehmen Sie bislang privat und beruflich, nur weil es für andere bequemer ist? Wo springen Sie laufend ein und verlieren so Zeit für das, was Sie »eigentlich« machen wollten? Prüfen Sie die Gewohnheiten, Projekte und Kontakte, die Sie nicht glücklich machen, die Ihnen nicht oder nicht mehr am Herzen liegen. Je früher, öfter und je konsequenter Sie ungewollte Verantwortung ablehnen bzw. anderen Leuten nicht mehr gewollte Verantwortung übertragen, desto eher sind Sie die Rolle des »Mädchen für alles« los.

Zeit können Sie nur einmal ausgeben

Bedenken Sie: Die Zeit und Energie, die Sie für Ihnen aufgeladene Aufgaben und ungeliebte Menschen einsetzen, fehlt Ihnen eins zu eins für diejenigen Menschen, Interessen und Projekte, die Ihnen wirklich am Herzen liegen. Entscheiden Sie deshalb ehrlich und mutig, welchen Beziehungen, Tätigkeiten, Gefälligkeiten Sie sich künftig weiter widmen wollen und welchen nicht mehr.

 ## Übung: Was ist mir wirklich wichtig?

Tragen Sie in Ihrem Projektbuch in drei Listen A, B und C ein,
- A: bei welchen Tätigkeiten und Menschen Sie sich wohlfühlen,
- B: welche Tätigkeiten und Menschen Sie weiterbringen oder weiterbringen würden und
- C: welchen Tätigkeiten und Menschen Sie zu viel Zeit und Energie widmen.

Auf Liste C stehen Ihre Loslass-Kandidaten, die Ihnen definitiv nicht guttun. Die dort aufgeführten Tätigkeiten sollten Sie schleunigst delegieren beziehungsweise den dort genannten Menschen nicht nur deutlich weniger Zeit widmen, sondern ihnen vielleicht ganz den Laufpass geben.

Prüfen Sie Ihren Besitz

Der Wunsch, sich mit etwas zu trösten, ist allen Profilen gemeinsam, am meisten dürften sich hier jedoch die treue Seele und Everybody's Darling wiedererkennen. Jedes »Zuviel« an Dingen, die Sie in der Hoffnung angesammelt haben, sich etwas Gutes damit zu tun, kostet auch viel Platz, Zeit und Mühe, »verwaltet« zu werden – seien es Möbel, Gerätschaften, Kleidung oder einfach nur Krimskrams.

Unnützes kostet Energie

Belasten Sie nicht auch all diese Dinge, die Sie besitzen, aber kaum benutzen, die Sie vielleicht noch nicht einmal mögen? Jeder dieser Gegenstände fordert immer wieder Aufmerksamkeit: »Ich sollte endlich den Stapel Fachzeitschriften lesen, mal nach einem der ausgeschnittenen Rezepte kochen, und da ist dann auch noch der Brotbackautomat …« Unversehens türmt sich ein überdimensionierter Berg an »Ich sollte« auf. Jeder Gegenstand, den Sie besitzen und der nutzlos vor sich hinstaubt, scheint beständig »Tu was mit mir« zu schreien – und nicht zuletzt mittels des schlechten Gewissens jede Menge Energie abzuziehen.

Wenn Sie unter dem Ballast der Sachen, die auf »irgendwann« warten, ächzen, ist es höchste Zeit, klar Schiff zu machen. Verabschieden Sie sich von den Dingen, die Sie nicht bzw. nicht mehr brauchen.

Warum wir festhalten

An einem Zuviel an Besitz festzuhalten, kann zum einen mit alten Mustern zu tun haben, etwa: »Bei uns zu Hause war nie genug Geld da, und jetzt will ich nie wieder Mangel erleben.« Zum anderen aber auch mit unerfüllten Wünschen, Sehnsüchten und Leidenschaften, die sich im Anhäufen vieler Dinge spiegeln: »Irgendwann einmal werde ich nach all diesen tollen Rezepten kochen und eine fabelhafte Gastgeberin sein …

irgendwann einmal werde ich so viel abgenommen haben, dass ich in diesem Kleid einfach super aussehe ... irgendwann einmal habe ich mir alles über Gartengestaltung angelesen und werde den schönsten Garten in der ganzen Nachbarschaft haben ...« Je mehr »geronnene Gefühle« in Form von alten Wünschen und Plänen in den einzelnen Dingen stecken, umso schwerer fällt es Ihnen wahrscheinlich, sie loszulassen. Doch bedenken Sie: Alles, wovon Sie sich trennen, brauchen Sie nicht mehr zu pflegen, abzustauben und zu verwahren. Wie viel Zeit und Energie werden frei!

 ## Übung: Die Umgebung fiktiv umgestalten

1 Entspannen Sie sich, schließen Sie die Augen und denken Sie an das Zimmer in Ihrer Wohnung, in dem Sie sich am meisten aufhalten.

2 Stellen Sie sich nun vor, in diesem Raum gäbe es nur noch Gegenstände, die Sie entweder wirklich häufig in Gebrauch haben oder die Sie sehr gerne mögen. Alle anderen Dinge hätten Sie verkauft oder verschenkt.

3 Gehen Sie in der Fantasie in Ihrem neuen Zimmer herum und genießen Sie den entstandenen Freiraum, die Übersicht, die Klarheit. Um Sie herum gibt es jetzt nur noch Dinge, die Ihnen wirklich etwas bedeuten, an denen Sie sich erfreuen oder die Sie tatsächlich benötigen ... Genießen Sie dieses Gefühl.

4 Jetzt ist auch genug Freiraum für Neues da. Sie können nun das eine oder andere ergänzen, dazutun, umstellen ... Maßstab ist stets Ihr Empfinden. Räume, in denen wir uns gerne aufhalten geben uns Kraft und fördern die gute Laune.

Laufen Sie sich warm

Mit dem Loslassen von Dingen, die für längst ausgeträumte Träume stehen (die hässliche Vase ganz hinten im Schrank, die man vom Ex zum dritten Hochzeitstag geschenkt bekommen hat), für uneingelöste Ansprüche (die vielen Kochbücher und damit gleichzeitig die Vorstellung, eine perfekte Köchin zu werden) oder für Gefühle der Verpflichtung (der sperrige Schrank von Tante Helga, weil man Erbstücke nicht einfach in den Sperrmüll geben darf), schafft man sich eben gleichzeitig auch seelischen Freiraum.

Sich von Gegenständen zu trennen ist zugleich eine effektive »Warmlauf-Übung«, um Loslassen ganz allgemein zu trainieren. **Kleine Trennungen bereiten den Boden für größere Abschiede.**

Beginnen Sie daher auch hier mit einfachen Dingen, bei denen es Ihnen leicht fällt, sich davon zu lösen. Machen Sie ein Spiel daraus: Gehen Sie einmal die Woche durch Ihre Wohnung und sammeln Sie zehn Dinge ein, die Sie nicht mehr brauchen – dann entsorgen oder verschenken Sie sie.

Lassen Sie alte Wunden heilen

Jeder hat es schon erlebt, ungerecht, beleidigend oder verletzend behandelt worden zu sein, hat Worte, Gesten oder Verhaltensweisen anderer als unangemessen und kränkend empfunden. Manche dieser Erlebnisse sind schnell vergessen, an anderen aber halten wir innerlich fest, oft für lange Zeit. Dieses Verhalten ist Ihnen sicher besonders vertraut, wenn Sie viele Anteile der chronischen Vergangenheitsbewältigerin haben. Alter Groll gerinnt jedoch zu Geschichten, die Sie sich immer wieder selbst und anderen erzählen. Und je öfter diese Geschichten Thema sind, desto mehr halten Sie daran fest und damit »die Glut weiter am Schwelen«.

Oft rührt der Groll von Geschehnissen her, an denen Sie im Nachhinein nichts mehr ändern können. Eigentlich wären Sie die Erinnerung daran auch gerne los, weil Sie spüren, dass Ihnen diese immerwährenden Gedankenschleifen und die damit verbundenen bitteren Gefühle nicht guttun.

Dennoch halten Sie weiter daran fest und empfinden es zunehmend als große Belastung. Das kann so weit gehen, dass Sie wirklich krank werden oder Ihre Gesundheit zumindest stark beeinträchtigt wird.

Das Opfer-Gefühl

Vielleicht haben Sie tatsächlich besonders viel Schlimmes erlebt, sind enttäuscht, verletzt, verlassen, hintergangen oder betrogen worden. Vielleicht gab es Belastendes in Ihrer Kindheit oder andere ungünstige Lebensumstände. Sie haben möglicherweise Geld verloren, Ihren Job, Ihren Mann oder Freunde, Sie wurden krank und »können gar nichts dafür«.

Das Gefühl, Opfer zu sein, ist vielen Menschen vertraut. Es führt dazu, sich in Acht zu nehmen und immer wieder an schlimme Erlebnisse zurückzudenken. Es gibt unterschiedliche Gründe dafür, in die Opferrolle zu geraten – durch Mobbing, Stalking, einen Vertrauensbruch, einen schlimmen Unfall, einen Überfall usw. und natürlich durch Erfahrungen in der Kindheit, wenn man mit Dingen konfrontiert war, die man nicht bewältigen konnte. Sicherlich ist der Blick zurück wichtig, um Muster und Zusammenhänge zu erkennen, die auf der Grundlage des Opfer-Gefühls entstanden sind. **Erlauben Sie es sich ruhig, Mitgefühl mit sich zu haben, wenn die Vergangenheit schwierig für Sie war.** All das ist okay und wichtig – solange Sie nicht dabei stehenbleiben.

Nach vorn schauen

Mittel- und langfristig geht es darum, das Gestern ziehen zu lassen und im Heute zu leben. Und zugleich im Heute gut für sich zu sorgen, damit es Ihnen auch morgen gut geht. Der erste Schritt dazu ist, nicht weiter die leidvollen Auswirkungen bestimmter Erlebnisse zu betrachten, sondern einen Blick auf die »Schätze« zu werfen, die in diesen Erfahrungen verborgen sind. Sie haben aus allem etwas gelernt. Sie sind gefordert, vielleicht auch überfordert worden und haben genau deswegen auch bestimmte

Stärken und Fähigkeiten entwickelt. Um sich darüber klar zu werden, welche das in Ihrem Leben sind, machen Sie die Übung unten.

Was es zu lernen galt

Wenn Sie sich als Kind in Ihrer Familie nicht gemocht und akzeptiert fühlten, haben Sie sich vielleicht Freunde gesucht, die Ihnen halfen, die Probleme zu Hause auszugleichen. Sie haben daraus gelernt, dass

 Übung: Die kleine Schatzkiste

Nehmen Sie Ihr Projektbuch zur Hand und beantworten Sie folgende Fragen:

1 Was hat Ihnen dabei geholfen, problematische Kindheitserlebnisse zu bewältigen?

2 Was haben Sie aus den Erlebnissen Ihrer Kindheit gelernt?

3 Wie, durch wen und wodurch haben Sie sich später im Leben die Erfahrungen erworben, die Ihnen in der Kindheit gefehlt haben?

Alles, was Sie im Leben erfahren haben, gerade auch die negativen und belastenden Dinge, die Ihnen zugestoßen sind, haben die Entwicklung entsprechender Fähigkeiten und Strategien in Ihnen gefördert, mit entsprechenden Erlebnissen zurechtzukommen. Denken Sie an die Muschel: Aus einem Sandkorn, das ins Innere gerät, wird schließlich eine Perle.

es wichtig ist, Freundschaften aufzubauen und zu pflegen. Wahrscheinlich haben Sie die Akzeptanz und Geborgenheit, die Ihnen als Kind gefehlt haben, später in einer Clique guter Freunde oder nach der Gründung der eigenen Familie erfahren.

Keine Energie mehr an alten Groll verschwenden

Halten Sie nicht an alten Kümmernissen fest, beklagen Sie sich nicht länger darüber, was andere Ihnen angetan haben. Sie entziehen sich damit Kraft und geben jenen, von denen Sie sich verletzt fühlen, Macht über sich. Wenn Sie an Vergangenem festhalten und die zugehörigen Gefühle immer wieder durchleben, führen Sie dem Belastenden unermüdlich neue Energie zu. Diese Gedankenschleifen können Sie nur durchbrechen, indem Sie beschließen, das, was war, loszulassen und Frieden mit dem Gewesenen zu schließen. Dazu gehört, dass Sie der Person, durch die Sie verletzt worden sind, vergeben.

Sie können nur gewinnen

Denen Amnestie zu gewähren, die Ihnen Unrecht zugefügt haben, nutzt in erster Linie Ihnen selbst. Es nutzt Ihrem Seelenfrieden und Ihrer Gesundheit, da unsere Gedanken und Gefühle stets auch auf körperliche Abläufe einwirken und selbst die Körperzellen beeinflussen. Indem Sie beginnen, anderen – und auch sich selbst – zu vergeben, initiieren Sie einen Heilungsprozess, der Ihre alten Wunden schließen kann, Ihnen Energie schenkt und Sie für Neues öffnet.

Hilfreiche Rituale

Hilfreich zum Loslassen alter Verletzungen sind Rituale, wie Sie sie auf den nächsten Seiten finden. Damit können Sie sich bewusst loslösen und einen Schlussstrich ziehen. Beginnen Sie, wenn Sie sich von quälenden Erinnerungen an erlittenes Unrecht befreien wollen, auch hier nicht mit dem schwierigsten Fall, sondern »üben« Sie zunächst mit leichteren Kränkungen.

Übung 1: Vergebung und Lernbedarf

1 Nehmen Sie etwas zur Hand, was symbolisch für die Person steht, der Sie vergeben möchten – etwa ein Foto, einen Gegenstand oder einen Zettel mit dem Namen der Person. Legen Sie das Symbol vor sich auf den Tisch in einem Abstand, der für Sie gefühlsmäßig stimmig ist.

2 Betrachten Sie den Stellvertreter der Person und schildern Sie ihr, welche Gefühle ihr Verhalten in Ihnen hervorgerufen hat. Ergehen Sie sich nicht in Beschimpfungen, sondern sprechen Sie nur von sich und Ihren Gefühlen. Nicht: »Du blöder Hund hast mich ...«, sondern: »Als du ... fühlte ich mich elend ...«.

3 Bedanken Sie sich dann bei der Person, dass sie Ihnen durch ihr damaliges Verhalten ermöglicht hat, einen Lernbedarf bei sich selbst zu erkennen, beziehungsweise bitten Sie darum, zu erkennen, was Ihre Lernaufgabe war. Wenn Sie die Lernbotschaft nicht gleich erkennen, dann geschieht das sehr wahrscheinlich in der Wiederholung.

4 Verabschieden Sie sich mit den Worten: »Ich vergebe dir.«

Machen Sie diese Übung eine Woche oder länger täglich, bis Ihre bitteren Gefühle der Person gegenüber abklingen.

Variante:
Wenn Sie sich selbst etwas vergeben wollen, üben Sie vor einem Spiegel. Schildern Sie, wie Sie sich heute mit dem, was Sie damals getan haben, fühlen. Keine Selbstbeschimpfung! Bedanken Sie sich bei Ihrem damaligen Ich für die Lektion und schließen Sie wieder mit den Worten: »Ich vergebe dir.«

Übung 2: Abschiedsbrief

Wenn Sie der Person, die Ihnen Unrecht getan hat, nicht mehr real gegenübersitzen und das direkte Gespräch mit ihr suchen könnten, schreiben Sie Ihr einen fiktiven Abschiedsbrief.

1 Nehmen Sie sich genügend Zeit; Sie können den Brief auch in mehreren Etappen schreiben.

2 Beenden Sie den Brief erst, wenn Sie sich alles Bedrückende von der Seele geschrieben haben und so weit sind, einen Schlussstrich zu ziehen und zu vergeben. Drücken Sie das, was Sie bewegt, deutlich aus, doch überlegen Sie, wie schon bei Übung 1, was Sie aus dem Geschehenen gelernt haben und wie Ihnen dies hier und heute nützlich sein kann. Es ist essenziell wichtig, dass Sie das Vergangene unter neuem Vorzeichen betrachten – als aktiv wertende und handelnde Person, nicht mehr aus dem früheren Opfer-Bewusstsein heraus.

3 Formulieren Sie Ihren Dank für das, was Sie lernen durften.

4 Wenn der Brief Ihnen stimmig erscheint, stecken Sie ihn in einen Umschlag und schreiben Sie Ihren Namen oder Ihre Initialen und die Initialen des Empfängers darauf.

5 Schicken Sie den Brief symbolisch ab: etwa indem Sie ihn verbrennen, von einem Fluss davontragen lassen usw.

6 Wichtig bei dieser Zeremonie ist, dass Sie in Gedanken ganz dabei sind und, wenn Sie sich gelöst haben, zu sich selbst etwas sagen wie »Es darf vorbei sein«.

7 Wenn künftig die Gedanken an die Person wieder auftauchen wollen, sagen Sie diesen Satz »Es darf vorbei sein« und erinnern sich an die Abschiedszeremonie.

Lösen Sie Bindungen

Es ist schon nicht einfach, unter vergangene Bindungen endlich den – symbolischen – Schlussstrich zu ziehen. Doch das Beenden bestehender Beziehungen ist eine noch viel größere Herausforderung. Vor allem, wenn Sie viele Anteile der treuen Seele in sich haben, ist das für Sie die Herausforderung schlechthin. Besonders schmerzhaft sind Trennungen, wenn man auf lange gemeinsame Jahre zurückblicken kann – diese müssen durchaus nicht immer glücklich gewesen sein. Die Zeit zu zweit schmiedet stets zusammen, im Guten wie im weniger Guten.

Wenn gemeinsame Jahre jedoch durch den anderen ein abruptes Ende finden, verliert man über den Schmerz hinaus oft die Orientierung. Denn gemeinsame Lebensentwürfe werden von demjenigen, der weggeht, oder vom Tod, der den Partner, ein Familienmitglied oder guten Freund aus dem Leben reißt, zerstört. Wer zurückbleibt, empfindet Trauer, Schmerz und oft auch Zorn darüber, nun allein dazustehen. Selbst wenn eine Trennung absehbar ist – wenn beispielsweise die erwachsen gewordenen Kinder ausziehen – ist dies oft mit viel Wehmut verbunden. Es kann sich ein Gefühl der Leere breit machen, vor allem wenn man sich vorher überwiegend über die Elternrolle definiert hat.

Bewusst Abschied nehmen

Um die Balance wiederzufinden und sich neu zu orientieren, benötigen Sie zunächst Zeit, dann aber auch die Bereitschaft, die Situation zu akzeptieren und schließlich Mut und Zuversicht, um neue Lebensperspektiven suchen zu können. Setzen Sie sich nicht unter Druck. **Die Gefühle, die mit dem Verlust verbunden sind, sind wichtig, um das Geschehene zu verarbeiten.** Haben Sie Geduld und unterstützen Sie sich selbst, indem Sie ganz bewusst Abschied nehmen. Wenn

Sie einen Ihnen nahestehenden Menschen, beispielsweise einen Expartner, einen Familienangehörigen, eine nahe Freundin usw., innerlich loslassen möchten, eignet sich zur Unterstützung gut die folgende Übung.

Phase 4: Schlagen Sie Ihren neuen Weg ein

Träume, Ideen und Visionen sind der Samen für die Realität von morgen. Nur was man sich vorstellen kann und für möglich hält,

 ## Übung: Abschieds-Visualisierung

1 Stellen Sie sich vor, dass Sie mit der betreffenden Person frühmorgens an einem malerischen Hafen stehen. Die Sonne ist gerade aufgegangen. Ihr Schiff liegt startklar am Kai.

2 Sie wenden sich der Person zu und verabschieden sich von ihr. Sie danken ihr für die gemeinsam verbrachte Zeit und wünschen ihr alles Gute.

3 Sie gehen an Bord und steuern Ihr Schiff in Richtung Sonne. Sie stehen ganz vorn, sehen nicht zurück, und am Ufer bleibt die Person zurück, wird immer kleiner, schrumpft zu einem Pünktchen.

4 Stellen Sie sich vor, dass ein neuer, schöner Ort (eine Stadt, eine Landschaft, was immer Sie sich wünschen) mit neuen, interessanten Menschen auf Sie wartet. Schmücken Sie diese Vorstellung mit den entsprechenden Details aus.

5 Wiederholen Sie diesen inneren »Film« gegebenenfalls hin und wieder, so oft, wie Sie es für notwendig halten. Wichtig ist, dass die Trauer, Abschied nehmen zu müssen, weicht und das Neue, worauf Sie zusteuern, Sie mehr und mehr mit freudiger Erwartung erfüllt.

kann man auch verwirklichen. Im Dreiklang von Wollen, Glauben und Planen vollzieht sich jegliche Veränderung.

Sie haben nun schon einen beachtlichen Weg zurückgelegt, indem Sie

- erkannt haben, wo Ihnen das Loslassen schwerfällt und in welchen Bereichen es gut für Sie wäre, mehr loslassen zu können.

- eine Vorstellung entwickelt haben, was Sie anstelle dessen, wovon Sie sich lösen wollen, gerne hätten.

- schon die ersten Schritte hin zur Praxis des Loslassens gemacht haben, vielleicht auch mithilfe der vorgeschlagenen Übungen oder Rituale.

Indem Sie Ihr »Weg-von« (zum Beispiel Perfektionsdrang, es allen recht machen zu wollen, etwas ganz Besonderes sein zu müssen, ständigem Hadern mit der Vergangenheit etc.) in ein »Hin-zu« (dem, was Sie anstelle dessen wollen) entwickelten, haben Sie sich für einen Veränderungsprozess geöffnet.

Heute Idee – morgen Realität

Wer wir heute sind, ist das Resultat dessen, was wir gestern gedacht und getan haben – oder auch, was wir unterlassen haben. Und wer wir morgen sind, ist das Resultat dessen, was wir heute denken und tun – oder was wir gerade unterlassen. Ein klares Zukunftsbild entwickelt eine Art »Zugkraft« in die entsprechende Richtung. Es erleichtert damit natürlich auch das Ausblenden derjenigen Dinge, die für die vorgestellte Zukunft kontraproduktiv sind. Eine klare Vision bewahrt Sie davor, sich zu verzetteln.

Wie fühlt es sich an in der Zukunft?

Versetzen Sie sich noch einmal innerlich in Ihre Zukunft, als hätten Sie Ihr Ziel schon erreicht. Genießen Sie das Gefühl, frei von dem zu sein, was Sie bisher bedrückt hat, und das verwirklicht zu haben, was Ihnen wichtig ist. Spüren Sie in sich hinein. Lassen Sie sich Zeit, Bilder und Gefühle aufsteigen zu lassen. Wie fühlt es sich beispielsweise an, inneren Frieden zu fühlen, anstatt immer wieder den Schmerz alter Kränkungen zu spüren? Wie fühlt es sich an, souverän nachzufragen, weshalb Ihr Gegenüber einen Vorschlag von Ihnen abgelehnt hat, statt sich wie bisher beleidigt in die Schmollecke zurückzuziehen?

Die Zielformulierung

Kleiden Sie die Essenz Ihrer Vision in klare Worte und formulieren Sie schriftlich einen Zielsatz, der möglichst genau ausdrückt, was Sie verwirklichen wollen. **Schriftliche Ziele schaffen Orientierung und fokussieren Ihre Aufmerksamkeit:**

- Beschreiben Sie das Ziel positiv und so präzise wie möglich.
- Verwenden Sie dabei die Gegenwartsform – als ob Sie das, was Sie anvisieren, bereits erreicht hätten. So sind Sie sich bewusst, dass Ihr Ziel durchaus in Reichweite ist.

- Formulieren Sie Ihren Zielsatz vergleichsfrei, etwa: »Ich weiß, was mir guttut und orientiere mich daran.« Mit einem »Weniger als« oder »Besser als« kann das Gehirn wenig anfangen.

Ihr Ziel sollte durch Sie selbst und Ihre Aktivitäten erreichbar und unabhängig von Verhaltensänderungen anderer oder sonstigen externen Faktoren sein. Ein Ziel, auf dessen Verwirklichung Sie keinen Einfluss haben, ist kein Ziel, sondern bleibt ein Wunsch. Beispiel: »Ich will, dass mein Freund zu mir zurückkommt«.

Wie hoch ist Ihre Motivation?
Fragen Sie sich, nachdem Sie Ihr Ziel formuliert haben: »Wie stark bin ich auf einer Skala von 1 bis 10 motiviert, mein Ziel zu erreichen?« Der Wert sollte mindestens 7 sein. Darunter ist die Energie, die Sie zur Verwirklichung brauchen, von starken Einwänden blockiert. Das ist dann so, als würden Sie mit angezogener Handbremse Auto fahren.

Übung: Einwände hinterfragen

Diese Übung hilft Ihnen dabei, zu klären, was hinter möglichen Einwänden stecken könnte. Nehmen Sie Ihr Projektbuch zur Hand und notieren Sie Ihre Antworten auf die folgenden Fragen:

● Entspricht das Erreichen des Ziels Ihren wichtigsten Wertvorstellungen? Was sagt Ihr Gefühl?

● Müssen Sie Ihre Zielformulierung noch einmal überarbeiten, weil etwas darin Ihre wichtigsten Wertvorstellungen verletzt?

● Welche Auswirkungen hat das Erreichen Ihres Ziels auf andere Menschen und auf Ihre Lebensumstände?

● Was verändert sich noch, wenn Sie Ihr Ziel erreichen? Verträgt sich das? Können Sie diese Konsequenzen akzeptieren?

● Was bekommen Sie gleichzeitig mit Ihrem Ziel, quasi als Dreingabe, was Sie vielleicht gar nicht haben wollen?

● Was gerät eventuell in Gefahr, verloren zu gehen, wenn Sie Ihr Ziel erreichen?

● Wem nützt es, wenn Sie Ihr Ziel nicht verwirklichen? Was ist der konkrete Nutzen?

● Wer leidet darunter, wenn Sie alles beim Alten lassen? Was ist der konkrete Schaden?

Integrieren Sie Ihre Einwände

Wenn Sie die Fragen durchgegangen sind und beantwortet haben, sehen Sie klarer, wo Befürchtungen lauern und wo Sie noch festhalten und warum. Welche Möglichkeiten haben Sie oder können Sie kreativ entwickeln, um den positiven Aspekt, der in Ihrem Einwand steckt, in der Zukunft beibehalten oder sichern zu können? Wenn Sie sich etwa vorgenommen haben, die Vorstellung loszulassen, jeder müsse

Sie nett finden, und sich zum Ziel gesetzt haben, eigene Maßstäbe zu entwickeln und eine eigene Meinung zu vertreten, dann könnte die Befürchtung auftauchen, dass Sie ausgegrenzt werden und die Zuneigung wichtiger Menschen verlieren.

Das Positive anders erreichen

Das Positive an diesem Einwand ist nun, dass Ihr bisheriges Verhalten dazu gedient hat, sich einer Gemeinschaft zugehörig zu fühlen. Was können Sie tun, um künftig als Persönlichkeit mit eigener Meinung dieses Zugehörigkeitsgefühl trotzdem zu spüren? Es gibt viele Wege, anderen Menschen Wertschätzung zu zeigen, etwa durch konzentriertes Zuhören, Blickkontakt, eine zugewandte Körperhaltung usw. Allesamt signalisieren, dass Sie den anderen wahrnehmen, womit Sie Ihrem Bedürfnis nach Zugehörigkeit Ausdruck verleihen können – ohne dass Sie jemandem nach dem Mund reden müssten. Mag sein, dass der eine oder andere, dessen Bedürfnis nach kritikloser Bestätigung Sie nun nicht mehr bedienen, sich abwendet. Ist das dann tatsächlich ein großer Verlust?

Experimentieren Sie

Betrachten Sie Ihre Einwände als wertvolle Impuls- und Ideengeber, die Sie auf zu berücksichtigende Bedürfnisse hinweisen. Überlegen Sie sich jeweils, wie Sie dem hinter einem Einwand steckenden Bedürfnis auf andere Weise gerecht werden können als bisher. Experimentieren Sie, wie Sie sie in Ihr Ziel integrieren können.

Sie haben sich beispielsweise vorgenommen, Ihr Arbeitszimmer gründlich zu entrümpeln und völlig neu zu gestalten. Weg von: dem Horten aller möglicher Unterlagen, da sie ja irgendwann einmal wieder gebraucht werden könnten – hin zu: Übersichtlichkeit, angenehmem Arbeitsklima, einem Raum, in dem man atmen kann. Ein Einwand, der als Bremse wirkt, könnte sein: »Und wenn ich später doch etwas brauche, was ich weggeworfen habe …?« Um diesem Einwand gerecht zu werden, könnten Sie sich beispielsweise vergegenwärtigen, was Sie im Fall der Fälle

- ohne viel Mühe im Internet wieder abrufen könnten,
- von Kollegen zur Verfügung gestellt bekommen könnten,
- in Bibliotheken entleihen könnten.

Das gibt die Sicherheit, dass nichts »verloren« ist, und so ist der Einwand ins Ziel »Entrümpeln« integriert. Messen Sie nun, nach der Bearbeitung bzw. Integration der Einwände, die Motivation für Ihr Ziel wieder auf einer Skala von 1 bis 10. Mit Ihrem Ergebnis und der klaren Orientierung können Sie sich nun auf den Weg machen und eine Strategie entwickeln.

Der Blick zurück aus der Zukunft

Denken Sie zurück an die »Wunderfrage« (siehe Seite 66). Bei dieser Übung hatten Sie sich in die Zukunft hineinversetzt. Sie hatten sich vorgestellt, wie Sie sich gänzlich von dem gelöst haben, was Sie bislang unglücklich gemacht hat, und dass Sie so leben, wie Sie sich das wünschen. Wandeln Sie diese Übung nun ein wenig ab und stellen Sie sich vor, Sie hätten sich in Ihrer vorgestellten Zukunft schon häuslich eingerichtet. Tun Sie so, als seien Sie in der Zukunft und hätten Ihr Ziel schon vor einem halben Jahr verwirklicht. Was haben Sie – aus dieser Perspektive betrachtet – damals getan, um Ihr Ziel zu erreichen? Wovon

»*Kein Weiser jammert um Verlust.*
Er sucht mit freud'gem Mut
ihn zu ersetzen.«

William Shakespeare

genau mussten Sie sich lösen, was mussten Sie anpacken, in die Wege leiten? Vielleicht Kenntnisse erweitern, Kontakte neu knüpfen, sich bewerben usw.? Machen Sie die Übung unten und notieren Sie die Antworten wieder in Ihrem Projektbuch.

Der Sinn der Übung

Indem Sie das Pferd sozusagen von hinten aufzäumen und von Ihrem Ziel aus zurückblicken, werden Ihnen Aspekte des Weges bewusst, die Sie beim gewohnten Blick nach vorn nicht erkennen können. Schauen Sie auf Ihr Ziel hin, ist es, als würden Sie einen Weg mit der Taschenlampe ausleuchten – Sie sehen ein Stück weit und dann verliert sich der Pfad im Ungewissen. Wenn Sie jedoch vom Ziel aus zurück schauen, überblicken Sie den ganzen Weg. Und Sie sehen deutlich, welche Schritte notwendig sind, was zu was führt und welche Zwischenschritte Sie vielleicht nicht im Blick hatten.

Schritt für Schritt

Konzentrieren Sie sich nun auf den ersten Schritt, den Sie unternehmen wollen, um Ihr Vorhaben zu verwirklichen. Erst durch konkretes Handeln können Sie real etwas bewegen.

 Übung: Rückblick vom Ziel aus

Was habe ich getan, das dazu geführt hat, mein Ziel Wirklichkeit werden zu lassen?
- Ich habe …
- Ich habe …
- Ich habe …

Was war in welcher Reihenfolge zu tun? Werden Sie sich über die wesentlichen Schritte klar, die Sie von Ihrem jetzigen zum gewünschten Zustand gebracht haben.

Übung: Zielführende Schritte entwickeln

Kehren Sie aus der Zukunfts-
fantasie ins Jetzt zurück und entwickeln Sie aus Ihren Etappen-
schritten einzelne Teilziele.
- Was wäre ein erster kleiner
Schritt?
- Was wäre aus dieser Situation
heraus der nächste Schritt?
- Stellen Sie sich vor, Sie haben
diesen Schritt bereits getan … –
Was hat sich verändert?

- Wie fühlen Sie sich, nachdem
Sie diesen Schritt getan haben?
- Was könnte ein weiterer kleiner Schritt sein, was dann ein
nächster …?

Nehmen Sie sich Ihr Projektbuch
vor und stellen Sie sich die folgenden Fragen immer wieder,
bis Sie in der Vorstellung an
Ihrem Ziel angekommen sind.

Wenn Sie beispielsweise die Erinnerung an alte Kränkungen loslassen
wollen und etwa formuliert haben:
»Ich fühle inneren Frieden und bin
ganz bei mir«, dann haben Sie sich
nun eine Reihe von Maßnahmen
überlegt, die geeignet sind, diesen
Frieden zu schließen und in sich
heimisch zu machen.
Ein erster kleiner Schritt könnte
sein, im Tagesablauf kurze Pausen
einzulegen und eine Bewusstheitsübung zu machen. Diese kann so
aussehen, dass Sie beim Einatmen
konzentriert an Frieden denken
und diese Qualität im Körper
spüren. Dann lassen Sie alles Be-
lastende in der Vorstellung mit
dem Ausatmen los. Das wiederholen Sie ein paar Male und genießen die einsetzende Entspannung. Gestalten Sie die ersten
Schritte in Richtung auf Ihr Ziel
hin stets angenehm, spielerisch
und so überschaubar, dass sie leicht
zu verwirklichen sind.

PRAXIS

»*Jedem Anfang* wohnt ein
Zauber inne, der uns beschützt
und der uns hilft zu leben.« — Hermann Hesse

Den Anfang machen

Ob es Ihnen um den Abschied vom
Perfektionsanspruch geht, um das
Entrümpeln der eigenen Wohnung
oder darum, Menschen zu vergeben, die Ihnen Schmerz zugefügt
haben: Bei all dem müssen Sie immer zuerst eines tun, nämlich beginnen. Manchmal ist das so, als
würde man einen Bann brechen,
als könnte man endlich wieder
richtig durchatmen. Und irgendwann fragt man sich, warum man
das Problem eigentlich so lange
Zeit mit sich herumgetragen hat.

Erfolge registrieren
Widerstehen Sie der Versuchung,
hundertprozentige Zielerreichung
anzustreben. Das würde nur Ihren
Forderungen an sich selbst, dem

»Ich sollte …« neue Nahrung geben
oder dazu führen, dass Sie frustriert
das Handtuch werfen. 80 Prozent
sind viel Erfolg versprechender,
auch mit 20 Prozent sind Sie schon
wesentlich weitergekommen. Es
geht nicht um neue Anforderungen
an sich selbst und nicht um Perfektion. Wichtig ist vielmehr, dass
Sie den ersten Schritt machen und
alles, was zu Ihrem Ziel führt – Ihre
großen und kleinen Erfolge – sorg-
fältig in Ihrem Projektbuch festhalten. Es gibt nichts, was nicht
aufgeschrieben werden könnte,
selbst wenn es von außen betrachtet unwesentlich zu sein scheint.
Wenn Ihnen zum Beispiel in einem
Meeting zum allerersten Mal auf-
fällt, dass Sie wieder reflexartig zu-
stimmen wollen und dann stattdessen etwas Abweichendes äußern,

dann ist das bemerkenswert! Selbst wenn Ihre Äußerung nicht weiter originell war. Sie haben in diesem Moment eine Struktur aufgebrochen – zum ersten Mal. Sie haben sich nicht erst hinterher über Ihren Reflex geärgert, sondern gleich reflektiert und gehandelt. Und wenn dieser Schritt einmal getan ist, ist die Wahrscheinlichkeit groß, dass sich das wiederholt und Sie – etliche Schritte weiter – sich angewöhnt haben, »Ihren Senf dazuzugeben«, und mit der Zeit schließlich dazu kommen, sich in Gesprächen ganz automatisch sicher und souverän zu verhalten. Wichtig ist auch hier, am Ball zu bleiben und Geduld mit sich selbst zu haben (siehe ab Seite 111).

Die Wochenübersicht

Um neues Verhalten zu üben, eignet sich eine Wochenübersicht. Eine Woche ist eine überschaubare Größe. Schlagen Sie Ihr Projektbuch auf und betrachten Sie, was Sie unter »zielführende Schritte«

notiert haben (siehe Seite 103). Diese Schritte setzen Sie nun in praktisches Tun um. Nehmen wir als Beispiel wieder »Ich fühle inneren Frieden und bin ganz bei mir«. Hier könnte nun in Ihrer Wochenübersicht stehen, sich anzugewöhnen, regelmäßig die Bewusstheitsübung zu machen.

Das könnte etwa so aussehen:
- Ich führe in der Woche vom … bis … mindestens einmal täglich die Bewusstheitsübung durch.
- Ich finde ein Symbol, das mich daran erinnert, und stelle es gut sichtbar auf meinen Schreibtisch.

Zusätzlich steht da vielleicht noch:
- Montag: Ich melde mich bei der Volkshochschule für den Schnupperworkshop »Progressive Muskelentspannung« am übernächsten Samstag an.
- Freitag: Ich mache nach der Arbeit einen Spaziergang durch den Stadtpark und konzentriere mich dabei ganz bewusst auf meine Schritte und meinen Atem, während ich gehe.

Oder: Ich nehme ganz bewusst die Pflanzen und Tiere im Park wahr. Egal, auf was Sie sich lieber konzentrieren, beides bringt Sie Ihrem Ziel »innerer Friede« näher.

So würde es weitergehen

In der nächsten Woche steht bei der Bewusstheitsübung schon »mindestens zweimal täglich«. Das ist außerdem die Woche, in der Sie im Workshop erkunden, ob die Progressive Muskelentspannung für Sie eine gute Entspannungsmethode ist. Wenn ja, entschließen Sie sich vielleicht, einmal wöchentlich in einer Gruppe zu üben. Konnten Sie der Methode nichts abgewinnen, starten Sie eventuell einen Versuch mit Yoga oder mit Meditation. Weitere Schritte würden bei diesem Beispiel erst dann erfolgen, wenn Sie die Bewusstheitsübung gewohnheitsmäßig mehrmals am Tag praktizieren, dies also »automatisiert« haben. Und wenn Sie eine Entspannungsmethode gefunden haben, die Sie regelmäßig durchführen.

Wenn Sie's eilig haben, lassen Sie sich Zeit

Planen Sie Zeiträume großzügig, also mit Zeitpuffern, sodass Unvorhergesehenes nicht Ihren Plan durcheinanderbringen kann. Die Planung soll Ihnen schließlich helfen, statt Sie erneut unter Druck zu setzen. Niemand drängt Sie. Es ist Ihre Entscheidung, etwas für sich zu tun und ungesunde Muster loszulassen. Sie bestimmen Ihr eigenes Tempo. Maßstab ist ausschließlich Ihr Wohlbefinden, nicht irgendwelche Ansprüche, denen Sie genügen müssen. Sie bestimmen, was Sie loslassen wollen und welchen neuen Weg Sie einschlagen. Sie bestimmen, wie Sie das tun und überlegen, wer und was Sie dabei unterstützen könnte.

Sie machen das, weil Ihnen an sich selbst gelegen ist und Sie sich achten und mögen. Sie nehmen sich die Zeit, die Sie brauchen, um die Änderungen, die Sie sich wünschen, herbeizuführen.

Kreislauf des Wohlbefindens

1 Am Anfang stehen
Ihre Gedanken und Erfahrungen.
Diese haben Einfluss auf …

8 … Freude und Wohlbefinden.
Diese beeinflussen wiederum:

2 … Ihre Vorstellung von sich selbst.
Diese hat Einfluss auf …

7 … Ergebnisse erzielen zu können.
Die Ergebnisse haben Einfluss auf …

3 … Ihr Selbstwertgefühl.
Das wiederum beeinflusst …

6 … Ihre Fähigkeit, tätig zu werden.
Das hat Einfluss darauf, …

4 … Ihre Wünsche und Energien.
Diese haben Einfluss auf …

5 … Ihre Motivation, zu lernen und
voranzukommen. Dies beeinflusst …

Nennen wir den Kreislauf »Engelskreis« – als Gegenstück zum »Teufelskreis«. Mit Teufelskreisen haben wir mehr Erfahrung als mit einem Engelskreis. Wir wissen intuitiv, dass abwertende, negative, selbstzerfleischende Gedanken einen Kreislauf in Gang setzen, der zur Schwächung des Selbstwertgefühls, zu unsinnigen Festhaltemanövern und zur systematischen Entmutigung führt. Weniger bewusst ist zumeist, dass wir bei unserer Gedanken- und Vorstellungswelt ansetzen müssen, um aus dem Teufels- einen Engelskreis zu machen.

PRAXIS

107

Was tun, wenn ich **feststecke?**

Um Altes loszuwerden und neue Wege zu gehen,
brauchen Sie Zeit, Geduld und Optimismus…

MIT DEM LOSLASSEN IST ES GENAUSO wie mit dem Verändern von anderen Denk- und Verhaltensmustern: Es braucht
Zeit, bis das Neue greift und schließlich wirklich zur zweiten Natur
geworden ist. Sich auf den Weg zu machen heißt also auch, zu akzeptieren, dass es nicht einfach schnurstracks gipfelwärts geht. Im Bann
eines neuen Anfangs erleben Sie oft in kurzer Zeit viele Einsichten und
Erkenntnisse, erstaunliche Veränderungen und haben richtig viel Power.
Wenn dann einige Wochen vergangen sind, hat sich der Reiz des Neuen
gelegt, und Sie fühlen sich vermutlich ein wenig ernüchtert. Zudem
hat der unmittelbare Veränderungsdruck nachgelassen, das »Weg-von«.
Sie haben schließlich schon einiges getan und gelassen, weshalb Sie sich
nun nicht mehr so gedrängt fühlen, Weiteres zu verändern. Das ist völlig
normal – Sie haben ein Lernplateau erreicht. Es kann sein, dass Sie auf
diesem Plateau für längere Zeit hängen bleiben und scheinbar auf der
Stelle treten. Vielleicht fallen Ihnen plötzlich auch weitere Baustellen auf,
die Ihnen bislang noch gar nicht bewusst waren. Auch das ist normal –
niemand verändert alte Muster einfach im Handumdrehen.

Was der Prozess des Loslassens erfordert

Unsere eingespurten Verhaltensmuster von einem auf den anderen Tag loswerden zu können ist also ein unerfüllbarer Wunsch. Wir haben sie uns oft über Jahrzehnte hinweg antrainiert und sie sind an bestimmte Auslöser, Stimmungen und Gefühle geknüpft. Diese haben sich verselbstständigt und mit dem ursprünglichen Zweck schon längst nichts mehr zu tun.

Plateaus und Rückschritte sind normal

Sie brauchen vor allem Geduld. Betrachten Sie die Phasen geduldiger Anstrengung und die Rückkehr alter Betrachtungs- und Verhaltensweisen als ebenso wichtig wie die Momente sprunghaften Fortschritts und Erfolgs. Wenn Sie das Gefühl haben, Ihr Vorhaben sei seit längerem ins Stocken geraten und nichts ginge weiter, dann ist es wichtig zu wissen, dass dies zu Ihrem Veränderungsprozess dazugehört, ebenso wie der eine oder andere Rückschritt in das Verhalten, das Sie eigentlich loslassen wollen.

So tauchen im Laufe des Loslass-Prozesses häufig besonders hartnäckige Themen wieder auf, oft in neuer Gestalt. Wer beispielsweise bisher einen starken Hang zur Perfektion hatte, könnte nun auch »perfekt« loslassen wollen, wer bisher ein großes Elitebewusstsein hatte, könnte versucht sein, das Loslassen als weitere Facette des individuellen »Ich-bin-besser-als-alle-anderen« zu betrachten. Hartnäckige Gewohnheiten loszulassen und **neue Wege zu gehen, kann frustrierend langsam zu verwirklichen sein. Lassen Sie sich davon nicht entmutigen!**

Wichtig: Weitermachen

Ebenso wichtig wie Geduld ist, dass Sie die hilfreichen Anregungen, Techniken und Werkzeuge, die Ihnen der »kleine Coach« bisher an die Hand gegeben hat, regelmäßig nutzen und ruhig auch immer wieder neue Methoden für sich austesten und sie trainieren. Damit gewinnen Sie doppelt: Sie bleiben bei der Stange, was Ihr Ziel betrifft. Und Sie erweitern Ihren Horizont und Ihre Fähigkeiten. Halten Sie Ihre Erfahrungen im Projektbuch fest, Erfolge genauso wie Rückschläge. Sie bilden Ihren persönlichen Lern-Weg darin ab.

Zum Loslassen gehört auch die Umsetzung der Erkenntnis, dass selten etwas von jetzt auf gleich funktioniert. Üben Sie während einer Plateauphase einfach kontinuierlich weiter. Über kurz oder lang werden Sie feststellen, dass sich plötzlich – vielleicht an ganz unerwarteter Stelle – etwas tut, was Sie Ihrem Ziel wieder näher bringt.

Irgendwann bemerken Sie zum Beispiel, dass Sie nach der Arbeit gut abschalten können und nicht mehr über das nachgrübeln, was an diesem Tag unerledigt geblieben ist, dass Ihre Nackenschmerzen nachlassen und Sie sich häufiger entspannt und glücklich fühlen – einfach so, ohne dass dem etwas Besonderes vorausgegangen ist. Genauso gut kann es passieren, dass Sie sich auf einmal in der Lage fühlen, sich von einem Stapel alter Zeitschriften zu trennen, ohne noch einen Blick hineinzuwerfen. Vielleicht beschließen Sie auch plötzlich, nicht mehr das willige Ohr für Ihre gewohnheitsmäßig jammernde Arbeitskollegin zu spielen, sondern in der Mittagspause lieber einen kleinen Spaziergang zu machen.

> »*Unsere größte Schwäche liegt im Aufgeben. Der sicherste Weg zum Erfolg ist immer, es noch einmal zu versuchen.*«   Thomas Alva Edison

Dies sind deutliche Indizien dafür, dass das Prinzip des Loslassens in Ihrem Leben Fuß gefasst hat – auch wenn Sie mit dem Loslass-Projekt, das Sie sich eigentlich ausgewählt haben, noch nicht so weit vorangekommen sind, wie Sie es sich gewünscht hätten. **Veränderungsprozesse haben stets ihre eigene Logik und Geschwindigkeit.** Lassen Sie sich überraschen.

Vier Wochen zum Ent-lernen und Er-lernen

Verhaltensforscher haben herausgefunden, dass ein Wandlungsprozess mindestens vier Wochen dauert. So lang braucht das Gehirn nämlich, um Gewohntes zu verlernen und Neues so zu er-lernen, dass es automatisch abläuft.
Das ist beim Loslassen nicht anders. Stellen Sie sich vor, Sie seien umgezogen und Ihre neue Wohnung befände sich zwar in der gleichen Stadt, aber in einem anderen Stadtteil. Die erste Zeit nach dem Umzug werden Sie nach Arbeitsschluss unwillkürlich den alten Weg nehmen wollen, haben ihn vielleicht schon automatisch eingeschlagen, bevor es Ihnen bewusst wird. Mit der Zeit aber werden Sie den alten Weg »ent-lernen« und den neuen so verinnerlicht haben, dass Sie ihn nun, so wie früher den alten Weg, ganz automatisch einschlagen.

Fortschritte wahrnehmen

Wenn Sie vier Wochen lang zwei Mal pro Woche Ihren Termin mit sich selbst eingehalten haben, sind Sie auf dem besten Wege, dabeizubleiben. Die Selbstwertschätzungs-Übung (siehe Seite 51) ist Ihnen dann bereits zum liebgewonnenen Ritual geworden und entfaltet ihre Wirkung ins Alltagsleben hinein, die abschließende Entspannungsübung (siehe Seite 62) lässt Sie immer leichter und müheloser zur Ruhe kommen. Ihr Gehirn hat entsprechende Synapsenverbindungen zwischen den relevanten Nervenzellen vollzogen, sodass die Reize nunmehr leicht von Zelle zu Zelle geleitet werden können.

Um die gemachten Fortschritte noch besser zu erkennen, lesen Sie am besten nach vier Wochen Ihr Projektbuch in einem Stück durch. Betrachten Sie Ihre Notizen zu den Übungen und die darin aufgezeichneten Veränderungen – Sie werden überrascht sein, was sich schon alles getan hat.

Wie Sie das Loslassen verinnerlichen

Außer der Maxime, Geduld zu haben und Phasen des Stillstands oder des Rückschritts als Bestandteil des Veränderungsprozesses zu sehen, gibt es noch weitere nützliche Strategien und Tipps. Mit diesen können Sie sich selbst dabei unterstützen, am Ball zu bleiben, bis Sie das Loslassen wirklich verinnerlicht haben und Ihr Ziel Schritt um Schritt verwirklichen.

Mikro-Loslassen

Machen Sie kleine Loslass-Übungen nebenbei – ähnlich den Fingerübungen beim Klavierspielen oder der Aufwärmgymnastik vor dem Training. Das sind kleine Aktionen, die Sie tagsüber durchführen können. Sie zielen darauf ab, eine gewohnte Verhaltensweise zu verändern – nur um mal etwas Neues auszuprobieren:

● Frühstücken Sie einmal anders als gewohnt.

● Wählen Sie einen neuen Weg zur Arbeit.

● Gehen oder fahren Sie – wenn möglich – früher oder später als sonst in die Arbeit.

● Benutzen Sie als Rechtshänder immer mal wieder anstelle der rechten bewusst die linke Hand – und umgekehrt.

● Kaufen Sie Ihren täglichen Bedarf in einem anderen Geschäft als gewohnt.

● Kochen Sie nach einem neuen, vielleicht exotischen Rezept.

● Machen Sie in der Mittagspause einen Spaziergang, statt in die Kantine zu gehen, usw.

Mit etwas Übung wird Ihnen noch viel mehr einfallen, was Sie mal so nebenher anders als sonst machen könnten. Oder auch Dinge, die Sie, anders als sonst, einfach nur bleiben lassen: Heute mal keinen Schokoriegel als Pausensnack nehmen, diesmal am ultimativen Schnäppchen einfach vorbeigehen, »Neinsagen« zum Nachschlag beim Mittagessen, gerade jetzt nicht surfen oder chatten. Was nicht heißt, dass Sie diese Dinge für ewig aus Ihrem Leben verbannen sollen – es sind nur momentane Fingerübungen für das Loslassen.

Muster auflockern

Nehmen Sie sich weniger vor. Eine weniger dichte Tagesagenda, ein schlankerer Terminkalender tragen viel dazu bei, mehr Gelassenheit zu entwickeln. Fragen Sie sich bei dem, was Sie tun, immer, ob es sich auch mit weniger Anstrengung be-

wältigen lässt – angefangen vom Halten eines Löffels bis hin zum Abwickeln eines Projekts. Es spielt keine Rolle, was genau Sie auswählen und ob Sie künftig dabei bleiben oder nicht. Wichtig ist nur das Spielerische, das Auflockern von Mustern, sodass Sie immer mehr verinnerlichen: **Loslassen ist eine Entscheidung, die Sie täglich und in jedem Moment neu treffen können.** Schreiben Sie Ihre Erlebisse mit diesen kleinen Experimenten in Ihr Projektbuch – Sie werden immer mehr Möglichkeiten finden.

Mit Ziel und Motiven in Kontakt bleiben

Denken Sie häufig an Ihr Vorhaben und vor allem auch an Ihre Motivation, aus der heraus Sie sich auf den Weg gemacht haben. Mit jeder dieser Vergegenwärtigungen aktiviert Ihr Gehirn Ihre Motivation aufs Neue und damit auch die mit dem Ziel verbundenen positiven Gedanken und Gefühle.

Motivation stärken

Es bleibt nicht aus, dass Sie sich mal entmutigt fühlen und geneigt sind, alles in Frage zu stellen. Ein Weg aus einem solchen Tief ist, sich daran zu erinnern, warum Ihnen Ihr Ziel wichtig ist. Diese Vergegenwärtigung, sowohl auf Gefühls- als auch auf rationaler Ebene, hilft Ihnen, Ihre Frustration zu überwinden und weiterzumachen.

Wenn Sie vor Ihrem geistigen Auge sehen, wie Sie das bereits erreicht haben, was Sie erreichen wollen – was nehmen Sie bei dieser Vorstellung wahr? Was sehen, hören, denken, tun Sie … welche Gefühle löst es aus? Freude? Erleichterung? Blättern Sie noch einmal auf Seite 71 zurück und sehen Sie sich die Übung »Zielmotivation stärken« an. Notieren Sie zunächst in Ihr Projektbuch, was Sie wahrgenommen haben, als Sie sich vorgestellt hatten, am Ziel Ihrer Wünsche zu sein. Dann beantworten Sie noch einmal die Übungsfragen, also warum es gut für Sie ist, dieses Ziel zu erreichen. Erweitern Sie die Übung um folgende Punkte:

- Schreiben Sie Ihre stärkste Motivation gleich hinter Ihr Ziel: (die stärkste Motivation ist die, die Ihre Gefühle am meisten anspricht). »Ich will … erreichen, weil …«
- Wählen Sie ein Symbol für Ihr Ziel und die damit verbundenen Gefühle und Motive und platzieren Sie es gut sichtbar am Arbeitsplatz oder zu Hause an einem Ort, an dem Sie oft genug vorbeikommen.

Was eignet sich als Symbol?

Wenn Sie sich etwa vorgenommen haben, Ihre Ängste vor Ablehnung loszulassen und künftig zu Ihrer eigenen Meinung zu stehen, können Sie sich mit einem Foto von einem starken Baum am Arbeitsplatz daran erinnern. Mut könnte auch das Bild einer Turmspringerin auf dem 10-Meter-Brett symbolisieren usw. Sie sollten nur einen starken inneren Bezug zu dem Symbol haben. Es sollte genau die Qualität ausdrücken, die Sie gerne hätten.

Züchten Sie unterstützende Überzeugungen

Gönnen Sie Ihrem inneren Kritiker möglichst oft ein paar freie Stunden. Selbstzweifel und destruktive innere Dialoge sind hinderlich für Selbstmotivation und Erfolg. Sagen Sie sich selbst häufiger am Tag bestärkende Sätze, beispielsweise:

- »Ich vertraue darauf, dass ich auf einem guten Weg bin.«
- »Schritt für Schritt komme ich meinem Ziel näher.«
- »Das krieg ich hin.«
- »Ich lasse los und spüre inneren Frieden.«
- »Loslassen gibt mir Entscheidungsfreiheit« usw.

Setzen Sie Gesten ein

Während Sie sich Ihren unterstützenden Sätzen widmen, beziehen Sie am besten auch Ihren Körper mit ein und unterstreichen Ihre Sätze mit Bewegungen und Gesten. Ist es zum Beispiel Ihr Ziel, häufiger inneren Frieden zu fühlen, dann führen Sie einfach eine Hand zu Ihrem Herzen. Wenn Sie »Ich vertraue darauf, dass ich auf einem guten Weg bin« oder »Schritt für Schritt komme ich meinem Ziel näher« unterstreichen wollen, dann gehen Sie, während Sie dies sagen, tatsächlich konzentriert ein paar Schritte in den Raum hinein und stellen sich dabei Ihren inneren Weg vor.

Vielleicht kommen Sie sich dabei anfangs etwas komisch vor – doch denken Sie daran: Unterstützende Gesten mobilisieren zusätzliche Energie für Ihr Ziel und verstärken die Wirksamkeit Ihrer Selbstunterstützung.

Bauen Sie Ihre Demotivatoren ab

Ebenso wichtig wie sich selbst zu bestärken, ist es, sensibel für das zu werden, was Sie für gewöhnlich demotiviert und dazu bringt, in altes Verhalten zurückzufallen. Ursache dafür können bestimmte

Situationen, Wahrnehmungen, Abläufe oder eigene Einstellungen sein, es kann der Kontakt zu Menschen sein, mit denen Sie nicht zurecht kommen – eben bestimmte Auslöser, die in Ihnen immer wieder Ihre klassischen Festhalte-Muster aktivieren. **Machen Sie sich Ihre persönliche Parade der Demotivatoren bewusst und entwickeln Sie Ideen, wie Sie sie umgehen, abschwächen oder abbauen können.** Vielleicht lassen Sie sich dabei von den folgenden Anregungen inspirieren:

Gedanken ersetzen

Wenn Sie spüren, dass Sie wieder in die alte Gewohnheit fallen, kann es helfen, Ihren negativen Gedankengang durch einen positiveren zu ersetzen. Statt »Ich schaffe es einfach nicht, mich zu entspannen, da kann ich machen was ich will!« denken Sie: »Ich entspanne mich jetzt einfach so gut, wie es mir möglich ist.« Sie können auch ein »aber« an negative Gedanken dranhängen. Aus »Ich trau mich einfach nicht« wird dann «Ich trau mich einfach nicht, ABER ich arbeite daran, und es wird mir bald besser gelingen«.

»Stopp!« sagen bei den alten Mustern

Jedes Mal, wenn Sie bemerken, dass Sie wieder in alte Gedankenschleifen hineingeraten oder sich bei dem Verhalten ertappen, das Sie ablegen wollen, denken oder sagen Sie »Stopp!« und wenden Sie sich etwas anderem zu, etwas, was nichts mit Ihrer »Baustelle« zu tun hat.

Wenn Sie beispielsweise in einer Gesprächssituation bemerken, dass Sie wieder in die Gewohnheit des automatischen »Ja-das-finde-ich-auch-Sagens« verfallen, um Ihrem Gegenüber gefallen zu wollen, sagen Sie innerlich »Stopp!« zu sich und verändern Sie rasch Ihre Steh- oder Sitzhaltung. Dann spüren Sie einen Moment lang in sich hinein, um anschließend wieder voll präsent zu sein.

Prioritäten setzen

Festhalten äußert sich oft dadurch, zu viel oder sogar alles auf einmal zu wollen. Wir blicken auf eine volle Tagesagenda und haben das Gefühl, unter Dauerstrom zu stehen.

Wir reden uns ein, dass keine der Aufgaben warten könne, alles sei wichtig, wichtig, wichtig. Besonders Miss Perfect ist anfällig für diese Form der Dauerüberlastung, da sie meint, nichts vernachlässigen zu dürfen. Und doch gibt es immer Aufgaben, die wesentlicher sind als andere. Hier hilft es, statt einer vollgeladenen To-do-Liste konsequent nur die drei wichtigsten Aufgaben des Tages aufzuschreiben. Sind die erledigt, ist der Tag erst einmal »gerettet«, egal, ob Sie dann noch etwas Zusätzliches schaffen.

Fahren Sie den Hang zum Vergleichen zurück

Vergleichen Sie sich weniger mit anderen, sondern konzentrieren Sie sich auf Ihren eigenen Weg und das, was Ihnen persönlich wichtig ist. Wann immer Sie merken, dass Sie beginnen, sich mit anderen zu vergleichen und sich beispielsweise fragen, wie viel besser der andere in was auch immer ist, dann halten Sie mit einem »Stopp!« kurz inne. Führen Sie den Gedanken nicht weiter, sondern wenden Sie Ihre Aufmerksamkeit sich selbst zu. Dazu können Sie beispielsweise Ihre Hand auf den Bauch legen, um sich besser zu spüren. Atmen Sie ein paar Mal tief durch und sagen Sie zu sich etwas wie »Ich bin ganz bei mir«.

Feiern Sie Ihre Erfolge

Belohnen Sie sich, wenn Ihnen etwas gelungen ist. Dazu gehören auch kleine Veränderungen. Manchmal sind es gerade diejenigen, die sich als bedeutsam erweisen. Widerstehen Sie der Versuchung, die Messlatte zu hoch zu hängen. Versichern Sie sich selbst: »Hey, das habe ich richtig gut hingekriegt!« Genießen Sie es, wenn Sie ein Ziel erreicht haben, beschenken Sie sich, feiern Sie! Erst dadurch bekommt der Erfolg den richtigen Stellenwert.

Bringen Sie Ihre Ressourcen ans Licht

Rufen Sie sich frühere Vorhaben in Erinnerung – sowohl solche, die Sie gut bewältigt haben, als auch solche, bei denen schnell die Luft raus war. **Die erinnerten Erfolge verstärken Ihre Kraft und Zuversicht für das Erreichen Ihrer zukünftigen Ziele.** Das, was nicht so gut lief, gibt Ihnen Anregungen, auf welche Fußangeln Sie sich für Ihre aktuellen Vorhaben möglicherweise einstellen müssen.

Denken Sie dabei durchaus auch an weit zurückliegende Dinge. Was wir als Kinder, als Jugendliche, als junge Erwachsene erlebt haben, hat zu den Denk- und Verhaltensmustern geführt, die auch heute in unserem Leben wirksam sind. Neh-

men Sie Ihr Projektbuch zur Hand und fertigen Sie zwei Listen an mit den folgenden Fragestellungen:

1. Was habe ich mir in der Vergangenheit vorgenommen und erfolgreich umgesetzt? (Etwa den Führerschein gemacht, ausdauernd auf etwas gespart, sich zu einer Trennung entschlossen und die entsprechenden Schritte getan usw.)

2. Womit bin ich gescheitert – vielleicht sogar in mehreren Anläufen? (Etwa sich beruflich verändern, dauerhaft weniger wiegen, eine Sprache lernen wollen.)

Nehmen Sie sich dann Ihre erfolgreichen und Ihre gescheiterten Vorhaben von früher genauer vor und überlegen Sie, wie wichtig oder unwichtig Ihnen die Sache jeweils war und was Ihre Motive dafür waren. Was entsprang einem inneren Anliegen (den Führerschein wollten Sie vielleicht machen, um sich ein Auto zu kaufen und flexibler zu sein), was waren Vorhaben, die Sie angegangen sind, weil andere es so von Ihnen erwarteten?

WIE SIE DAS LOSLASSEN VERINNERLICHEN

> »*Es gibt mehr Leute, die kapitulieren, als solche, die scheitern.*« Henry Ford

Führen Sie sich vor Augen, was Sie damals dazu bewogen hat, ein Vorhaben nur halbherzig anzugehen oder vorzeitig aufzugeben. Hatten Sie es sich nicht wirklich zugetraut, das Ziel zu erreichen? War es nicht Ihr eigenes Ziel, sondern etwas, was Sie nach Ansicht anderer tun »sollten«? Oder haben Sie einfach das Interesse verloren, weil etwas, das Ihnen wichtiger war, in den Vordergrund getreten ist?

Betrachten Sie jedoch genauso intensiv Ihre erfolgreich umgesetzten Ziele und Entscheidungen: Was hat dazu geführt, dass Sie Ihr Vorhaben verwirklichen konnten? Welche Ihrer Stärken, Talente, Fähigkeiten und Fertigkeiten haben Sie eingesetzt? Was hat Sie bei der Stange gehalten? Was war für Ihre längerfristige Motivation wichtig? Wie haben Sie sich nach dem Erreichen Ihres Zieles gefühlt? Notieren Sie Ihre

Gedanken dazu in Ihr Projektbuch. Viele der Qualitäten, die Ihnen schon früher beim Umsetzen eines Vorhabens hilfreich waren, können Sie auch heute einsetzen.

Der Weg ist das Ziel ...

... oder zumindest ein großer Teil davon. Die Kunst der Achtsamkeit zu pflegen heißt, dem gewöhnlichen Alltagsgeschehen ebenso viel Bedeutung beizumessen wie den Ereignissen persönlicher Sternstunden. Sich einzig und allein auf das Erreichen des anvisierten Zieles zu konzentrieren würde das »Dazwischen«, die vielen gelebten Stunden entwerten, die die Zeit zwischen Start und Ziel ausmachen. Bei der achtsamen Art des Unterwegsseins kommt es nicht darauf an, wie schnell Sie von A nach B kommen, sondern darauf, wie Sie Ihrem eingeschlagenen Weg folgen und was Sie unterwegs entdecken und erfahren. Nicht nur in den spirituellen Traditionen gilt die Achtsamkeit als der Schlüssel dafür, die Wahrnehmung von sich selbst, von anderen Menschen und den wechselnden Umgebungen zu verändern.

Achtsamkeit üben Sie, indem Sie zunächst sich selbst – also Ihren Körper, Ihre Gedanken und Gefühle – wahrnehmen, jedoch ohne zu werten. Einfach nur registrieren, wie es Ihnen im Moment geht, wie Sie sich fühlen, welche Bedürfnisse vielleicht da sind und dann auch andere Menschen und Ihre Umgebung so wahrnehmen, ohne bestimmte Absicht, ohne etwas einordnen zu wollen.

Diese absichtslose Aufmerksamkeit macht Sie besonders in Situationen, in denen Sie aufgeregt, aufgebracht oder gestresst sind, ganz automatisch wieder ruhiger und gelassener. Sie gewinnen mehr Abstand zum Geschehen und können wieder klar denken.

Achtsamkeit können Sie auch gezielt einsetzen, wenn es darum geht, diffusen Unzufriedenheitsgefühlen auf die Spur zu kommen, denn diese legen sich wie ein Grauschleier über die Motivation. Wenn Sie wissen, was hinter Ihrer Verstimmung steckt, können Sie viel leichter gegensteuern. Wenn Sie also merken, dass Sie in einer Situation zusehends unzufriedener werden und eigentlich gar nicht so recht wissen, was los ist, dann fragen Sie sich:

- Was genau ist es, was mich jetzt stört?
- Was sind im Augenblick meine Bedürfnisse?
- Welche Erwartungen habe ich momentan?
- Kann ich an dieser Situation etwas verändern? Was genau?
- Welche Alternativen habe ich?

Stellen Sie sich diese Fragen, sooft Sie mit einer Situation unzufrieden sind. Bei der Beantwortung erkennen Sie rasch, wie Sie wieder klar Schiff machen können.

Ein Rückfall! Kleiner »Erste-Hilfe«-Leitfaden

Sie merken, dass Sie immer wieder alten Mustern folgen, statt Ihren neuen Weg zu gehen? Vielleicht macht sich Entmutigung breit, vielleicht ist es auch Trägheit. Eigentlich ist Ihnen klar, was Sie wollen und was nicht mehr. Sie möchten vorankommen … wenn da nur nicht xyz wäre! Was Ihnen da in die Quere kommt, kann ein Motivationsloch sein (»Ich kann mich nicht aufraffen«), es kann sich auch um diffuse Ängste handeln (»Wenn ich das wirklich tue, passiert etwas Schlimmes«) oder es sind negative Feedbacks von der Familie, aus dem Freundeskreis oder von Kollegen (»Früher warst du hilfsbereiter«).

Nehmen Sie innere Einwände ernst

Wann immer Sie spüren, dass etwas in Ihnen sich gegen Ihre geplante Veränderung sträubt, dann ist das in der Regel ein nicht ausgeräumter innerer Einwand. Sie befürchten – meist unbewusst – dass die Veränderung keine Verbesserung, sondern eine Verschlechterung nach sich zieht. Das, was Sie sich zum Ziel gesetzt haben, wiegt nicht auf, was Sie eigentlich loslassen wollen. **Es hat keinen Sinn, einen solchen Einwand mittels Härte oder Disziplin wegdrücken zu wollen.** Worauf glauben Sie, verzichten zu müssen, wenn Sie loslassen? Was genau ist Ihnen so wichtig an dem, was Sie offenbar unbedingt festhalten wollen? Was verbinden Sie innerlich damit? Schließlich hat das Verhaltensmuster in der Vergangenheit einen bestimmten Zweck erfüllt.

Dem Sinn auf der Spur

Nahezu alle Gewohnheiten haben oder hatten früher mal irgendeinen »Sinn«, auch wenn Sie sie heute vielleicht nur mehr als lästig oder schädlich betrachten.
Wenn jemand beispielsweise daran gewöhnt ist, seine Abende Chips

mampfend vor dem Fernseher zu verbringen und wahllos so ziemlich alles zu gucken, was daherkommt – egal ob Castingshow, Familiendrama oder Thriller – dann tut er dies ja nicht mit dem Ziel, seinen Geist abzustumpfen, seine Kondition zu ruinieren oder einen Rettungsring um die Taille zu züchten. Vielmehr befriedigt er mit diesem »Abhängen« bestimmte Bedürfnisse – etwa, sich zu entspannen und Abstand zum Arbeitstag zu schaffen. An diesen Bedürfnissen ist an sich auch überhaupt nichts »falsch« – es geht vielmehr darum, ihnen auf eine andere Art als bisher gerecht werden zu können und sich zu fragen, welche anderen Verhaltensweisen dieses Bedürfnis nach Abstand und Entspannung auch gut bedienen könnten – ohne schädliche Nebenwirkungen. Fragen Sie sich also:

- Welche Bedeutung hatte das »alte« Verhalten für mich?
- Wozu habe ich es gebraucht?
- Welche Gefühle rief es hervor?
- Was will ich jetzt an seine Stelle setzen?
- Was muss gewährleistet sein, damit die Veränderung funktionieren kann?

Entdramatisieren Sie das Geschehen

Ein Rückfall in alte Verhaltensmuster ist kein Beinbruch. Häufig sind mehrere Versuche nötig, um ans Ziel zu kommen. Es gibt immer Gründe, warum Sand ins Getriebe gekommen ist. Vielleicht waren die anvisierten Schritte zum Ziel zu ehrgeizig bemessen, vielleicht war ganz einfach nicht »Ihr Tag«, vielleicht sind Sie auch stark in der Vorstellung gefangen, Ihre Ergebnisse stets bewerten zu müssen oder gehen gewohnheitsmäßig streng mit sich selbst um. Lernen funktioniert aber nicht nach dem Alles-oder-nichts-Prinzip. Werten Sie Fehlversuche nicht als Scheitern, sondern als Erfahrung, aus der Sie lernen können.

Auch helfen wieder bestimmte Fragen, den Rückfall für Ihre Weiterentwicklung fruchtbar zu machen:

- Warum hat es in dieser Situation nicht funktioniert?
- Was zeigt mir diese Erfahrung? Was kann ich daraus lernen?
- Wie gehe ich das nächste Mal in einer solchen Situation vor?

Damit ordnen Sie das Geschehen in Ihren Lernprozess ein, statt es als persönliche Unfähigkeit zu verallgemeinern. Das ist wichtig, denn in Schimpfen gegenüber sich selbst zu verfallen, würde nur den Druck erhöhen – und genau das wäre kontraproduktiv für den weiteren Weg.

Seien Sie sich eine gute Freundin

Ein schlechter Tag gefährdet nicht gleich das ganze Vorhaben. Blockieren Sie sich also nicht mit negativen Suggestionen wie »Ich schaffe das sowieso nicht!«. Nehmen Sie vielmehr gerade jetzt die Ihnen schon vertraute Haltung der guten Freundin ein. Wie würden Sie reagieren, wenn jemandem, den Sie mögen, etwas misslungen ist? Doch wohl kaum damit, Ihr Gegenüber abzukanzeln, zu beschimpfen und zu entmutigen …?

Konzentrieren Sie also Ihre Energie lieber wieder auf das, was Sie ändern wollen.

Relativieren Sie

Es geht nicht um Fehlerlosigkeit und nicht darum, dass Sie irgendwem etwas beweisen müssen. Auch sind sogenannte Misserfolge oft nur Interpretationssache aus einer momentanen Sichtweise heraus. Wenn Sie in Ihrem Projektbuch die Notizen zum Thema Ressourcen betrachten (siehe »Die kleine Schatzkiste«, Seite 91), so werden Sie wahrscheinlich erkennen, dass so manches, was sich ereignet hat, anfänglich als »Misserfolg« daherkam. Später hat es sich dann als ein wichtiger Schritt hin zu einer positiven Entwicklung herausgestellt. Letztlich ist die Botschaft eines Misserfolges nur, dass Sie einen anderen Lösungsweg ausprobieren sollten. Viele große Erfindungen sind nur deshalb gemacht worden, weil Menschen nach einem Misserfolg eben nicht einfach die Flinte ins Korn geworfen haben, sondern, aus den Fehlern lernend, schließlich an ihrem Ziel angekommen sind.

Halten Sie bei einem sogenannten Misserfolg also einfach inne und fragen Sie sich: »Wo genau war die Schwachstelle, und wie kann ich beim nächsten Mal an diesem Punkt besonders achtsam sein? Was könnte mich dabei unterstützen?«

Wie Sie auf Kurs bleiben

Nachdem Sie die Lehre aus dem Misserfolg gezogen haben, gehen Sie – wieder ein wenig gescheiter geworden – weiter Ihres Weges. Vergegenwärtigen Sie sich immer wieder Ihr Ziel und auch Ihre Motive. Sorgen Sie dafür, dass Sie Ihren Tag möglichst bewusst gestalten und häufig ganz bei sich sind. Dass Sie also registrieren, wie es Ihnen gerade geht, was Sie denken und fühlen und was Sie vielleicht gerade jetzt loslassen können, um Ihrem Ziel näherzukommen.

Je bewusster Sie Ihr Leben gestalten, desto gezielter können Sie auch lenkend eingreifen, wenn Sie mal wieder in Versuchung sind, zu den alten Mustern zu greifen. Diesen Bewusstheitsprozess können Sie mit Entspannungsübungen unterstützen. Wenn Sie Ihren Körper regelmäßig entspannen, fällt es Ihnen auch im Alltag leichter, Ängste, Ansprüche und Erwartungshaltungen loszulassen. Belegen Sie einen Yoga-, Tai-Chi- oder Qi-Gong-Kurs oder meditieren Sie, um tiefere Entspannungszustände zu erreichen. So finden Sie Ihren eigenen Rhythmus, der Sie dabei unterstützt, sich neue Ziele zu wählen und Ihre Vorhaben auch umzusetzen. Ich wünsche Ihnen viel Erfolg dabei!

Bücher, die weiterhelfen

Abend, Matt G.: Leben heißt Loslassen. Alles, was wir festhalten, hält auch uns fest, Verlag Via Nova

Engelbrecht, Sigrid: Richtig gute Laune kriegen, Droemer Knaur Verlag

Daiker, Ilona: Gelassen wie ein Buddha, GRÄFE UND UNZER VERLAG

Kast, Verena: Sich einlassen und loslassen. Neue Lebensmöglichkeiten bei Trennung und Trauer, Herder Verlag

Lindinger, Karin: Lass los und … gewinne! GRÄFE UND UNZER VERLAG

Mannschatz, Marie: Buddhas Anleitung zum Glücklichsein, GRÄFE UND UNZER VERLAG

Dies.: Mit Buddha die Trennung meistern, GRÄFE UND UNZER VERLAG

Matschnig, Monika: Mehr Mut zum Ich – Sei du selbst und lebe glücklicher, GRÄFE UND UNZER VERLAG

Müller-Ebert, Johanna: Trennungskompetenz in allen Lebenslagen, Kösel Verlag

Müller-Kainz, Elfrida und Hajdu, Hedwig: Loslassen, Integral Verlag

Münchhausen, Marco von: Entrümpeln mit dem inneren Schweinehund, GRÄFE UND UNZER VERLAG

Tarr, Irmtraud: Loslassen - die Kunst, die vieles leichter macht, Herder Verlag

Dank

Mein Dank für Anregungen, Kritik und tatkräftige Unterstützung geht insbesondere an meine Tochter Ariadne Engelbrecht. Bei meinen Seminarteilnehmerinnen und -teilnehmern bedanke ich mich für ihre inspirierenden Praxisbeispiele und persönlichen Tipps. Und meiner Lektorin, Angela Hermann-Heene, danke ich für ihr fachkundiges und sehr engagiertes Lektorat.

Übungsregister

Programmleitung: Ulrich Ehrlenspiel

Redaktion: Anja Schmidt

Lektorat: Angela Hermann-Heene

Korrektorat: Armin Gierth

Innenlayout, Typographie und Umschlaggestaltung: independent Medien-Design, München

Coverfoto: Getty

Satz: Knipping Werbung GmbH, Berg/Starnberg

Herstellung: Susanne Mühldorfer

Reproduktion: Longo AG, Bozen

Druck und Bindung: Printer, Trento

ISBN 978-3-8338-1370-2
5. Auflage 2010

Unsere Garantie

Liebe Leserin, lieber Leser,

wir freuen uns, dass Sie sich für ein GU-Buch entschieden haben. Mit Ihrem Kauf setzen Sie auf die Qualität, Kompetenz und Aktualität unserer Ratgeber. Dafür sagen wir Danke! Wir wollen als führender Ratgeberverlag noch besser werden. Daher ist uns Ihre Meinung wichtig. Bitte senden Sie uns Ihre Anregungen, Ihre Kritik oder Ihr Lob zu unseren Büchern. Haben Sie Fragen oder benötigen Sie weiteren Rat zum Thema? Wir freuen uns auf Ihre Nachricht!

Wir sind für Sie da! *(0,14 €/Min. aus dem dt. Festnetz/ Mobilfunkpreise maximal 0,42 €/Min.)
Montag–Donnerstag: 8.00–18.00 Uhr;
Freitag: 8.00–16.00 Uhr
Tel.: 0180-5 00 50 54*
Fax: 0180-5 01 20 54*
E-Mail: leserservice@graefe-und-unzer.de

P.S.: Wollen Sie noch mehr Aktuelles von GU wissen, dann abonnieren Sie doch unseren kostenlosen GU-Online-Newsletter und/oder unsere kostenlosen Kundenmagazine.

GRÄFE UND UNZER VERLAG
Leserservice
Postfach 86 03 13
81630 München

Ein Unternehmen der
GANSKE VERLAGSGRUPPE

Mosby's atlas of functional human anatomy

Mosby's atlas of

Functional human anatomy

Ernest W. Beck, B.S., M.A.

Medical Illustrator, Lake Forest, Illinois; formerly Executive
Managing Editor, Journal of the American Medical Association
and AMA's Specialty Journals; Member and Past President,
Association of Medical Illustrators; formerly Editor of
The Journal of Biocommunication

with

Maureen Groër, R.N., Ph.D.

College of Nursing, University of Tennessee, Knoxville, Tennessee

edited by

Harry Monsen, Ph.D.

Professor of Anatomy, Department of Anatomy,
University of Illinois, College of Medicine, Chicago, Illinois

With 267 illustrations, 170 in full color

The C. V. Mosby Company

ST. LOUIS · TORONTO · LONDON   1982

A TRADITION OF PUBLISHING EXCELLENCE

Editor: Thomas Allen Manning
Assistant editor: Nancy Mullins
Manuscript editor: Roger McWilliams
Design: Diane Beasley
Production: Diane Beasley

The C.V. Mosby Company
11830 Westline Industrial Drive, St. Louis, Missouri 63141

Library of Congress Cataloging in Publication Data

Beck, Ernest W., 1923-
  Mosby's atlas of functional human anatomy.

  Includes index.
  1. Anatomy, Human—Atlases. 2. Abnormalities,
Human—Atlases. I. Groër, Maureen E., 1944-
II. Monsen, Harry, 1924-   . III. Title.
[DNLM: 1. Anatomy—Atlases. QS 17 M894]
QM25.B424   611   81-14110
ISBN 0-8016-0554-7   AACR2

VT/VH/VH 9 8 7 6 5 4 3 2 1   02/C/227

Consultants

Ruthanna Dyer, Ph.D.
Coordinator, Department of Human Biology,
Seneca College of Applied Arts and Technology,
Ontario, Canada

Anthony J. Gaudin, Ph.D.
Department of Human Sciences,
California State University,
Northridge, California

Edward J. Greding, Ph.D.
Assistant Professor,
Department of Human Biology,
Del Mar College,
Corpus Christi, Texas

Louise D. Hall
Professor, Department of Nursing,
Mohawk Valley Community College,
Utica, New York

Barbara Hansen, Ph.D.
Professor of Physiology,
School of Medicine,
University of Michigan,
Ann Arbor, Michigan

Carl Hoegler, Ph.D.
Associate Professor of Biology,
Marymount College,
Tarrytown, New York

Raymond Kahn, Ph.D.
Professor of Anatomy,
School of Medicine,
University of Michigan,
Ann Arbor, Michigan

Mary Jane Myers, Ph.D.
Chairman, Department of Human Sciences,
Clarke College,
Newton, Mississippi

Anna Marie Parmeley, M.A.
Associate Professor of Biology,
California State University,
Long Beach, California

Steven J. Person, Ph.D.
Assistant Professor of Biology,
Lake Superior State College,
Sault Ste. Marie, Michigan

John A. Pitts, Ph.D.
Head, Department of Biology,
North Shore Community College,
Beverly, Massachusetts

Melvin R. Schmid, Ph.D.
Professor, Department of Human Sciences,
Trenton State College,
Trenton, New Jersey

To my wife, **Joan,**
and to our children, **Christopher** and **Melinda,**
for offering daily encouragement and support.

Preface

This atlas is for students and practitioners in many health and life science fields. It makes no pretense of being complete; what is of interest and importance to one specialty may only be of passing curiosity to another. The subject matter of each plate has been carefully considered for its usefulness as standard reference material for the understanding of human anatomy, physiological principles, and frequently encountered pathological conditions. Some commonly practiced surgical procedures are also included, along with other subjects of interest and concern to those who provide patient care and treatment. Text copy has purposely been kept at a minimum to allow presentation of as many illustrations as possible.

This book consists of thirteen chapters. The first introduces readers to topographic anatomy, a depiction of parts of the body in relation to a definite and limited area of the surface. It is an attempt to orient superficial structures, including skeletal landmarks, to related structures that lie at a deeper level. The body is then examined in microscopic and macroscopic detail; the remaining chapters show essential features of the various systems of the body—integumentary, skeletal, muscular, nervous, special senses, endocrine, respiratory, circulatory, lymphatic and reticuloendothelial, digestive, and urogenital. The final chapter illustrates common surgical positions in select clinical procedures.

This traditional presentation of human anatomy provides illustrative and succinct textual support to courses in human anatomy, physiology, and integrated coverage of anatomy and physiology. Although primarily designed as a tool for quick reference in many courses, this atlas is flexible enough to be used in various settings by students, practitioners, and scientists alike.

Ernest W. Beck
Maureen Groër
Harry Monsen

Author's note and acknowledgment

Throughout my career as a medical illustrator, the questions most often asked by those for whom the drawings and paintings are created have been "Can I have it tomorrow?" and "How much will it cost?" My answers are invariably "No" and "Enough to pay my bills." Few for whom the work is created fully realize the time required for thinking and planning—the preparation of a preliminary sketch frequently takes more hours than the final rendering. Developing a thorough understanding of what is to be shown, arranging components in a layout, sizing within space limitations, depicting subject matter with clarity and precision, naming anatomical parts, writing succinct, pertinent legends and text useful to the reader—all of these are parts of the process, and each requires deliberateness and care. This atlas was created from the start with the knowledge that no artist/author is omniscient and that no single book can be all-inclusive. It is a beginning, with many more plates planned in future editions.

For one who daily for more than 30 years has done little else than prepare medical illustrations for other authors, pharmaceutical companies, practitioners, and encyclopedias, I am grateful to the C.V. Mosby Company for asking me to prepare this atlas. My thanks to Chet Dow, Tom Manning, Nancy Mullins, Roger McWilliams, Diane Beasley, and the production personnel for their separate roles in coordinating the many factors necessary to produce this book. The distinguished consultants listed elsewhere have been of immeasurable help in selecting subject matter and critiquing text and illustration content.

To those educators, practitioners, authors, and other medical illustrators who have contributed to my understanding of the human body, I am most grateful.

For assistance in authoring the text portion I am deeply indebted to Maureen Groër; for meticulous editing and scrutiny for anatomical accuracy I am particularly appreciative to the distinguished anatomist, Harry Monsen.

My gratitude also to Catherine P. Anthony and Gary A. Thibodeau, authors of *Textbook of Anatomy and Physiology,* for allowing use of several plates developed for that text.

I want to acknowledge specifically those medical illustrators, past and present, whose standards of excellence and achievement have influenced my style of rendering: William Brudon, Robert Demarest, Vincent Destro, Robert Drake, Mary Dixon Elder, Gerald Hodge, Emil Hospodar, Tom Jones, Lucille Cassel Innes, Carl Linden, David Mascaro, Jean McConnell, Biagio Melloni, Laurel Schaubert, William Schwarz, Willard Shepard, and many more.

Ernest W. Beck

Contents

3 | The skeletal system

4 | The muscular system

8 | The respiratory system

9 | The circulatory system

10 | The lymphatic and reticuloendothelial system

11 The digestive system

12 The urogenital system

13 | Common surgical positions

Mosby's atlas of functional human anatomy

1 | Topographic anatomy

1|1

Directions and planes of section

The human body can be pictorially represented in many planes and with many reference points. The term *anatomical position* indicates an erect, or upright, posture. The head is untilted; eyes are looking straight ahead; the chin is not elevated or depressed; and the nose is in the center line of the body. The arms are at the sides, with elbows fully straightened touching the flanks; forearms and hands are rotated so that the palms face forward (supinated). The feet are also directed forward. When the body is in this position, it can be divided by imaginary planes either vertically or horizontally.

The median, or midsagittal, plane divides the body into equal right and left halves. Surfaces parallel to the median plane are termed paramedian, or parasagittal. Planes at right angles to the median plane are coronal, or frontal, planes. Also pictured are transverse, or horizontal, planes.

Several other anatomical terms denote general location or position of a structure relative to other structures. Thus anterior, or ventral, refers to the front of the body; posterior, or dorsal, to the back; cephalad (cranial), or superior, to the head region; caudal, or inferior, to the tail or lower end of the body; and lateral to the sides. Proximal suggests that the structure is nearer to the attached end of the limb; a distal structure is toward the free end of the limb.

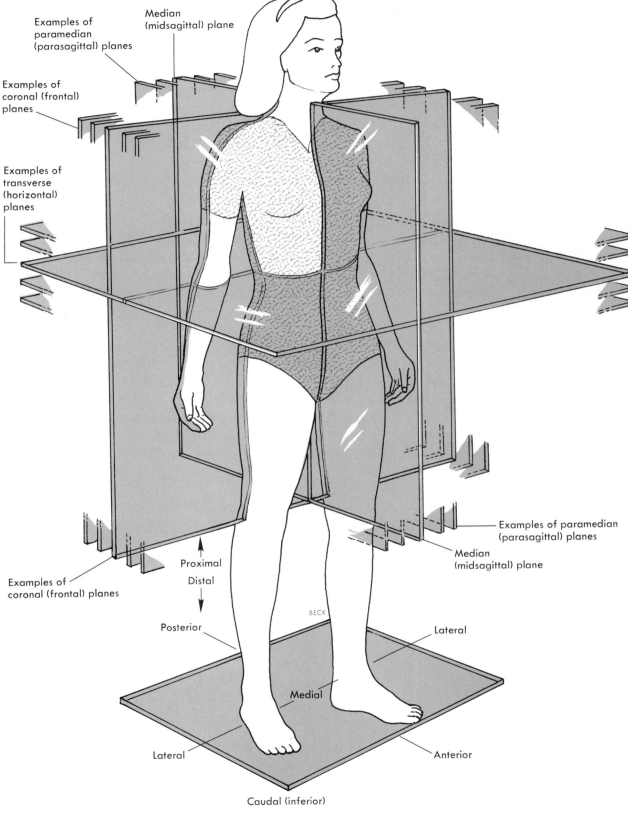

Cephalad (superior)

Examples of paramedian (parasagittal) planes

Median (midsagittal) plane

Examples of coronal (frontal) planes

Examples of transverse (horizontal) planes

Examples of coronal (frontal) planes

Examples of paramedian (parasagittal) planes

Median (midsagittal) plane

Proximal

Distal

Posterior

Lateral

Medial

Lateral

Anterior

Caudal (inferior)

BECK

1|2

Surface relationships of the skull

Shown is a lateral projection of the head with surface relationships of the skull, face, and jaw bones. Internationally accepted techniques of measurement of the skull (craniometry) have led to the designation of a number of terms to standardize points of measurement. These include the glabella, nasion, gnathion, gonion, inion, lambda, vertex, bregma, and pterion.

The cranium consists of eight bones: the unpaired frontal, two parietal, two temporal, occipital, sphenoid, and ethmoid. The fourteen bones that form the face are two maxillary, two zygomatic (malar), two nasal, mandible, two lacrimal, two palatine, and the vomer. All the face bones are paired except the mandible and vomer. The cranium is formed by flat bones that join together at immovable joints called sutures. At birth and in infancy these bones are separated by six membranous intervals (fontanels, or "soft spots") at the angles of the parietal bones.

The articulation of the lower jaw (mandible) with the temporal bone just in front of the ear may be characterized as a combination of a shallow ball-and-socket joint and a hinge joint.

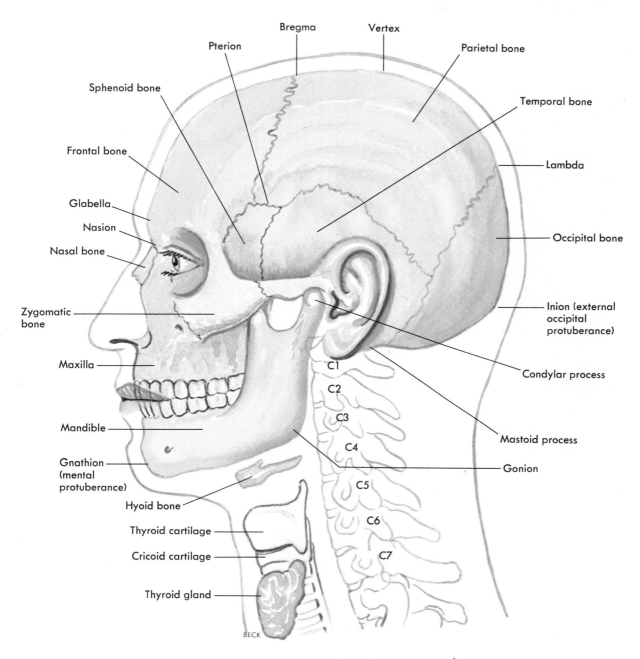

Bregma

Vertex

Pterion

Parietal bone

Sphenoid bone

Temporal bone

Frontal bone

Lambda

Glabella

Nasion

Occipital bone

Nasal bone

Zygomatic
bone

Inion (external
occipital
protuberance)

Maxilla

C1

Condylar process

C2

Mandible

C3

C4

Gnathion
(mental
protuberance)

C5

Mastoid process

Gonion

Hyoid bone

C6

Thyroid cartilage

Cricoid cartilage

C7

Thyroid gland

BECK

Lateral projection of the head showing surface
relationships of the skull, face, and jaw bones.
C1 to C7   Cervical vertebrae

5

1|3

Paranasal sinuses; oral and nasal cavities

Shown are projections of the paranasal air sinuses and oral and nasal cavities of the skull and face. Outlines of cavities and sinuses are indicated in color. Paranasal sinuses include the frontal, sphenoidal, ethmoidal, and maxillary and are connected by channels within bones to the nasal cavity. The sinuses have the same lining tissue (epithelium) and vascular and nerve supply as the nasal mucous membrane from which the sinuses developed. Mucus produced in the epithelial lining of the sinuses drains into the nose. It serves as protection against microorganisms and foreign material. When drainage is blocked by inflamed tissue, the sinuses are frequent sites of upper respiratory infection. The resulting pressure can lead to severe "sinus" headache.

Because of the extremely thin walls of the sinuses, infections may extend through the bone and spread to the protective coverings of the brain (meninges). This may lead to meningitis, a severe infection that results in neurological symptoms, high fever, and possible neurological damage.

The sphenoid, ethmoid, and maxillary sinuses are present at birth but are usually mere slits or grooves in the bone. Frontal sinuses appear after the second year. All paranasal sinuses enlarge gradually until puberty and rapidly after puberty. Maxillary sinuses do not reach their full size until after the eruption of permanent teeth.

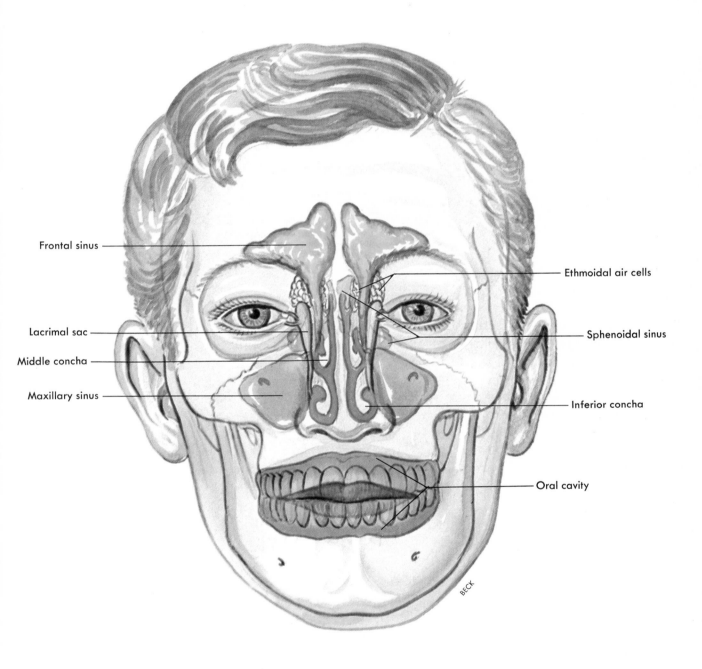

Frontal sinus

Ethmoidal air cells

Lacrimal sac

Sphenoidal sinus

Middle concha

Maxillary sinus

Inferior concha

Oral cavity

1|4

Sound areas as determined by percussion

Percussion is a technique used in physical assessment and diagnosis. It consists of the production of sound waves through striking the surface of the body. It can be direct or indirect. Indirect percussion is most commonly used: the middle finger of one hand is struck below the nail with the extended end of the middle finger of the other hand. The percussion note thus obtained will characterize the density of the underlying tissue or organ. A very solid structure such as compact bone will produce a very *flat* percussion note. Less dense tissue such as liver produces a *dull* sound when struck. Air-filled tissue such as lungs gives off a *resonant* sound, and if overinflation occurs, the sound is *hyperresonant.* A drumlike sound (*tympany*) is obtained over the stomach and intestines because of the presence of gas bubbles in these organs.

The production of characteristic notes through percussion on the body surface is useful for the detection of abnormal organ position or size. It can also yield useful information about pathology in different organ systems and can help locate abnormal growths. Percussion can also be used to assess for tender areas; for example, tenderness on percussion over the costal (rib) vertebral angle is typical of renal disease.

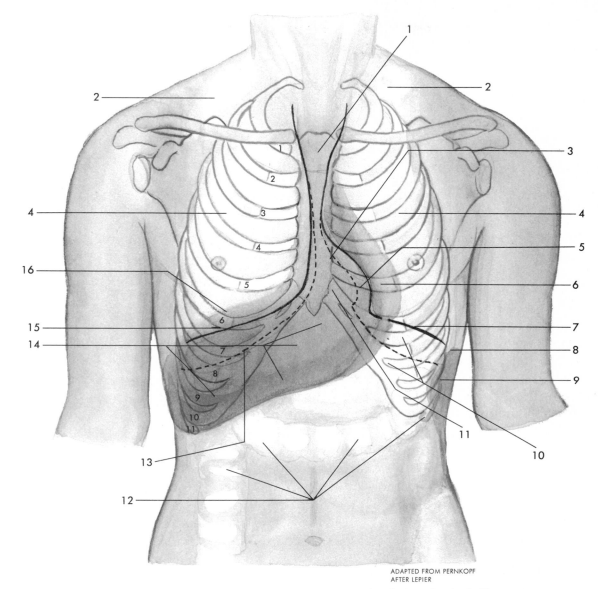

ADAPTED FROM PERNKOPF
AFTER LEPIER

1 Supracardiac (mediastinal) dullness
2 Apical lung sound
3 Anterior pulmonary margin during inspiration
4 Lung sound
5 Anterior pulmonary margin during expiration
6 Relative cardiac dullness
7 Inferior pulmonary margin during expiration
8 Relative splenic dullness

9 Absolute splenic dullness
10 Vesiculotympanic sound (air in stomach)
11 Absolute cardiac dullness
12 Tympanic sound (gas in colon)
13 Inferior pulmonary margin during inspiration
14 Absolute hepatic dullness
15 Inferior pulmonary margin during expiration
16 Relative hepatic dullness

Smaller numbers, 1 to 11 Ribs

Lightest shade—area of tympanic sound; lightly
toned—area of lung sounds; medium shade—area
of relative dullness; darkest shade—area of
absolute dullness.

1|5

Topography of projected thoracic and abdominal viscera—ventral view

Shown is the anterior aspect of the trunk (chest and abdomen), revealing surface topography of the organs in their relationships to bony landmarks.

The lower border of the heart sac crosses the juncture of the sixth rib cartilages with the body of the sternum and the upper end of the xiphoid process. The aortic arch emerges from the left ventricle at the juncture of the left third costal cartilage with the body of the sternum. The dome of the diaphragm is higher on the right side than on the left and is at a level with the fifth costal cartilage. The left dome usually reaches no higher than the fifth intercostal space. During exhalation the diaphragm rises on the right side to the fourth intercostal space opposite the nipple.

Posteriorly, the esophagus extends from the level of the sixth cervical vertebra to that of the ninth thoracic vertebra, where it enters the abdomen through the esophageal opening in the diaphragm slightly to the left of the midline. The stomach lies almost entirely in the left hypochondriac region, with its lesser curvature in the left half of the epigastric region. The pylorus (juncture of stomach with the duodenum) lies behind the quadrate lobe of the liver in the transpyloric plane slightly to the right of the median plane.

The right colic flexure lies between the lowest part of the liver and the lower part of the right kidney to the right of the gallbladder, opposite the tenth costal cartilage. The transverse colon crosses the bodies of the second and third lumbar vertebrae. The splenic flexure is higher than the right colic flexure.

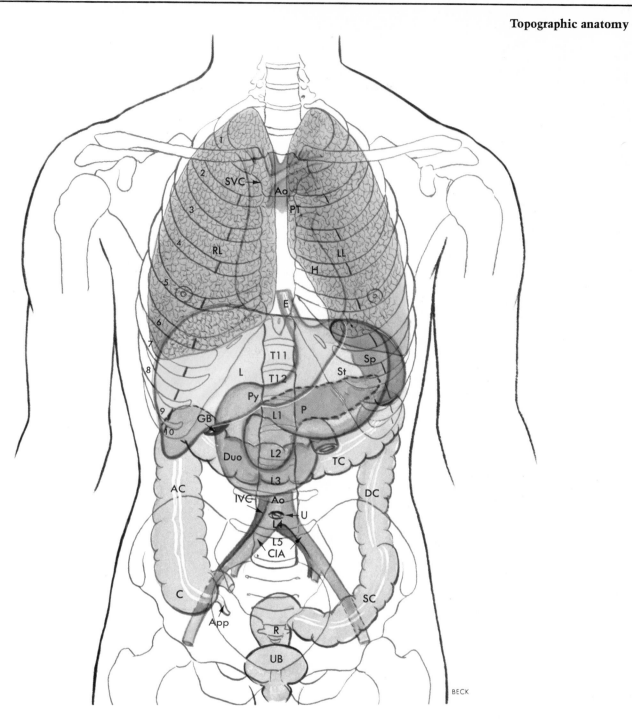

AC	Ascending colon	H	Heart	SC	Sigmoid colon
Ao	Aorta	IVC	Inferior vena cava	Sp	Spleen
App	Appendix	L	Liver	St	Stomach
C	Cecum	LL	Left lung	SVC	Superior vena cava
CIA	Common iliac artery	P	Pancreas	TC	Transverse colon
DC	Descending colon	PT	Pulmonary trunk	U	Umbilicus
Duo	Duodenum	Py	Pylorus	UB	Urinary bladder
E	Esophagus	R	Rectum	T11, T12	Thoracic vertebrae
GB	Gallbladder	RL	Right lung	L1 to L5	Lumbar vertebrae

Smaller numbers, 1 to 10   Ribs

1|6

Topography of projected thoracic and abdominal viscera—dorsal view

As in the ventral view (Plate 1-5), the vertebral column and ribs provide landmarks for identifying the borders of organs.

In this dorsal view the retroperitoneal abdominal organs and their anatomical relationships to each other and to bony landmarks are highlighted. The posterior retroperitoneal location of the kidneys makes them almost inaccessible to palpation through the ventral abdominal wall. However, on deep inspiration the lowest pole of the right kidney may occasionally be felt because it is placed slightly lower than the left kidney.

The spleen also is inaccessible to palpation except when enlarged. The pancreas is such a friable, diffuse organ that it is normally not palpable. Because of the musculature of the back, none of these organs can be felt posteriorly.

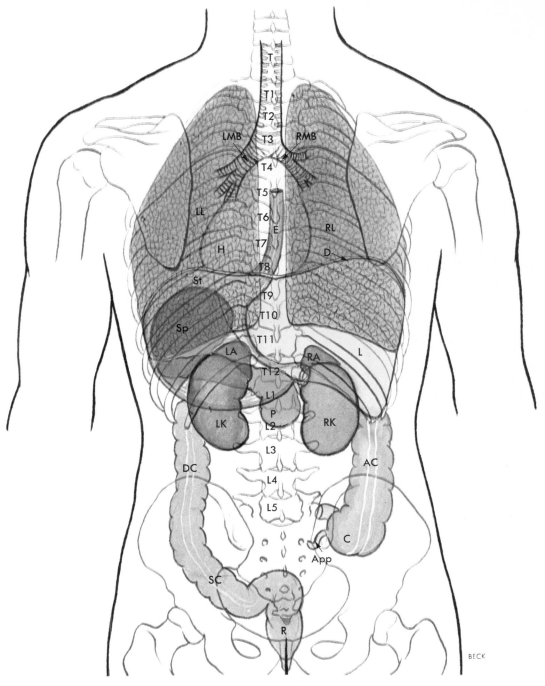

AC	Ascending colon	LA	Left adrenal gland	RL	Right lung
App	Appendix	LK	Left kidney	RMB	Right main bronchus
C	Cecum	LL	Left lung	SC	Sigmoid colon
D	Diaphragm	LMB	Left main bronchus	Sp	Spleen
DC	Descending colon	P	Pancreas	St	Stomach
E	Esophagus	R	Rectum	T	Trachea
H	Heart	RA	Right adrenal gland	T1 to T12	Thoracic vertebrae
L	Liver	RK	Right kidney	L1 to L5	Lumbar vertebrae

1|7

Projection of heart and great vessels to anterior wall of thorax

The individual valves of the heart project their closing sounds, the typical "lub" and "dub" of the heartbeat, to different parts of the chest wall. Listening to the heart sounds with a stethoscope at these particular areas yields information about the quality of heart function in general and about the condition of the four major heart valves.

The mitral (bicuspid) valve is behind the left half of the sternum, at the level of the fourth costal cartilage; it is directed forward, downward, and to the left. Its sound is heard in the the fifth intercostal space at the midclavicular line. The area is known as the apical area, and the heart sounds are loudest here.

The tricuspid valve is nearer the anterior chest wall than the mitral valve and is opposite the middle of the sternum at the level of the fourth and fifth cartilages. Its sound is best heard at the left border of the sternal body in the fourth intercostal space. The first heart sound (lub) is produced by closure of the mitral and tricuspid valves.

The pulmonary valve lies opposite the third left costal cartilage and is directed upward and backward. It is best heard along the left sternal border at the second intercostal space.

The aortic valve is behind the left margin of the sternum, opposite the lower border of the third intercostal space. Its sound is best heard along the right sternal border at the second intercostal space. The second heart sound (dub), because of closure of the aortic and pulmonary valves, is most pronounced at the base of the heart at the second intercostal space.

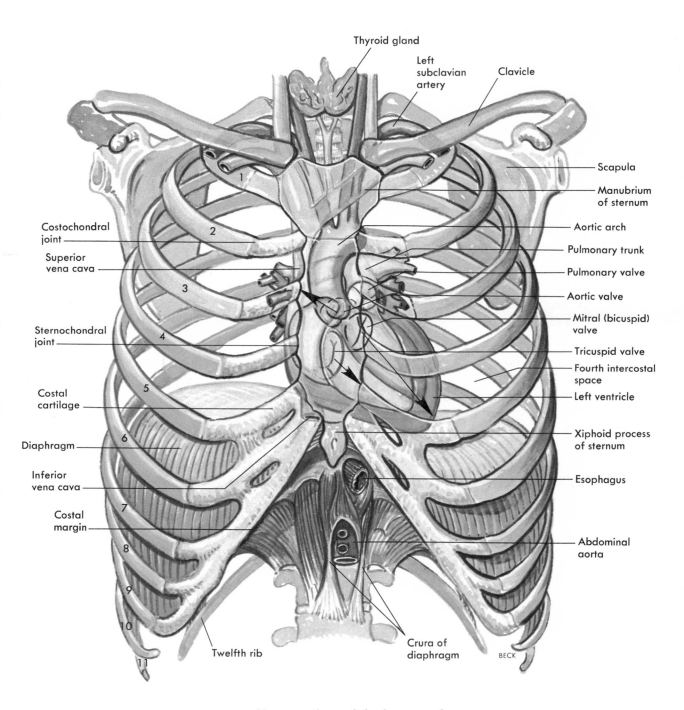

Thyroid gland

Left subclavian artery

Clavicle

Scapula

Manubrium of sternum

Aortic arch

Pulmonary trunk

Pulmonary valve

Aortic valve

Mitral (bicuspid) valve

Tricuspid valve

Fourth intercostal space

Left ventricle

Xiphoid process of sternum

Esophagus

Abdominal aorta

Costochondral joint

Superior vena cava

Sternochondral joint

Costal cartilage

Diaphragm

Inferior vena cava

Costal margin

Twelfth rib

Crura of diaphragm

BECK

Projection of heart, valves of the heart, and great
vessels to anterior wall of thorax (sternum, costal
cartilages, clavicles).

1|8

Projection of lungs and bronchi to rib cage

The points on the rib cage to which different parts of the bronchi and lungs project are illustrated. While listening with a stethoscope placed on the chest wall at different locations, one can hear the movement of air in and out of the respiratory structures. The quality of the sound is indicative of the health of the respiratory tubes. Pain that emanates from the bronchi and lungs may be projected to the walls (pleura) of the thoracic cage, the muscles between ribs, and overlying chest and back muscles.

The illustration shows the extensive branching of the bronchial tree in both lungs from main bronchi to smaller bronchioles and to alveolar ducts and alveolar sacs (not illustrated). The cartilages encircling the larger branches are progressively lost as the bronchi branch and become smaller.

Breath sounds high in the chest cavity at the level of the sternoclavicular joints are described as "bronchial," with expiration sounding louder and lasting longer than elsewhere in the chest cavity. At the level of the tracheal bifurcation the inspiration sounds almost as loud and lasts as long as expiration; the breath sound here is described as "bronchovesicular." Expiration is normally more prolonged and louder than expiration in the lung fields themselves, leading to the soft "vesicular" sounds.

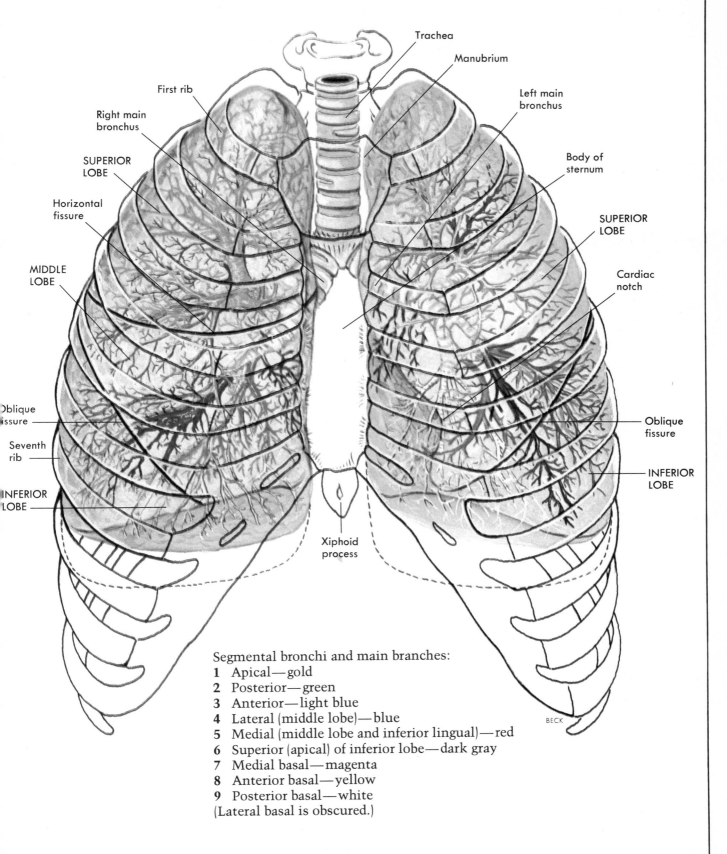

Trachea

Manubrium

First rib

Right main
bronchus

Left main
bronchus

SUPERIOR
LOBE

Body of
sternum

Horizontal
fissure

SUPERIOR
LOBE

MIDDLE
LOBE

Cardiac
notch

Oblique
fissure

Oblique
fissure

Seventh
rib

INFERIOR
LOBE

INFERIOR
LOBE

Xiphoid
process

BECK

Segmental bronchi and main branches:
1 Apical—gold
2 Posterior—green
3 Anterior—light blue
4 Lateral (middle lobe)—blue
5 Medial (middle lobe and inferior lingual)—red
6 Superior (apical) of inferior lobe—dark gray
7 Medial basal—magenta
8 Anterior basal—yellow
9 Posterior basal—white
(Lateral basal is obscured.)

1|9

Regions of the abdomen

For purposes of description and convenience the abdomen is divided into nine regions by means of two primary horizontal lines and two vertical lines (shown as interrupted lines). The upper horizontal plane, or line, passes through the pylorus and is called the transpyloric plane. It passes through the body of the first lumbar vertebra. The lower horizontal plane passes through the tubercles of the iliac crest and is called the transtubercular plane. It is about midway between the xiphosternal junction and the umbilicus. The vertical planes pass through the middle of the right and left inguinal ligaments. The arrows medial to these lines indicate the planes created by the lateral margins of the rectus abdominis muscles (lateral rectus planes).

The regions bounded by these planes are the right and left hypochondriac and epigastric regions above the transpyloric plane; the right and left lumbar and umbilical regions between the two horizontal lines; the right and left inguinal, or iliac, and hypogastric regions below the lowest horizontal line (interspinous plane). The subcostal plane is at the most caudal part of the tenth costal cartilage. The supracristal plane passes through the highest points of the iliac crest.

Because of individual body differences and the wide range of variation in the position of the abdominal contents, the subdivisions thus created are only approximate.

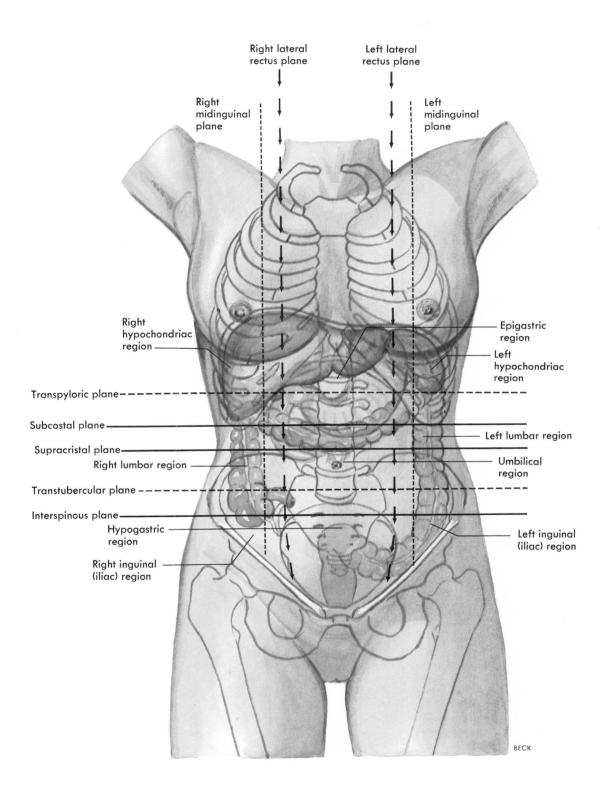

Right lateral
rectus plane

Left lateral
rectus plane

Right
midinguinal
plane

Left
midinguinal
plane

Right
hypochondriac
region

Epigastric
region

Left
hypochondriac
region

Transpyloric plane

Subcostal plane

Left lumbar region

Supracristal plane

Right lumbar region

Umbilical
region

Transtubercular plane

Interspinous plane

Hypogastric
region

Left inguinal
(iliac) region

Right inguinal
(iliac) region

BECK

1|10

Abdominal and pelvic viscera from the right side

This lateral perspective of the adult female body shows the proportionately great space that the intestinal tract and abdominal organs occupy. Notice the length of the ureters as they pass from the flank location of the kidneys to the pelvic cavity, where they enter the bladder.

The dome-shaped diaphragm permits the lungs to project downward on either side. The numbering of the ribs (4 to 12), intercostal spaces, and vertebrae (thoracic 8 to 12, lumbar 1 to 4) provide landmarks for locating structures.

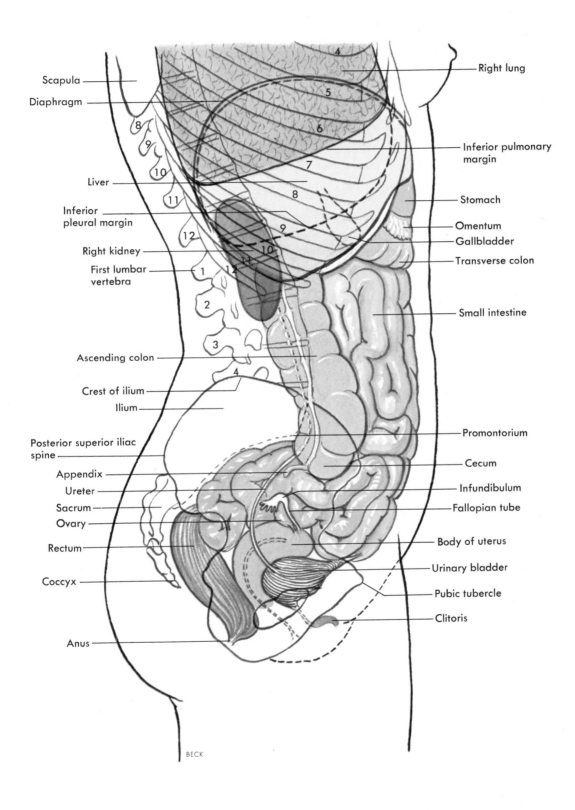

Scapula

Diaphragm

Liver

Inferior
pleural margin

Right kidney

First lumbar
vertebra

Ascending colon

Crest of ilium

Ilium

Posterior superior iliac
spine

Appendix

Ureter

Sacrum

Ovary

Rectum

Coccyx

Anus

Right lung

Inferior pulmonary
margin

Stomach

Omentum

Gallbladder

Transverse colon

Small intestine

Promontorium

Cecum

Infundibulum

Fallopian tube

Body of uterus

Urinary bladder

Pubic tubercle

Clitoris

BECK

1|11

Abdominal and pelvic viscera from the left side

This view of the adult male body from the left side shows relationships of the lungs and abdominal organs to the ribs (4 to 12), vertebrae (thoracic 8 to 12, lumbar 1 to 4), and bones of the pelvis. The dome of the diaphragm reaches the fifth intercostal space. The left kidney extends from the middle of the body of the tenth thoracic vertebra to the lower part of the twelfth thoracic vertebra. The descending colon is seen extending from the left colic (splenic) flexure to the level of the anterior superior iliac spine, where it bends posteriorly and from there on is named the sigmoid colon. The spleen occupies a left posterolateral position, extending from behind the stomach to a level even with the third lumbar vertebra.

The crest of the ilium is easily palpable in all but extremely obese persons and is an important bony landmark.

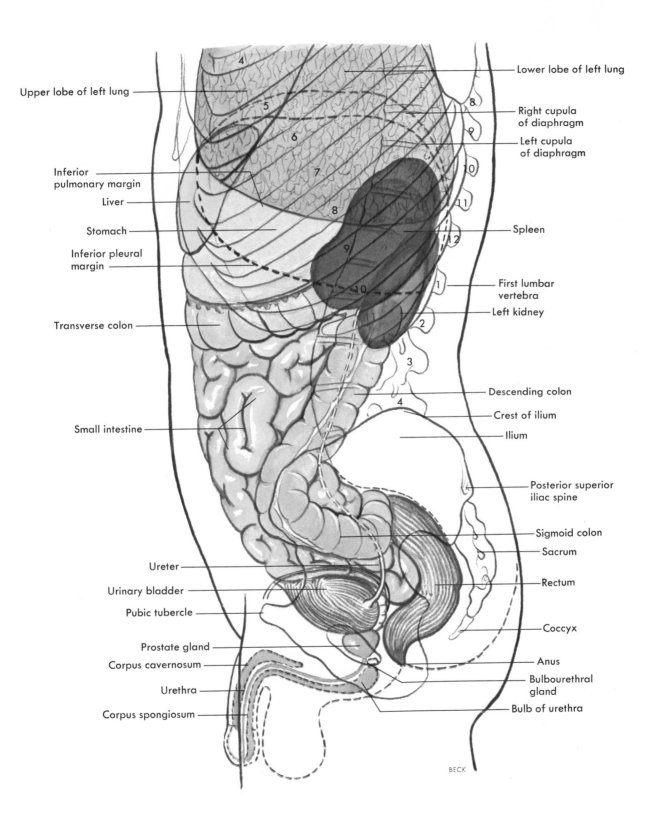

Upper lobe of left lung

Inferior
pulmonary margin

Liver

Stomach

Inferior pleural
margin

Transverse colon

Small intestine

Ureter

Urinary bladder

Pubic tubercle

Prostate gland

Corpus cavernosum

Urethra

Corpus spongiosum

Lower lobe of left lung

Right cupula
of diaphragm

Left cupula
of diaphragm

Spleen

First lumbar
vertebra

Left kidney

Descending colon

Crest of ilium

Ilium

Posterior superior
iliac spine

Sigmoid colon

Sacrum

Rectum

Coccyx

Anus

Bulbourethral
gland

Bulb of urethra

BECK

1|12

The peritoneum

An extensive serous membrane, the peritoneum, binds and protects the gastrointestinal tract, holding its components loosely in place. It lines the walls of the entire abdominal cavity (parietal layer) and also forms the serous outer coat of the organs (visceral layer). Its relections from the small intestine to the posterior abdominal wall (lumbar region) are called mesenteries. This great fan of peritoneum is variable in length and consists of two serous layers, between which blood vessels and nerves reach the gut walls. A less extensive fold of peritoneum, the transverse mesocolon, attaches the transverse colon to the posterior abdominal wall. The greater omentum is a downward continuation of the serosa of the greater curvature of the stomach. It is variable in length and hangs like an apron to cover and protect the small bowel. The lesser omentum, or gastrohepatic and hepatoduodenal ligaments, connects the lesser curvature of the stomach to the liver.

These folds of peritoneum provide a lubricating fluid to ensure smooth and unimpeded movements of the intestinal loops against the surrounding viscera. The peritoneum also serves as a fat storage organ, and can help wall off local inflammations within the abdominal cavity. Peritoneal fluid is rich in white blood cells that serve as phagocytes.

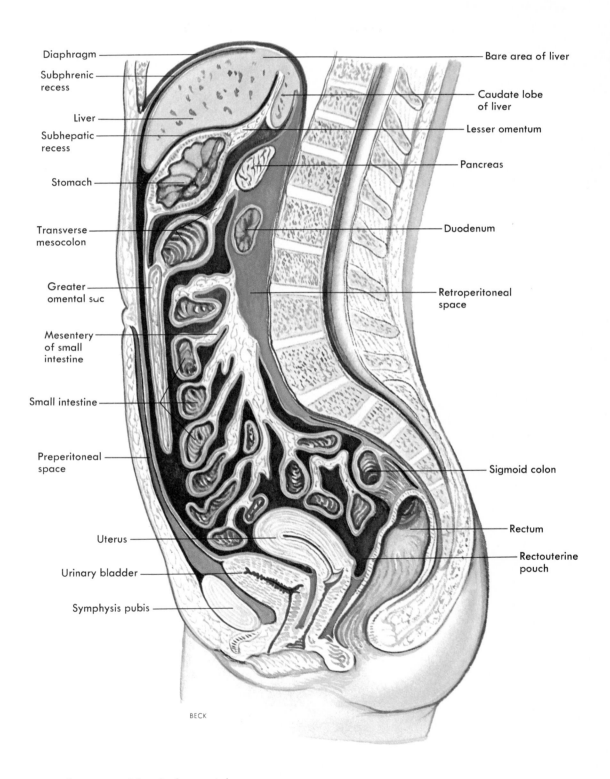

Diaphragm

Subphrenic recess

Liver

Subhepatic recess

Stomach

Transverse mesocolon

Greater omental sac

Mesentery of small intestine

Small intestine

Preperitoneal space

Uterus

Urinary bladder

Symphysis pubis

Bare area of liver

Caudate lobe of liver

Lesser omentum

Pancreas

Duodenum

Retroperitoneal space

Sigmoid colon

Rectum

Rectouterine pouch

BECK

Peritoneal cavity—blue (schematic)
Retroperitoneal spaces—green (schematic)

1|13

Full-term pregnancy (in relation to viscera)

The full-term pregnant uterus occupies an enormous amount of intraabdominal space. Many anatomical and physiological adaptations must take place, and there are also many annoying side effects. The colon becomes compressed, typically causing constipation in later pregnancy. A lumbar lordosis develops and combined with muscle stretching and straining, often causes backache. The diaphragm is elevated, leading to minor respiratory discomfort and a faster respiratory rate. The stomach is also elevated and compressed, leading to reflux of stomach contents into the esophagus. This causes the typical heartburn of later pregnancy. The rectus abdominis muscle is greatly stretched, as is the overlying skin. This may lead to a midline separation of the muscle after pregnancy (diastasis recti) and to stretch marks.

The pregnant uterus also exerts pressure on the easily collapsible large veins. Thus the pregnant woman may tend to develop varicose veins and hemorrhoids.

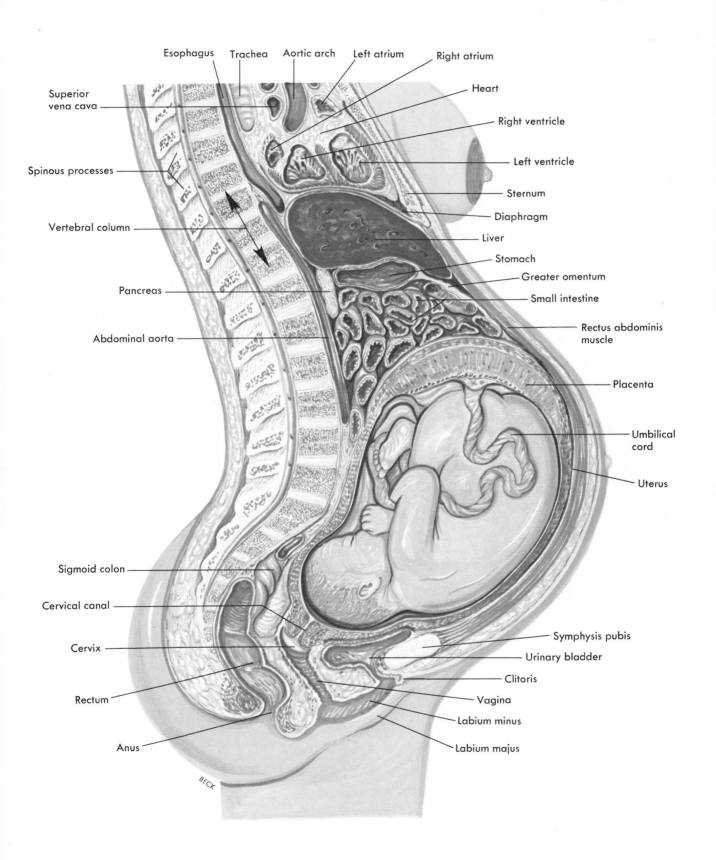

Esophagus   Trachea   Aortic arch   Left atrium   Right atrium

Superior vena cava

Heart

Right ventricle

Left ventricle

Spinous processes

Sternum

Diaphragm

Vertebral column

Liver

Stomach

Greater omentum

Pancreas

Small intestine

Abdominal aorta

Rectus abdominis muscle

Placenta

Umbilical cord

Uterus

Sigmoid colon

Cervical canal

Symphysis pubis

Cervix

Urinary bladder

Clitoris

Rectum

Vagina

Labium minus

Anus

Labium majus

BECK

27

2 | **The integumentary system**

The skin
Common skin disorders

2|1

The skin

The external appearance of the skin is deceptively homogenous and simple. The visible outer layer is composed of a cornified layer of dead cells. Cells are constantly shed from this layer and replaced by cells that are produced in the basal layer of the epidermis. The germinating cells divide continually and new cells are pushed upward, forming the stratifications of the epidermal epithelium. The epithelial layers are separated from the connective tissue dermis by a basement membrane. Epidermal elements dip down into the dermis, however, and include sweat and oil glands and the hair follicles. Thus the dermis can serve as a source of new epidermis if this layer should be destroyed, as may happen in a severe burn. The functions of the dermis, which is largely composed of dense, white connective tissue, are supportive. The fibers are collagen and elastin, which give the dermis form and substance. There are many nerves and blood vessels running through the dermis, and the skin is amply provided with sensory nerve endings for pressure, touch, pain, and temperature. Some areas of the skin are more richly innervated than others and include the hands, feet, genitalia, and face.

The skin is a very vascular organ and plays an extremely important role in temperature regulation. The blood vessels to the skin are organized so that blood may be shunted directly from arteries to veins through vessels larger than arteriole and venule size (arteriovenous anastomoses), thus bypassing the capillaries. When the needs of the body require elevation of the internal body temperature, these shunts are open. However, if excessive heat is produced internally and must be lost from the body, such as occurs in prolonged muscular exercise, then the arteriovenous anastomoses are closed and a large volume of blood moves to the skin, where excessive heat can be radiated into the environment. The skin also functions in temperature regulation by providing a large surface for evaporative water loss, and sweat glands provide an additional source of heat and water loss as well. Besides temperature regulation, the skin protects the body from environmental extremes, excesses of temperature, and trauma and provides the nervous system with valuable information about the environment.

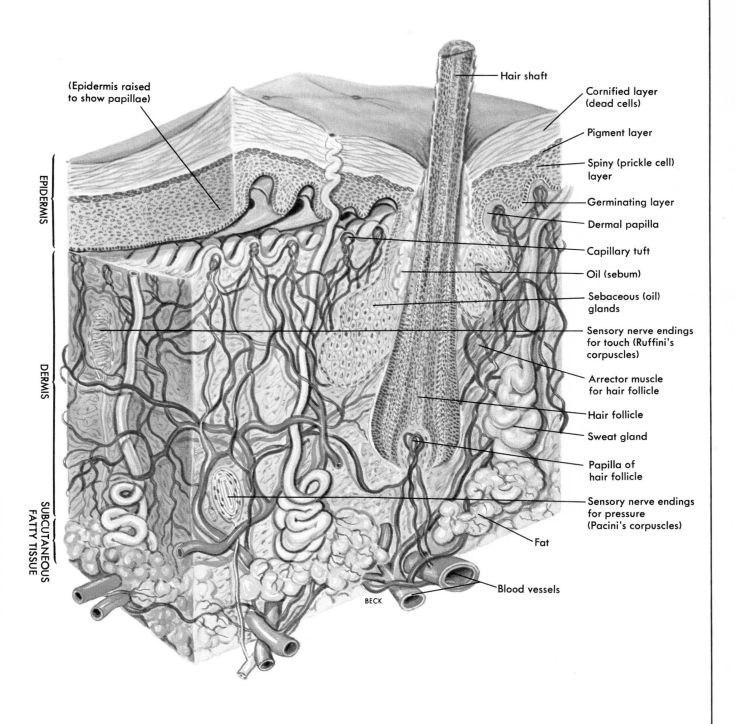

(Epidermis raised
to show papillae)

Hair shaft

Cornified layer
(dead cells)

Pigment layer

Spiny (prickle cell)
layer

Germinating layer

Dermal papilla

Capillary tuft

Oil (sebum)

Sebaceous (oil)
glands

Sensory nerve endings
for touch (Ruffini's
corpuscles)

Arrector muscle
for hair follicle

Hair follicle

Sweat gland

Papilla of
hair follicle

Sensory nerve endings
for pressure
(Pacini's corpuscles)

Fat

Blood vessels

EPIDERMIS

DERMIS

SUBCUTANEOUS
FATTY TISSUE

BECK

2|2

Common skin disorders—acne; warts; moles

The illustrations in Plates 2-2 and 2-3 depict some of the most common dermatological problems that occur in human beings.

Acne is most common in the adolescent age group, although it can be seen at any point in the life cycle. Acne is the result of excessive secretion of oil from the facial oil glands. There may be hypersecretion of oil on other parts of the body as well. A major problem that complicates the clinical course of acne is secondary infection. Bacterial invasion and growth result in unsightly reddening and swelling. This may lead to further handling and provoking of the lesions, and a vicious cycle ensues.

Warts are the result of a viral skin disease that produces small, benign tumors. They are the only known human tumors caused by viruses, although there is evidence for a viral origin for many benign and malignant tumors in other animals.

Moles are probably the most common skin lesions and vary in coloration from light brown to deep black. The amount of pigment present determines the color. The most serious skin cancer arises from a previously benign mole and is known as malignant melanoma. Often the mole is heavily pigmented and may be subject to irritation or excessive exposure to sunlight before it actually becomes transformed into a malignant growth.

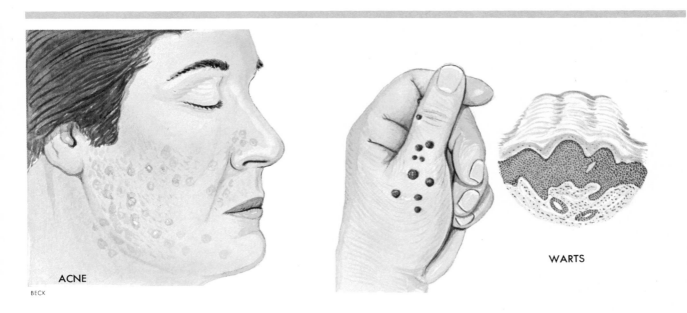

ACNE

BECK

WARTS

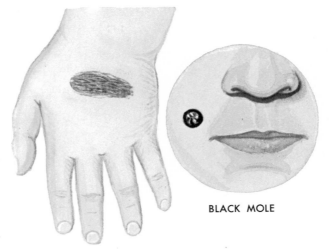

BROWN MOLE

BLACK MOLE

Common skin disorders—basal cell and squamous cell carcinoma; athlete's foot; poison ivy

Skin cancer is the most common form of human cancer, and generally is highly curable. Two common cancers are illustrated here in histological section. Basal cell carcinoma is thought to arise from malignant transformation of a cell in the stratum basalis of the epidermis. It appears as a small, pearly lesion on the skin. The malignancy shown here is a deep growth into the dermis but separated from the dermis by the basement membrane. The squamous cell carcinoma often arises from a patch of hyperpigmented skin and initially has a wartlike appearance. This type of skin cancer often is diffuse and ulcerated; necrosis is common. The histological pattern frequently shows deep fixation to and invasion of underlying structures.

Athlete's foot, or tinea pedis (ringworm of the foot), is a frequent problem affecting the creases between the toes and the sole of the foot. It thrives in a warm, moist environment and is caused by a fungus.

Poison ivy is an allergic response to a plant substance that leads to a reddened, wet, itchy dermatitis. The scratching and handling of these lesions may lead to spreading, skin breakdown, and infection.

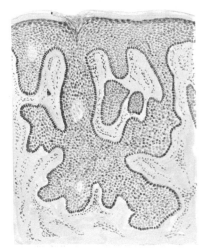

BASAL CELL CARCINOMA

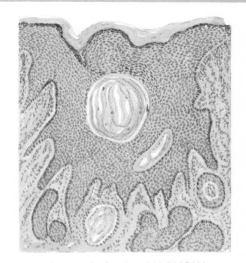

SQUAMOUS CELL CARCINOMA

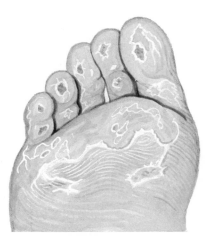

ATHLETE'S FOOT

POISON IVY

3 | The skeletal system

Structure of long bone
Microscopic structure of bone
The skull
Fetal skull
The skeleton (in relation to body outline)
Cartilages of the nose
The vertebral column
Male and female bony pelvis (compared)
Skeleton of the thorax
Hip joint
Shoulder joint
Elbow joint
Wrist joint
Knee joint
Pathology of gouty arthritis
Bones of the foot
Arches of the foot
Clubfoot (talipes)
Bone growth—upper limbs
Bone growth—lower limbs
Longitudinal section of a molar tooth and surrounding
    structures
Deciduous arch (temporary teeth) and permanent teeth

3|1

Structure of long bone

Long bones consist of a cortex, or outer covering, of hard, compact bone. This is protected externally by the periosteum, a connective tissue covering. The endosteum covers the compact bone's surface facing the internal medullary, or marrow, cavity. In the fetus, infant, and young child these cavities are filled with red marrow, which produces blood cells. With age the red marrow is replaced with fatty tissue, the yellow marrow. The flat bones generally function more in blood cell formation in the adult and retain the red bone marrow.

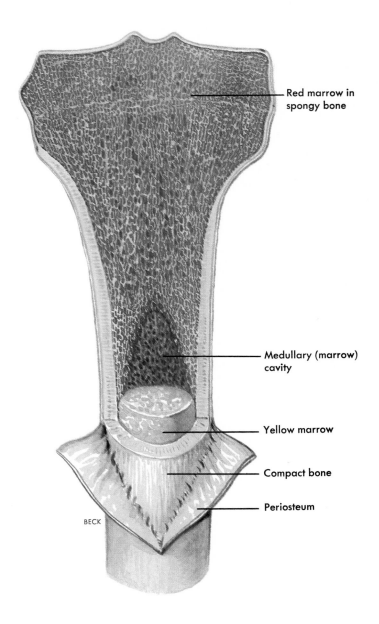

Red marrow in
spongy bone

Medullary (marrow)
cavity

Yellow marrow

Compact bone

Periosteum

BECK

3|2

Microscopic structure of bone

Microscopically, bone is seen to be honeycombed with cavities and tiny canals. Within these structures are osteocytes (bone cells) and long cytoplasmic extensions of osteocytes. The haversian system is the anatomical unit of bone. One haversian system is made up of concentric layers of cells, lacunae containing osteocytes, canaliculi extending between the lacunae, and a central haversian canal that contains blood vessels.

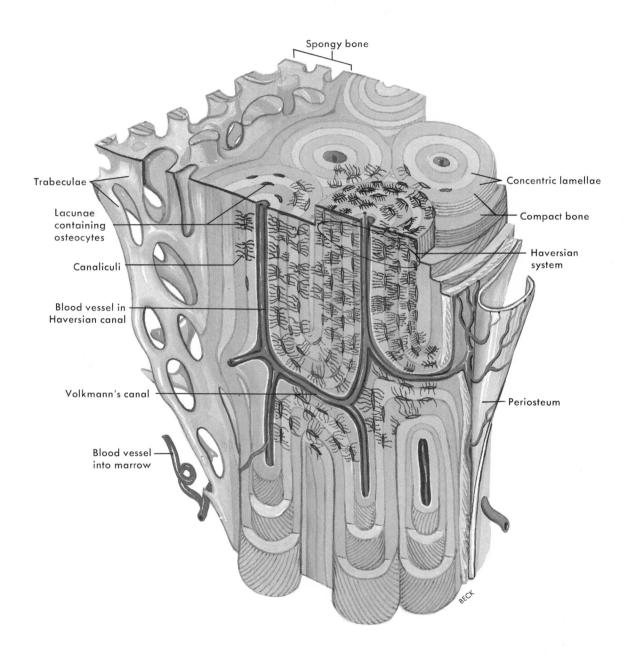

Spongy bone

Trabeculae

Lacunae
containing
osteocytes

Canaliculi

Blood vessel in
Haversian canal

Volkmann's canal

Blood vessel
into marrow

Concentric lamellae

Compact bone

Haversian
system

Periosteum

BECK

3|3

The skull

The adult human skull is an extraordinarily strong bony encasement for the soft, easily damaged brain. The protective capacity of the skull is well attested to by the many head traumas that people can endure without injury to the brain itself. There are 28 separate bones making up the skull. The cranium is made up of several flat bones that are joined together at the sutures. Although fused in the adult, these bones nevertheless are considered anatomically to articulate with each other through a type of joint known as a synarthrotic (nonmovable) fibrous joint.

The cranial bones include the frontal, parietal, temporal, and occipital. Two other cranial bones, the ethmoid and the sphenoid, make up the floor of the cranium. The skull is also composed of separate bones that form the face. The maxillae and mandible make up the jaw; the zygomatic bones, the cheeks; and the nasal bone, the nose. Numerous other thin, irregular bones also help form the interior nasal and palatal structure, and the tiny middle ear bones (ossicles) are responsible for sound transmission to the inner ears.

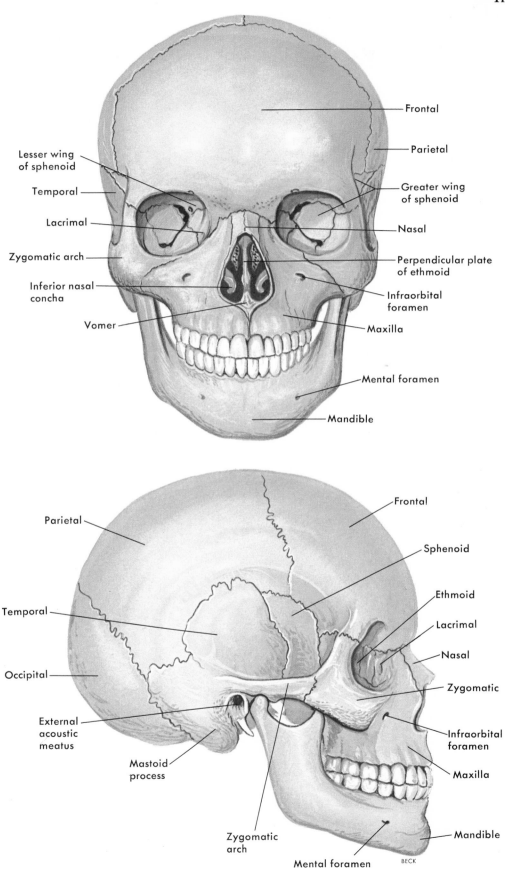

Frontal

Parietal

Lesser wing
of sphenoid

Greater wing
of sphenoid

Temporal

Nasal

Lacrimal

Perpendicular plate
of ethmoid

Zygomatic arch

Inferior nasal
concha

Infraorbital
foramen

Vomer

Maxilla

Mental foramen

Mandible

Parietal

Frontal

Sphenoid

Temporal

Ethmoid

Lacrimal

Occipital

Nasal

Zygomatic

External
acoustic
meatus

Infraorbital
foramen

Mastoid
process

Maxilla

Zygomatic
arch

Mandible

Mental foramen

BECK

3|4

Fetal skull

The skull is proportionately larger and softer in the fetus, infant, and young child as compared to the adult. The flat bones of the skull are not articulated at birth and are separated by sutures and fontanels. The frontal, or anterior, fontanel is most easily palpable at birth and is commonly called the "soft spot." The absence of fusion of the skull bones permits molding of the infant's head as it is pushed through the birth canal.

Molding refers to the changes in shape of the fetal head that result when the cranial bones move and shift position during birth. Molding may permit delivery of the fetal head in situations where there is mild disproportion between the maternal pelvis and the diameter of the head. The most common type of molding is a slipping of the occipital bone beneath the parietal bones.

Growth of the brain is permitted during the first year of life by the presence of sutures and fontanels. When abnormal closure of the sutures and fontanels occurs, the brain can no longer grow and mental retardation usually results. The posterolateral fontanel is small and closes by the second month. The larger anterior fontanel can be felt up to 18 months. Until then the infant's head is vulnerable to trauma and temperature extremes.

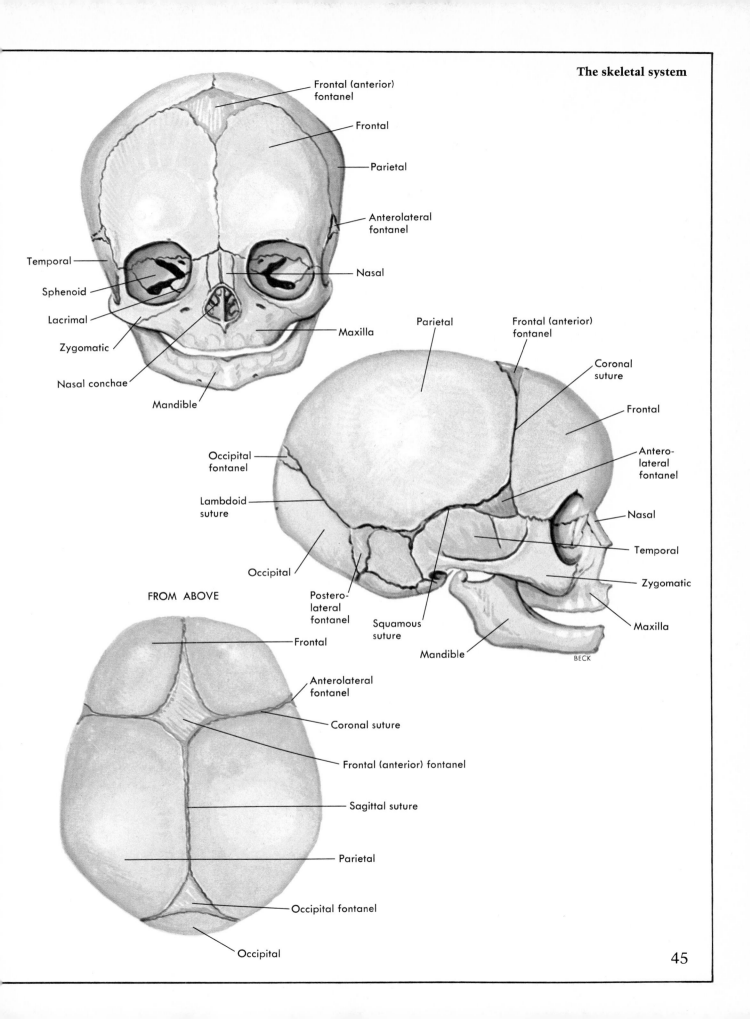

Frontal (anterior) fontanel

Frontal

Parietal

Anterolateral fontanel

Nasal

Temporal

Sphenoid

Lacrimal

Zygomatic

Nasal conchae

Mandible

Maxilla

Parietal

Frontal (anterior) fontanel

Coronal suture

Frontal

Antero-lateral fontanel

Nasal

Temporal

Zygomatic

Maxilla

Occipital fontanel

Lambdoid suture

Occipital

Postero-lateral fontanel

Squamous suture

Mandible

BECK

FROM ABOVE

Frontal

Anterolateral fontanel

Coronal suture

Frontal (anterior) fontanel

Sagittal suture

Parietal

Occipital fontanel

Occipital

45

3|5

The skeleton (in relation to body outline)

The human skeleton consists of an axial system (bones of the head, vertebral column, sternum, and rib cage) and an appendicular system (bones supporting and forming the upper and lower extremities). Together these systems contain 206 bones. The skeletal system functions in support and movement, providing both a structural framework and a system of levers and fulcrums for muscle action.

Bone itself is a type of connective tissue calcified into a mineralized lattice in which bone cells are imbedded. Bone is an extremely dynamic tissue, constantly being remodeled, that not only grows during childhood but also responds to stress by breakdown and regrowth throughout life. Bone also serves as a storage tissue for calcium and phosphorous, readily releasing these minerals when stimulated by parathyroid hormone. The internal medullary cavities of flat bones in adults are occupied by red bone marrow, which produces blood cells. Both long bones and flat bones function in blood cell production during early years of life.

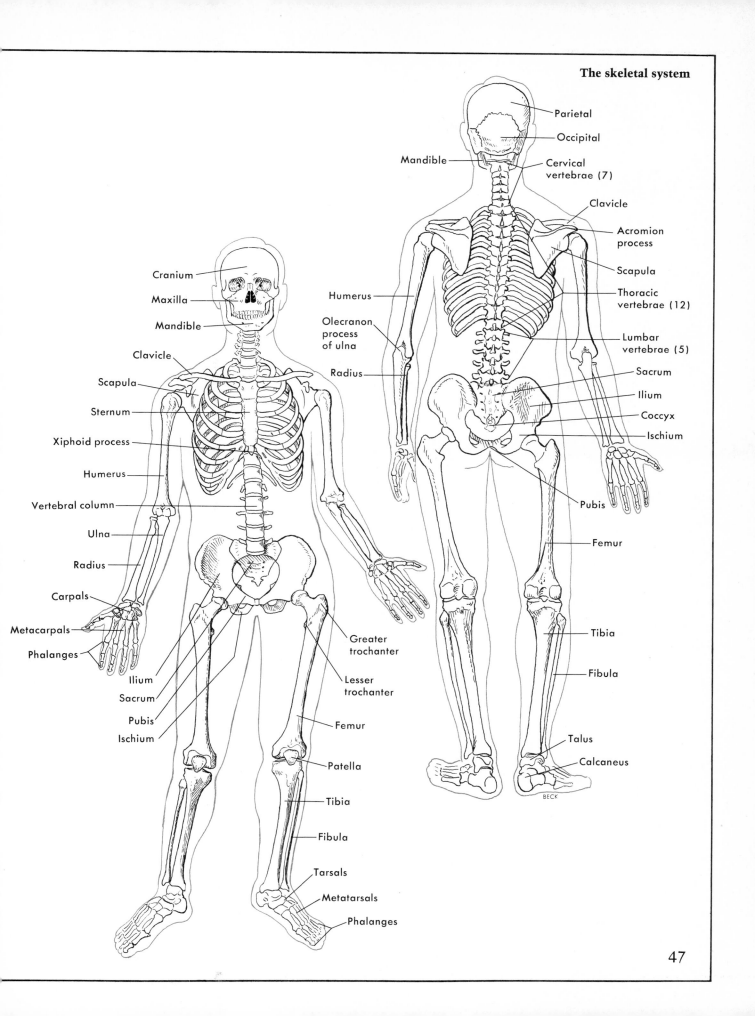

Parietal

Occipital

Mandible

Cervical
vertebrae (7)

Clavicle

Acromion
process

Scapula

Humerus

Thoracic
vertebrae (12)

Olecranon
process
of ulna

Lumbar
vertebrae (5)

Radius

Sacrum

Ilium

Coccyx

Ischium

Pubis

Femur

Tibia

Fibula

Talus

Calcaneus

BECK

Cranium

Maxilla

Mandible

Clavicle

Scapula

Sternum

Xiphoid process

Humerus

Vertebral column

Ulna

Radius

Carpals

Metacarpals

Phalanges

Ilium

Sacrum

Pubis

Ischium

Greater
trochanter

Lesser
trochanter

Femur

Patella

Tibia

Fibula

Tarsals

Metatarsals

Phalanges

47

3|6

Cartilages of the nose

The nose is composed of both bony and cartilaginous parts. The nasal bone and nasal processes of the frontal and maxillary bones form the root and dorsum of the nose; the cartilages form the distal part, the tip, and the external and internal nares. The separate cartilaginous plates are held tightly together by connective tissue and muscular attachments. These parts allow the nares and external nasal cavities to change shape and dilate, contributing to facial expressiveness. Flaring of the nares is not normally visible during respiration and can be an important indicator of respiratory distress.

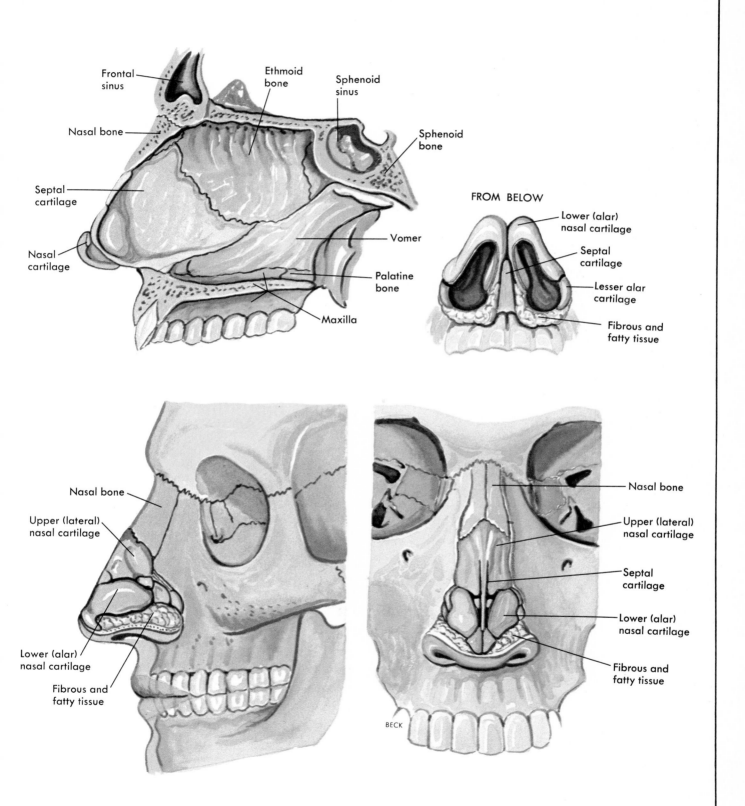

Frontal sinus

Ethmoid bone

Sphenoid sinus

Sphenoid bone

Nasal bone

Septal cartilage

Nasal cartilage

Vomer

Palatine bone

Maxilla

FROM BELOW

Lower (alar) nasal cartilage

Septal cartilage

Lesser alar cartilage

Fibrous and fatty tissue

Nasal bone

Upper (lateral) nasal cartilage

Lower (alar) nasal cartilage

Fibrous and fatty tissue

Nasal bone

Upper (lateral) nasal cartilage

Septal cartilage

Lower (alar) nasal cartilage

Fibrous and fatty tissue

BECK

3|7

The vertebral column

The vertebral column is a semirigid, bony pillar that supports muscles and encases and protects the spinal cord. The individual vertebrae are separated by cartilaginous disks. Intervertebral foramina provide openings through which the spinal nerves pass from the spinal cord to their points of innervation. There are typical curvatures in the vertebral column; the cervical and lumbar curves, which are concave, and the thoracic and sacral, which are convex. These curves develop as the child learns to hold the head up and then later to walk. Certain abnormalities of curvature can occur. Scoliosis is a lateral curvature that develops most commonly in pubescent girls. Kyphosis is an exaggerated thoracic curvature that is a normal part of aging but can occur pathologically earlier in life. Lordosis results when the lumbar curvature is more pronounced than normal.

The separate divisions of the vertebral column are characterized by structural differences in the vertebrae that allow for support and appropriate movement. Nevertheless, the back is one of the weaker parts of the human musculoskeletal system. Back pain is a common ailment; muscle weakness often leads to back sprains. A more serious problem is related to the intervertebral disks, whose soft centers may herniate and create pressure on nerves and severe pain. The disks also become worn and thinned as a result of aging.

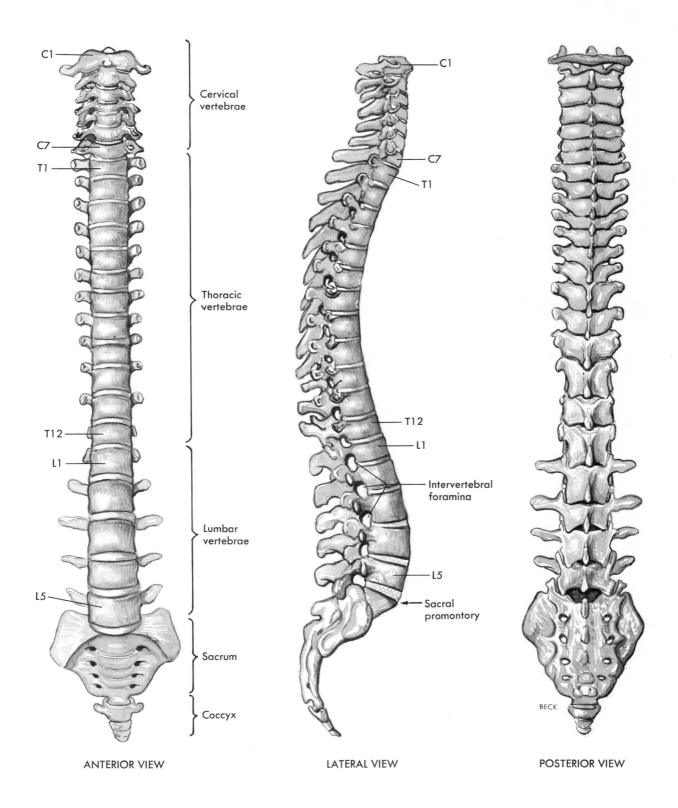

C1

Cervical
vertebrae

C7

T1

Thoracic
vertebrae

T12

L1

Lumbar
vertebrae

L5

Sacrum

Coccyx

ANTERIOR VIEW

C1

C7

T1

T12

L1

Intervertebral
foramina

L5

Sacral
promontory

LATERAL VIEW

BECK

POSTERIOR VIEW

3|8

Male and female bony pelvis (compared)

The pelvis is formed by the sacrum, coccyx, and two innominate bones. The male pelvis is shorter, heavier, and narrower in all dimensions when compared to the female pelvis. Generally, the wider and longer female pelvic outlet is a characteristic associated with the childbearing function. However, the female pelvis can also be classified into different types, depending on the dimensions of the pelvic inlet, including anthropoid, gynecoid, android, and platypelloid. This classification is based on the shape of the anterior and posterior segment of the pelvis if an imaginary line is drawn across the widest transverse diameter of the pelvic inlet. Gynecoid is the most common type in the white female and is characterized by a rounded posterior segment, while the anthropoid type, of a more oval shape, is more common in non-Caucasian women. The other types are less common and are often associated with problems in delivery of the fetus.

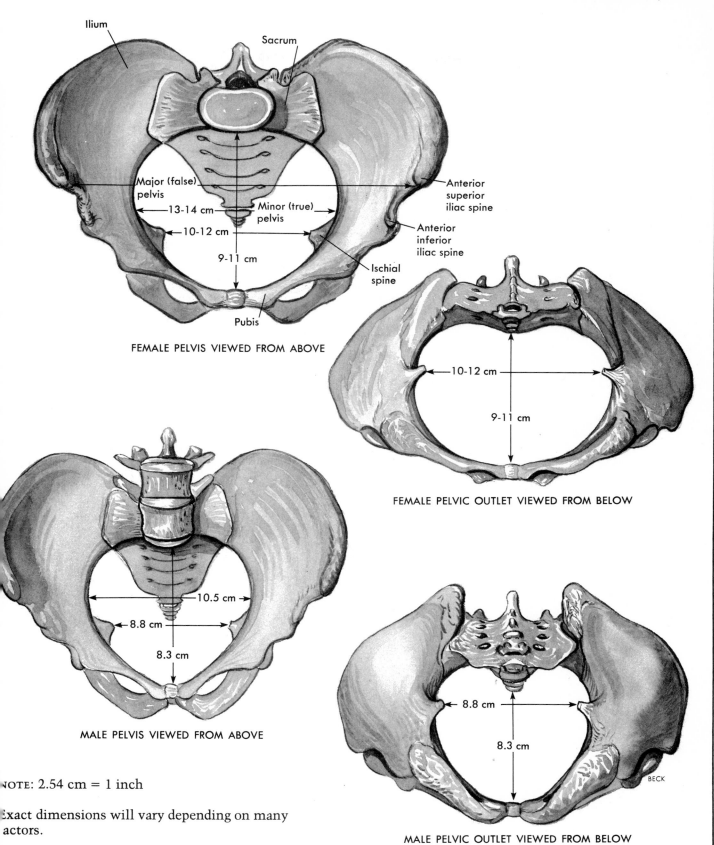

Ilium

Sacrum

Major (false) pelvis

Minor (true) pelvis

13-14 cm

10-12 cm

9-11 cm

Anterior superior iliac spine

Anterior inferior iliac spine

Ischial spine

Pubis

FEMALE PELVIS VIEWED FROM ABOVE

10-12 cm

9-11 cm

FEMALE PELVIC OUTLET VIEWED FROM BELOW

10.5 cm

8.8 cm

8.3 cm

MALE PELVIS VIEWED FROM ABOVE

8.8 cm

8.3 cm

BECK

MALE PELVIC OUTLET VIEWED FROM BELOW

NOTE: 2.54 cm = 1 inch

Exact dimensions will vary depending on many factors.

3|9

Skeleton of the thorax

The thoracic cage provides protection for the thoracic and mediastinal organs. The sternum, or breastbone, lies in the midline and is shield-shaped, consisting of the manubrium, sternal body, and xiphoid process. Notice the articulations of the ribs with the sternum via the costal cartilages. Posteriorly, a typical rib articulates with a transverse process and the bodies of two adjacent vertebrae and the intervening disk. There are 12 pairs of ribs, with the eleventh and twelfth ribs not articulating with the sternum or the costal cartilages, thus often called the "floating ribs." The ribs project forward and downward to completely encircle the thoracic organs. The clavicles, or collarbones, together with the two scapula bones form the shoulder girdle. The anatomical arrangement of the shoulder girdle permits the extreme flexibility and mobility of the shoulder.

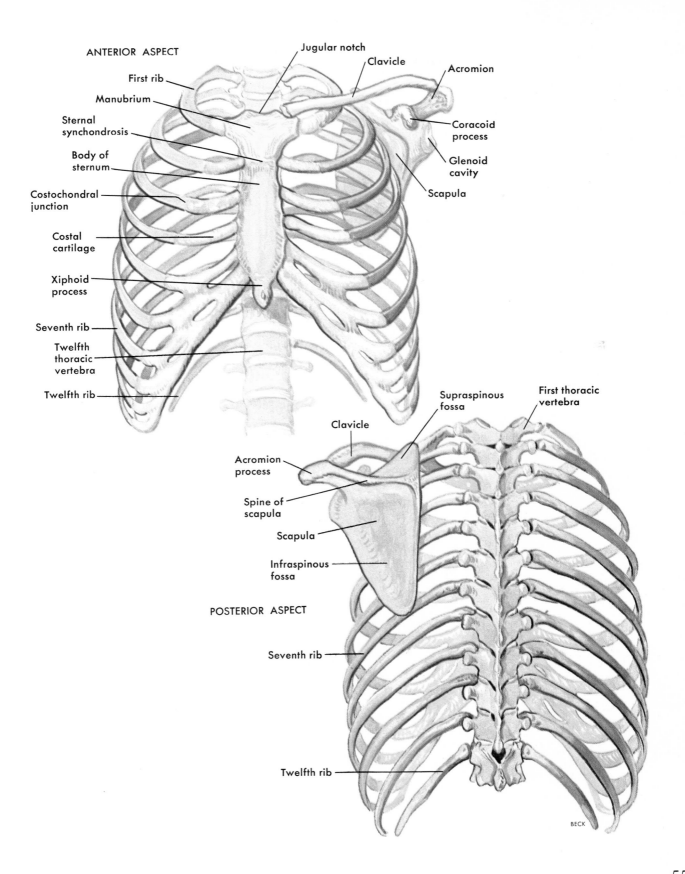

ANTERIOR ASPECT

Jugular notch

Clavicle

Acromion

First rib

Manubrium

Coracoid process

Sternal synchondrosis

Glenoid cavity

Body of sternum

Scapula

Costochondral junction

Costal cartilage

Xiphoid process

Seventh rib

Twelfth thoracic vertebra

Twelfth rib

Supraspinous fossa

First thoracic vertebra

Clavicle

Acromion process

Spine of scapula

Scapula

Infraspinous fossa

POSTERIOR ASPECT

Seventh rib

Twelfth rib

BECK

55

3|10

Hip joint

The head of the femur fits tightly into the acetabulum, forming the ball-and-socket joint of the hip. This joint permits a wide range of motion and is exceptionally strong. The iliofemoral ligament binds the greater trochanter to the ilium, reinforcing the articular capsule. The femur is the largest, heaviest bone in the body, but its weakest part is the neck region. It is here that a fracture is most likely to occur, especially in the elderly.

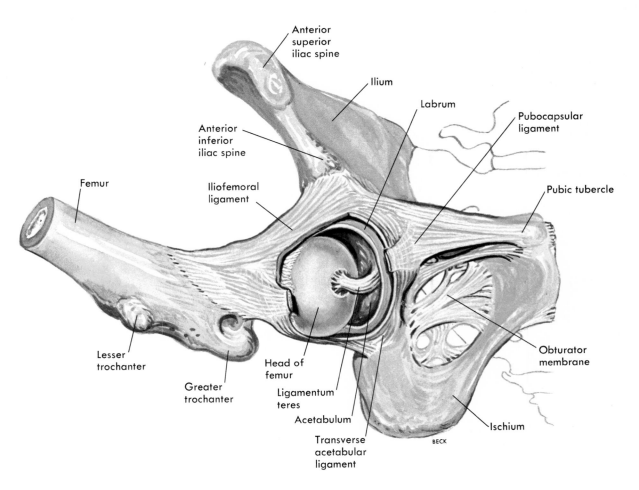

Hip joint—femur abducted and rotated laterally
(a portion of the iliofemoral ligament is removed)

3|11

Shoulder joint

The shoulder joint is also a ball-and-socket joint, even more flexible than the hip joint. This additional mobility is permitted because of the relatively shallow glenoid cavity as compared to the acetabulum and because the ligaments are less tightly binding. Several bursae (not illustrated) are present to cushion the muscles and joint capsule. Bursitis occurs in the shoulder joint more often than in other joints and usually affects the subacromial bursa, which is between the acromion process and the supraspinous muscle.
The most prominent symptom is pain on movement. Dislocation of the glenohumeral joint is a common athletic injury—the humeral head dislocates out of the glenoid fossa in an anterior direction, and the shoulder is slightly externally rotated and appears more angular. Often a dislocation of this type can readily be manipulated back into position.

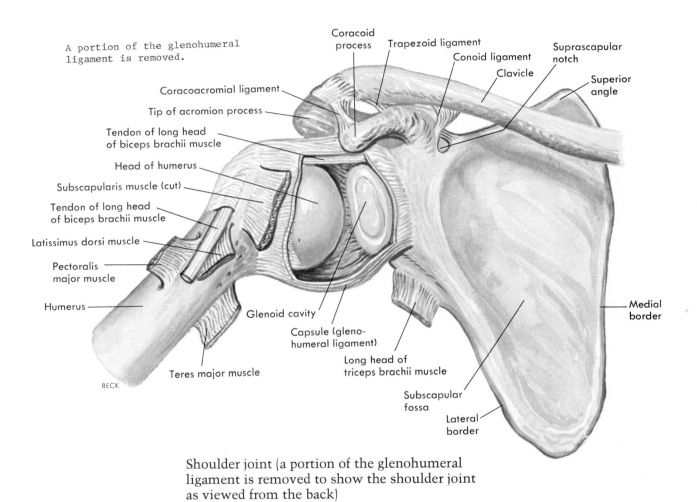

A portion of the glenohumeral
ligament is removed.

Coracoid
process

Trapezoid ligament

Conoid ligament

Clavicle

Suprascapular
notch

Superior
angle

Coracoacromial ligament

Tip of acromion process

Tendon of long head
of biceps brachii muscle

Head of humerus

Subscapularis muscle (cut)

Tendon of long head
of biceps brachii muscle

Latissimus dorsi muscle

Pectoralis
major muscle

Humerus

Glenoid cavity

Capsule (gleno-
humeral ligament)

Teres major muscle

Long head of
triceps brachii muscle

Subscapular
fossa

Lateral
border

Medial
border

BECK

Shoulder joint (a portion of the glenohumeral
ligament is removed to show the shoulder joint
as viewed from the back)

3|12

Elbow joint

The elbow joint is a movable hinge-and-pivot joint, articulating the radius and ulna to form the pivoting joint and the humerus and ulna to form the hinge joint. This hinge-and-pivot joint allows several types of movement: flexion, extension, supination, pronation, and rotation. The most frequent disturbance of the elbow joint is "tennis elbow," which can result from many activities involving rotation and shock to the elbow joint. Inflammation of the lateral epicondyle and the associated extensor tendons is usually the cause. Pain, mainly when the arm is used in a position of pronation, is marked, and the area over the lateral epicondyle is usually extremely tender to touch.

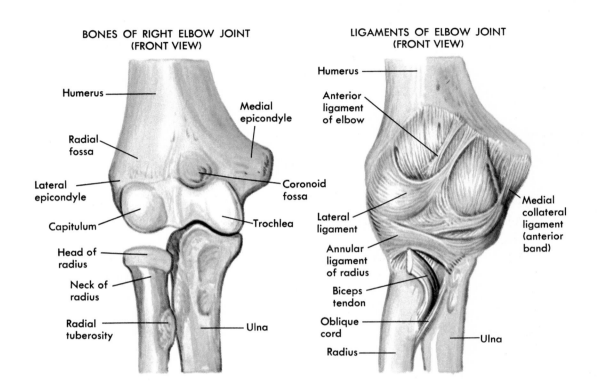

BONES OF RIGHT ELBOW JOINT
(FRONT VIEW)

Humerus

Radial
fossa

Lateral
epicondyle

Capitulum

Head of
radius

Neck of
radius

Radial
tuberosity

Medial
epicondyle

Coronoid
fossa

Trochlea

Ulna

LIGAMENTS OF ELBOW JOINT
(FRONT VIEW)

Humerus

Anterior
ligament
of elbow

Lateral
ligament

Annular
ligament
of radius

Biceps
tendon

Oblique
cord

Radius

Medial
collateral
ligament
(anterior
band)

Ulna

LATERAL COLLATERAL LIGAMENT OF ELBOW JOINT

Capitulum

Head of radius

Lateral collateral ligament of elbow

Annular ligament of radius

Radius

Lateral
epicondyle

Olecranon

Ulna

BECK

MEDIAL COLLATERAL LIGAMENT OF ELBOW JOINT

Humerus

Medial
epicondyle

Biceps
tendon

Annular
ligament

Oblique cord

Ulna   Anterior part

Posterior part   Oblique part

Olecranon

61

3|13

Wrist joint

The wrist joint articulates the radius with the scaphoid, lunate, and triquetrum bones, which form the proximal row of the carpal bones. This joint is capable of flexion, extension, adduction, and abduction of the hand. The extensor tendons of the fingers are located over the dorsal aspect of the wrist, and the flexors are present on the ventral surface. Wrist pain commonly results from synovitis (inflammation of the synovial membrane) of these tendons. One particular disorder, the carpal tunnel syndrome, is caused by synovitis of the flexor tendon and accompanying neuritis of the median nerve. This leads to a specific pattern of pain in the thumb, index finger, middle finger, and radial aspect of the ring finger. The pain is most marked on flexion of the wrist.

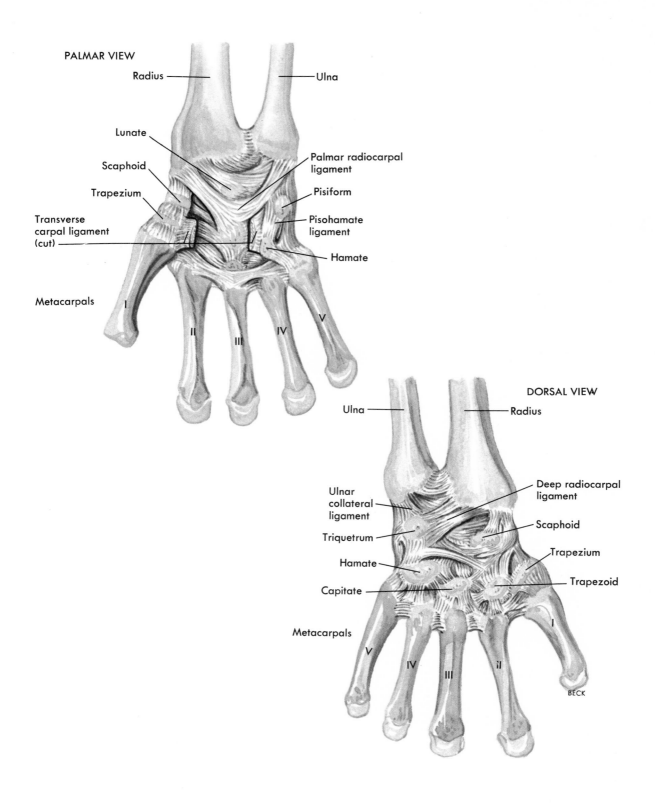

PALMAR VIEW

Radius

Ulna

Lunate

Palmar radiocarpal ligament

Scaphoid

Pisiform

Trapezium

Pisohamate ligament

Transverse carpal ligament (cut)

Hamate

Metacarpals

I

II

III

IV

V

DORSAL VIEW

Ulna

Radius

Ulnar collateral ligament

Deep radiocarpal ligament

Triquetrum

Scaphoid

Hamate

Trapezium

Capitate

Trapezoid

Metacarpals

I

V

IV

III

II

BECK

3|14

Knee joint

The knee is a strong hinge joint, held in alignment by ligaments and muscles and capable of flexion, extension, and very slight rotation. The knee is cushioned by bursae located strategically to pad the joint, the largest one located in front of the patella. The knee is capable of considerable weight-bearing and stress but is still a common site for injury, particularly in athletes. Arthritic changes in the knee joint also routinely occur during old age and can be painful and crippling.

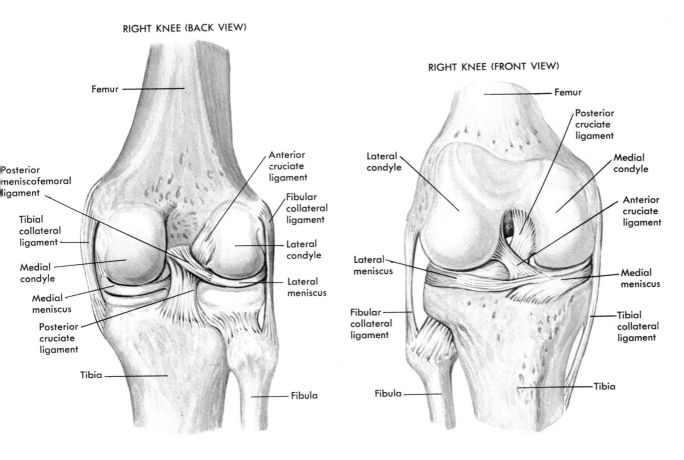

RIGHT KNEE (BACK VIEW)

Femur

Posterior meniscofemoral ligament

Tibial collateral ligament

Medial condyle

Medial meniscus

Posterior cruciate ligament

Tibia

Anterior cruciate ligament

Fibular collateral ligament

Lateral condyle

Lateral meniscus

Fibula

RIGHT KNEE (FRONT VIEW)

Femur

Posterior cruciate ligament

Lateral condyle

Medial condyle

Anterior cruciate ligament

Lateral meniscus

Medial meniscus

Fibular collateral ligament

Tibial collateral ligament

Fibula

Tibia

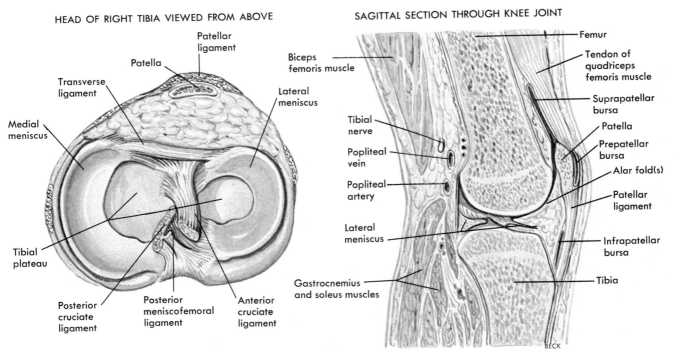

HEAD OF RIGHT TIBIA VIEWED FROM ABOVE

Patellar ligament

Patella

Transverse ligament

Medial meniscus

Lateral meniscus

Tibial plateau

Posterior cruciate ligament

Posterior meniscofemoral ligament

Anterior cruciate ligament

SAGITTAL SECTION THROUGH KNEE JOINT

Biceps femoris muscle

Tibial nerve

Popliteal vein

Popliteal artery

Lateral meniscus

Gastrocnemius and soleus muscles

Femur

Tendon of quadriceps femoris muscle

Suprapatellar bursa

Patella

Prepatellar bursa

Alar fold(s)

Patellar ligament

Infrapatellar bursa

Tibia

BECK

3|15

Pathology of gouty arthritis

Gout has often been described as a disorder of "excessive living" because it can be associated with overeating and overdrinking. It is found most often in men, and the tendency toward gout may be inherited. The pathophysiology involves a defect in purine metabolism, which leads to an accumulation of excess uric acid in the blood and extracellular fluid. The uric acid and its salt (sodium urate) collect in joint capsules and cause an acute inflammatory process that is marked by swelling, redness, and exquisite pain of the involved joint. The joint most commonly involved is that between the first metatarsal and the proximal phalanx, as illustrated. If the disease progresses, many other joints may also be affected. Ultimately, a chronic inflammatory process and foreign body reaction develop, which may eventually result in joint destruction. In addition, tophi can develop in the subcutaneous tissue and in joints and further impair function. The tophi can sometimes be palpated and consist of gritty salts and granulomatous tissue.

Various drugs are used to treat gout, both in its acute and chronic form, and patients are usually advised to decrease consumption of rich foods and alcohol and lose weight.

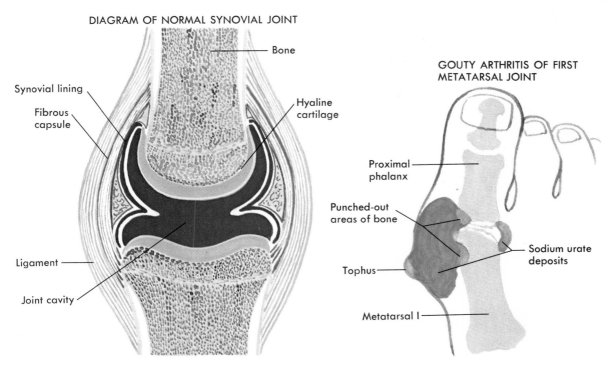

DIAGRAM OF NORMAL SYNOVIAL JOINT

Bone

Synovial lining

Fibrous
capsule

Hyaline
cartilage

Ligament

Joint cavity

GOUTY ARTHRITIS OF FIRST
METATARSAL JOINT

Proximal
phalanx

Punched-out
areas of bone

Tophus

Sodium urate
deposits

Metatarsal I

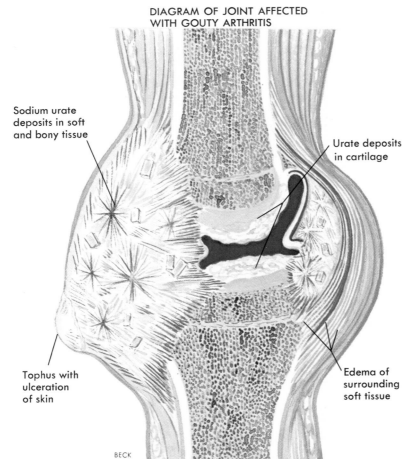

DIAGRAM OF JOINT AFFECTED
WITH GOUTY ARTHRITIS

Sodium urate
deposits in soft
and bony tissue

Urate deposits
in cartilage

Tophus with
ulceration
of skin

Edema of
surrounding
soft tissue

BECK

67

3|16

Bones of the foot

The skeleton of the foot is made up of tarsal, metatarsal, and phalangeal bones. Of the tarsal bones, the calcaneus contributes to the configuration of the heel; the talus articulates with the distal extremities of the tibia and fibula to form the ankle joint; the navicular bone is inserted between the talus and the three cuneiforms; and the cuneiforms and the cuboid articulate with the five metatarsals. The toes are numbered one to five, with the big toe number one. The toes are formed by proximal, middle, and distal phalanges, with the big toe having only two phalanges.

The bones of the foot are held together by strong ligaments and musculotendinous attachments. The joints formed between the tarsal bones are capable of gliding, inversion, and eversion; those between the metatarsals and phalanges permit flexion, extension, adduction, and abduction; and the phalangeal joints allow flexion and extension.

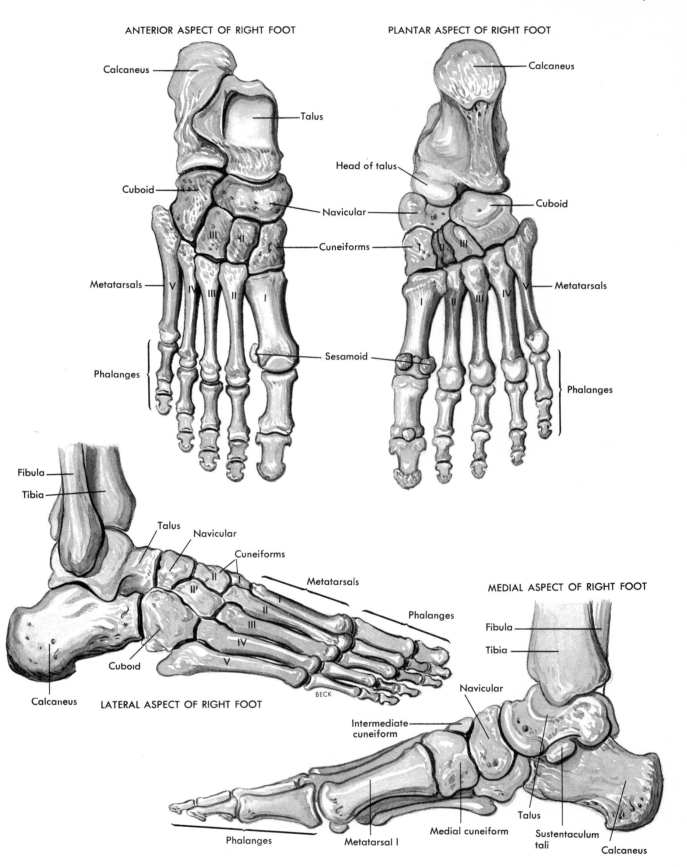

ANTERIOR ASPECT OF RIGHT FOOT

Calcaneus
Talus
Cuboid
Navicular
Cuneiforms
Metatarsals
Phalanges
Sesamoid

PLANTAR ASPECT OF RIGHT FOOT

Calcaneus
Head of talus
Cuboid
Metatarsals
Phalanges

Fibula
Tibia
Talus
Navicular
Cuneiforms
Metatarsals
Phalanges
Cuboid
Calcaneus

LATERAL ASPECT OF RIGHT FOOT

BECK

MEDIAL ASPECT OF RIGHT FOOT

Fibula
Tibia
Navicular
Intermediate cuneiform
Medial cuneiform
Talus
Sustentaculum tali
Calcaneus
Phalanges
Metatarsal I

69

3|17

Arches of the foot

The feet bear the body's weight in the normal stance and must absorb the shocks created by walking or running. In the erect posture the lateral side of the feet, the heads of the metatarsal, and the distal phalanges are in contact with the supporting surface. The bones form three arches, which are maintained through ligamentous and tendinous attachments. The medial longitudinal arch is formed by the calcaneus, talus, navicular, cuneiforms, and three medial metatarsals. The lateral longitudinal arch is formed by the calcaneus, cuboid, and two lateral metatarsals. The transverse arch is present at the level of the tarsometatarsal joints.

Flatfoot occurs when ligaments connecting the tarsal bones are weakened. A shortened Achilles tendon may cause the calcaneus to flatten, tilting the talus and other tarsal bones downward. These disorders usually cause problems in posture and alignments. Back pain is also often associated with problems of the feet.

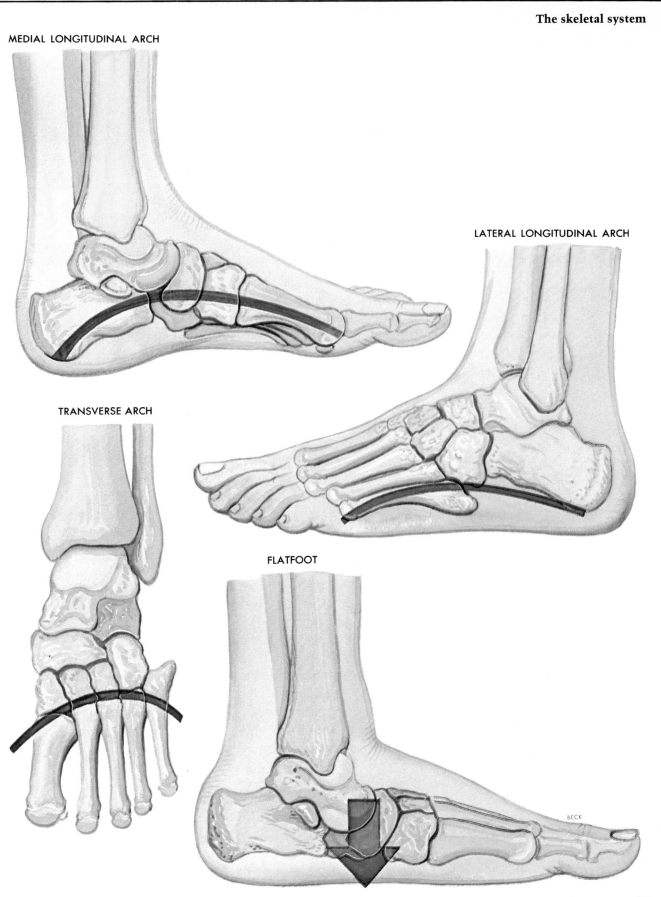

MEDIAL LONGITUDINAL ARCH

LATERAL LONGITUDINAL ARCH

TRANSVERSE ARCH

FLATFOOT

BECK

3|18

Clubfoot (talipes)

Clubfoot is the most common and important defect or deformity of the foot and ankle. Clubfoot may be congenital or acquired. *Talipes* is the term used for foot deformities of congenital origin. Treatment includes manipulation with or without anesthesia, use of retention devices, and in resistant cases surgical intervention.

Talipes equinovarus. The primary deformity is medial and plantar deviation of the anterior part of the talus. The heel is inverted and the forefoot is adducted and inverted. There is often an associated cavus deformity, with the forefoot plantar flexed on the hindfoot at the midtarsal joint. Incidence is 1:1000 births. About 75% of congenital clubfeet are of this type.

Talipes equinovalgus. The heel is everted and the forefoot is abducted and everted. The entire foot is fixed in plantar flexion at the subtalar and ankle joints. This condition is relatively rare.

Metatarsus varus. All five metatarsals are adducted and inverted at the tarsometatarsal joints. The hindfoot is usually in slight or moderate valgus position. The navicular bone is laterally displaced on the head of the talus. This is considered a mild or incomplete form of clubfoot.

Talipes equinus. The foot is plantar flexed and the toes are at a lower level than the heel. In this condition there is usually a shortened Achilles tendon.

Talipes calcaneovalgus. The entire foot is dorsiflexed and everted. Soft tissues on the dorsum and lateral aspect of the foot are contracted and limit plantar flexion and inversion.

TALIPES EQUINOVARUS

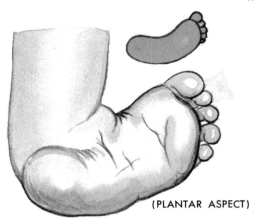

(PLANTAR ASPECT)　　　　　　(DORSAL ASPECT)

TALIPES EQUINOVALGUS　　　　　　METATARSUS VARUS

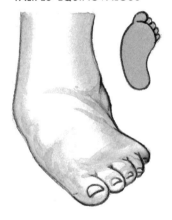

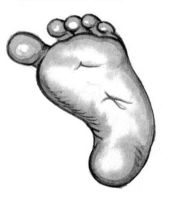

TALIPES EQUINUS　　　　　　TALIPES CALCANEOVALGUS

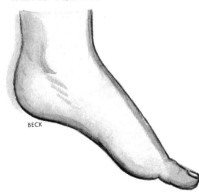

BECK

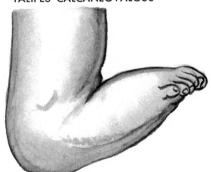

3|19

Bone growth—upper limbs

Plates 3-19 and 3-20 show those areas of the upper and lower limbs involved in bone growth in males and females, with the epiphyseal centers of ossification and their average time of appearance. Long-bone growth takes place at the epiphyses and continues until the epiphyses have fully ossified (closed). The microscopic structure of the epiphyseal plate is rows of cartilaginous cells that separate the diaphysis from the epiphysis and provide new matrix for bone growth, which proceeds through formation of new bone by osteoblast cells and subsequent calcification.

Radiographic study of the skeletal system, with particular attention to epiphyseal closures, gives an accurate bone age, which in some pathological states differs from chronological age. Certain hormonal insufficiencies or imbalances may lead to delayed or early closures. Gigantism, which is produced by excessive growth hormone production by the anterior lobe of the pituitary gland, leads to remarkable body heights. Delayed epiphyseal closure during growth causes the increased stature. Insufficient growth hormone on the other hand leads to early closure of the epiphyses and results in abnormally short stature.

A particular note of interest is that the clavicle is the last long bone of the upper limb to fully ossify.

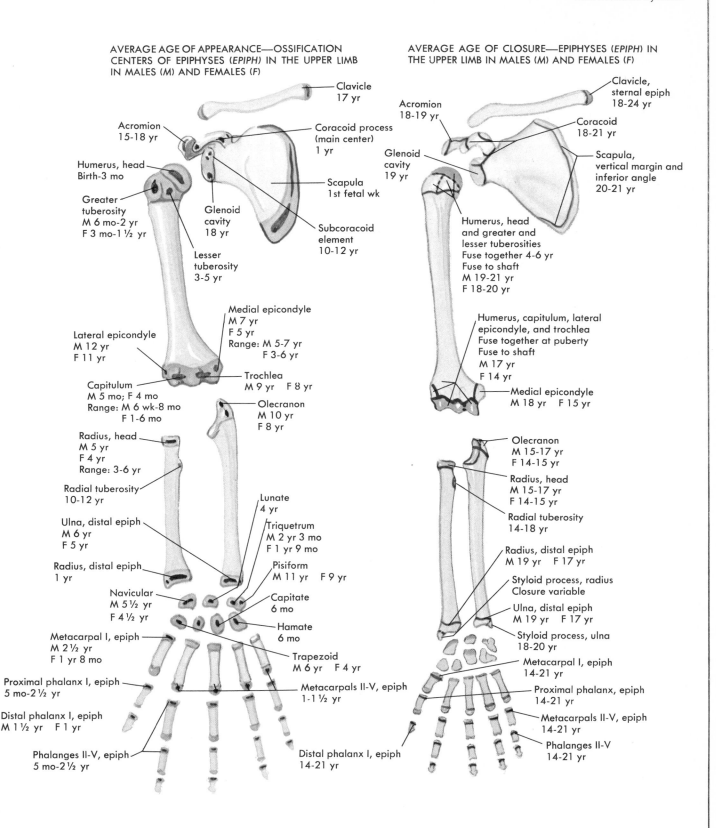

AVERAGE AGE OF APPEARANCE—OSSIFICATION
CENTERS OF EPIPHYSES (*EPIPH*) IN THE UPPER LIMB
IN MALES (*M*) AND FEMALES (*F*)

AVERAGE AGE OF CLOSURE—EPIPHYSES (*EPIPH*) IN
THE UPPER LIMB IN MALES (*M*) AND FEMALES (*F*)

Clavicle
17 yr

Acromion
15-18 yr

Coracoid process
(main center)
1 yr

Humerus, head
Birth-3 mo

Greater
tuberosity
M 6 mo-2 yr
F 3 mo-1½ yr

Glenoid
cavity
18 yr

Scapula
1st fetal wk

Subcoracoid
element
10-12 yr

Lesser
tuberosity
3-5 yr

Medial epicondyle
M 7 yr
F 5 yr
Range: M 5-7 yr
F 3-6 yr

Lateral epicondyle
M 12 yr
F 11 yr

Capitulum
M 5 mo; F 4 mo
Range: M 6 wk-8 mo
F 1-6 mo

Trochlea
M 9 yr   F 8 yr

Olecranon
M 10 yr
F 8 yr

Radius, head
M 5 yr
F 4 yr
Range: 3-6 yr

Radial tuberosity
10-12 yr

Lunate
4 yr

Triquetrum
M 2 yr 3 mo
F 1 yr 9 mo

Ulna, distal epiph
M 6 yr
F 5 yr

Pisiform
M 11 yr   F 9 yr

Radius, distal epiph
1 yr

Navicular
M 5½ yr
F 4½ yr

Capitate
6 mo

Hamate
6 mo

Metacarpal I, epiph
M 2½ yr
F 1 yr 8 mo

Trapezoid
M 6 yr   F 4 yr

Proximal phalanx I, epiph
5 mo-2½ yr

Metacarpals II-V, epiph
1-1½ yr

Distal phalanx I, epiph
M 1½ yr   F 1 yr

Phalanges II-V, epiph
5 mo-2½ yr

Distal phalanx I, epiph
14-21 yr

Clavicle,
sternal epiph
18-24 yr

Acromion
18-19 yr

Coracoid
18-21 yr

Glenoid
cavity
19 yr

Scapula,
vertical margin and
inferior angle
20-21 yr

Humerus, head
and greater and
lesser tuberosities
Fuse together 4-6 yr
Fuse to shaft
M 19-21 yr
F 18-20 yr

Humerus, capitulum, lateral
epicondyle, and trochlea
Fuse together at puberty
Fuse to shaft
M 17 yr
F 14 yr

Medial epicondyle
M 18 yr   F 15 yr

Olecranon
M 15-17 yr
F 14-15 yr

Radius, head
M 15-17 yr
F 14-15 yr

Radial tuberosity
14-18 yr

Radius, distal epiph
M 19 yr   F 17 yr

Styloid process, radius
Closure variable

Ulna, distal epiph
M 19 yr   F 17 yr

Styloid process, ulna
18-20 yr

Metacarpal I, epiph
14-21 yr

Proximal phalanx, epiph
14-21 yr

Metacarpals II-V, epiph
14-21 yr

Phalanges II-V
14-21 yr

Adapted from Tachdjian, M.O.: Pediatric orthopedics, Philadelphia, 1972, W.B. Saunders Co.

3|20

Bone growth—lower limbs

The lower limbs undergo epiphyseal growth and ultimate epiphyseal closure in a manner similar to that of the upper limbs. In general, bony growth of the lower limbs is complete by the eighteenth through twentieth years. As with the upper limbs, the female epiphyseal centers generally appear later and close earlier. Bone growth is stimulated by the male sex hormones, which partly accounts for greater length and heavier bones.

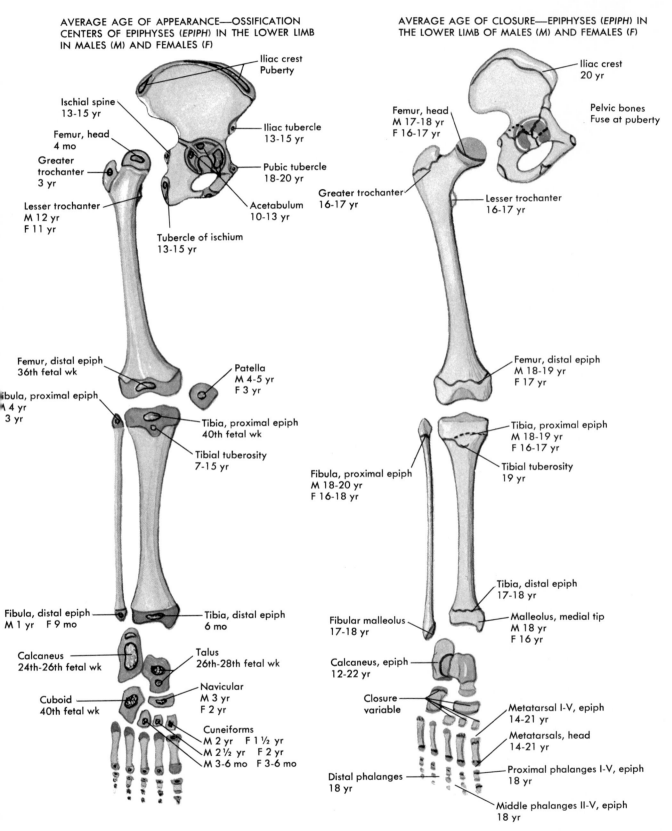

AVERAGE AGE OF APPEARANCE—OSSIFICATION CENTERS OF EPIPHYSES (*EPIPH*) IN THE LOWER LIMB IN MALES (*M*) AND FEMALES (*F*)

Iliac crest
Puberty

Ischial spine
13-15 yr

Femur, head
4 mo

Greater trochanter
3 yr

Lesser trochanter
M 12 yr
F 11 yr

Iliac tubercle
13-15 yr

Pubic tubercle
18-20 yr

Acetabulum
10-13 yr

Tubercle of ischium
13-15 yr

Femur, distal epiph
36th fetal wk

Fibula, proximal epiph
M 4 yr
3 yr

Patella
M 4-5 yr
F 3 yr

Tibia, proximal epiph
40th fetal wk

Tibial tuberosity
7-15 yr

Fibula, distal epiph
M 1 yr   F 9 mo

Tibia, distal epiph
6 mo

Calcaneus
24th-26th fetal wk

Talus
26th-28th fetal wk

Cuboid
40th fetal wk

Navicular
M 3 yr
F 2 yr

Cuneiforms
M 2 yr   F 1 ½ yr
M 2½ yr   F 2 yr
M 3-6 mo   F 3-6 mo

AVERAGE AGE OF CLOSURE—EPIPHYSES (*EPIPH*) IN THE LOWER LIMB OF MALES (*M*) AND FEMALES (*F*)

Iliac crest
20 yr

Femur, head
M 17-18 yr
F 16-17 yr

Pelvic bones
Fuse at puberty

Greater trochanter
16-17 yr

Lesser trochanter
16-17 yr

Femur, distal epiph
M 18-19 yr
F 17 yr

Tibia, proximal epiph
M 18-19 yr
F 16-17 yr

Tibial tuberosity
19 yr

Fibula, proximal epiph
M 18-20 yr
F 16-18 yr

Tibia, distal epiph
17-18 yr

Fibular malleolus
17-18 yr

Malleolus, medial tip
M 18 yr
F 16 yr

Calcaneus, epiph
12-22 yr

Closure variable

Metatarsal I-V, epiph
14-21 yr

Metatarsals, head
14-21 yr

Proximal phalanges I-V, epiph
18 yr

Distal phalanges
18 yr

Middle phalanges II-V, epiph
18 yr

Adapted from Tachdjian, M.O.: Pediatric orthopedics, Philadelphia, 1972, W.B. Saunders Co.

3|21

Longitudinal section of a molar tooth and surrounding structures

The molar tooth is illustrated in a sectioned view to show both the nonliving enamel surfaces and the vascular supply and nerves contained in the pulp. The tooth is divided into the crown, neck, and root. The enamel protects the vulnerable tissues of the dentin and pulp. Once decay occurs, it is easy to see that bacterial invasion of these tissues could lead to pain and tissue death, with ultimate loss of the tooth.

Gingivitis is another common problem and involves inflammation, swelling, and infection of the gums. This is probably the most common dental problem in the elderly, whereas decay takes its major toll in children.

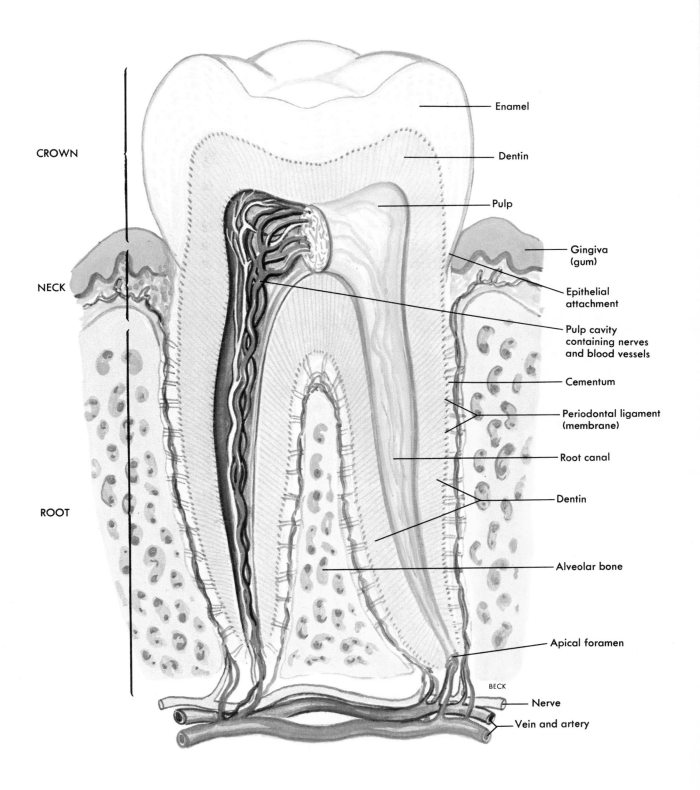

CROWN

NECK

ROOT

Enamel

Dentin

Pulp

Gingiva (gum)

Epithelial attachment

Pulp cavity containing nerves and blood vessels

Cementum

Periodontal ligament (membrane)

Root canal

Dentin

Alveolar bone

Apical foramen

BECK

Nerve

Vein and artery

Deciduous arch (temporary teeth) and permanent teeth

Shown at upper right are the 20 temporary teeth forming the deciduous arch. There are no premolars (bicuspids) and only two pairs of molars in each jaw. These teeth begin to appear at about 6 months of age and are lost during childhood beginning at about 6 years of age. The primary teeth are replaced by the 32 permanent teeth. The lower teeth generally begin to erupt before the upper teeth and usually appear earlier in girls than in boys.

The second part of the plate illustrates the full adult dentition of permanent teeth.

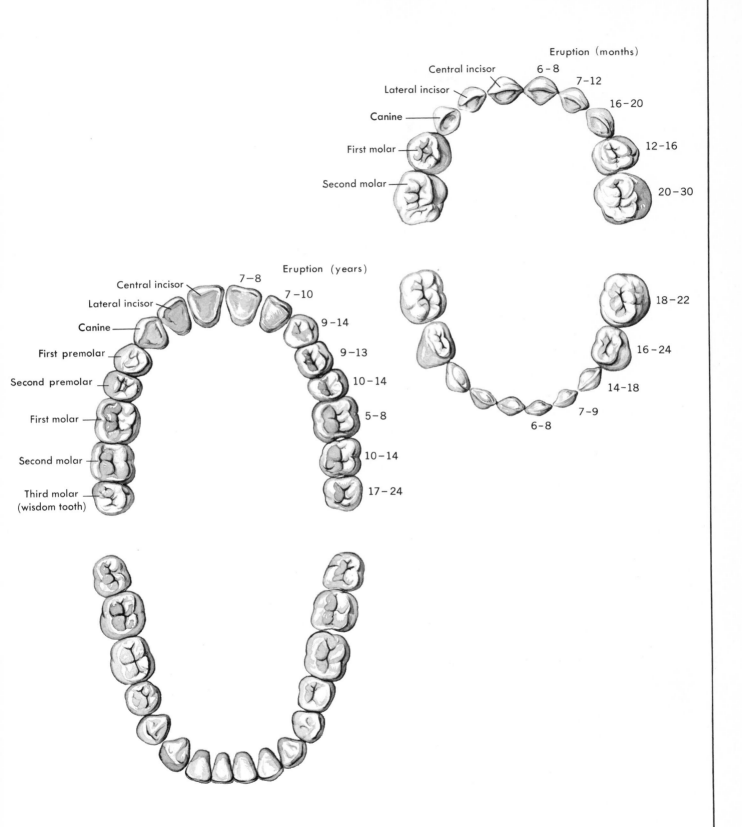

Eruption (months)

Central incisor — 6 - 8

Lateral incisor — 7 - 12

Canine — 16 - 20

First molar — 12 - 16

Second molar — 20 - 30

18 - 22

16 - 24

14 - 18

7 - 9

6 - 8

Eruption (years)

Central incisor — 7 - 8

Lateral incisor — 7 - 10

Canine — 9 - 14

First premolar — 9 - 13

Second premolar — 10 - 14

First molar — 5 - 8

Second molar — 10 - 14

Third molar (wisdom tooth) — 17 - 24

4 | The muscular system

4|1

Structure of skeletal muscle

This illustration shows the increasingly more detailed submicroscopic structure of a skeletal muscle fiber. The muscle belly is subdivided into connective tissue–sheathed bundles of separate fibers.

Within the muscle fiber is a subcellular system of tubules and fibrils. A muscle fiber is a single muscle cell and like all cells has cytoplasmic components and nuclear material. The muscle cell has an elaborate tubular system that is composed of the sarcoplasmic reticulum and the T tubules. The function of these tubes is to communicate with the cell membrane, and thus respond to muscle cell membrane depolarization, and store calcium ions, which are needed for normal muscle contraction. The muscle fiber appears striped under the microscope because of the myofibrils that are lined up along the cells. These myofibrils are made up of filaments of protein, actin, and myosin, which are linearly arranged in very specific configuration.

The sarcomere is the functional unit of muscle and is the distance between two Z lines. Notice that filaments of actin are attached at the Z line. Overriding actin filaments are the mysosin filaments. In reality the actin and mysosin filaments are attached to each other by minute projections, or cross-bridges, arising from the myosin. Muscle contraction is the result of sliding of actin filaments over mysosin filaments through movement of these cross-bridges. During muscle contraction calcium is released from the tubular system into the areas around the sarcomeres. This then initiates the movement of the cross-bridges and sliding of the filaments. During muscle contraction the Z lines move up to the A bands and the H zone disappears. Contraction is immediately followed by relaxation. The process requires a constant energy supply and adequate availability of calcium.

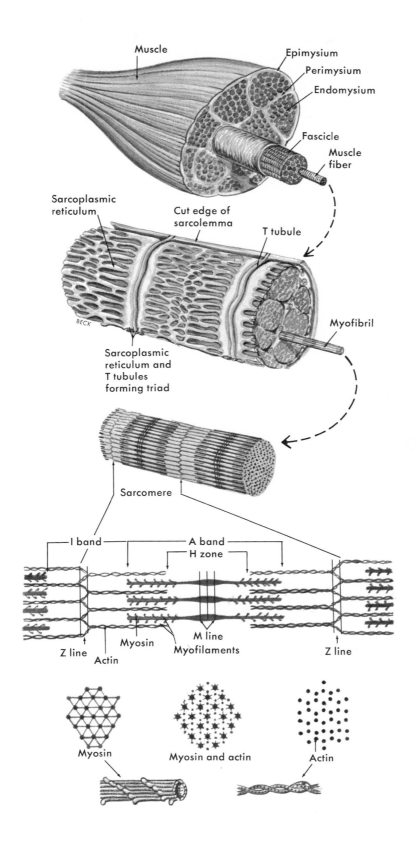

Muscle

Epimysium

Perimysium

Endomysium

Fascicle

Muscle fiber

Sarcoplasmic reticulum

Cut edge of sarcolemma

T tubule

Sarcoplasmic reticulum and T tubules forming triad

Myofibril

Sarcomere

I band

A band

H zone

Z line

Actin

Myosin

M line

Myofilaments

Z line

Myosin

Myosin and actin

Actin

Muscles of facial expression

Unlike most skeletal muscles, the muscles that permit facial expressions are thin and have their origin on skin, connective tissue, or bone. Most of them surround the orifices of the face: the eyes, nose, and mouth. The contraction or dilation of these muscles produces a variety of facial expressions and conveys such emotions as surprise, disgust, doubt, fear, pleasure, and worry. The simple act of dilating the nostrils, as in showing fear, anger, or disdain, is produced by two muscles, the dilator naris and depressor septi. Constricting the nostrils, as in showing sternness, results from action of the compressor naris. Wrinkling the nose is accomplished by a number of small muscles, including the compressor naris, procerus, nasalis, and some fibers of the corrugator supercilii. Smiling is produced through contraction of the buccinator muscle, the same muscle used to produce a trumpeter's musical note.

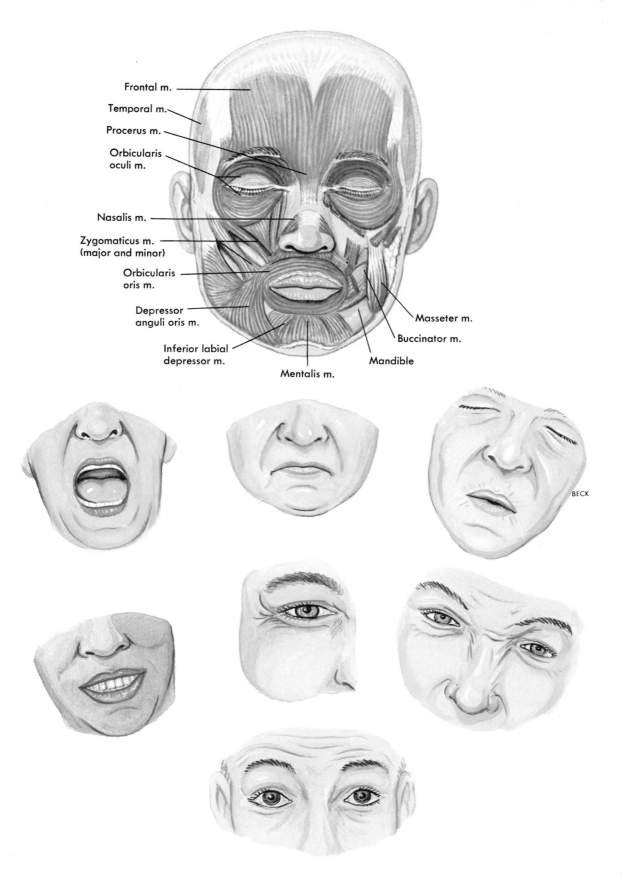

Frontal m.

Temporal m.

Procerus m.

Orbicularis
oculi m.

Nasalis m.

Zygomaticus m.
(major and minor)

Orbicularis
oris m.

Depressor
anguli oris m.

Inferior labial
depressor m.

Mentalis m.

Mandible

Buccinator m.

Masseter m.

BECK

4|3

Muscles of the upper limb

Muscles that move the arms are not only those of the upper limb, but also muscles of the thorax (Plate 4-4), such as the trapezius, levator scapulae, rhomboid major and minor, and serratus anterior, which move the scapula. The pectoralis major adducts the humerus, as does the latissimus dorsi. The major shoulder muscle is the deltoid, originating from the clavicle, acromion, and scapula and inserting on the side of the humerus. The deltoid participates in flexion, adduction, abduction, and extension of the humerus. Major muscles of the upper arm are the biceps and triceps. The biceps brachii primarily acts to allow supinations of the forearm and hand, whereas the triceps extends the forearm.

The anterior muscles of the forearm consist of superficial flexors, such as the pronator teres, flexor carpi radialis, palmaris longus, and the flexor carpi ulnaris. Superficial extensors are the extensor carpi radialis longus and brevis, extensor carpi ulnaris, and extensor digitorum; these muscles are located on the posterior side of the forearm. There are intermediate and deep layers of posterior and anterior flexors and extensors in the forearm. Some of these muscles insert on the metacarpals and phalanges and therefore control movements of the fingers.

Individual muscles of the hand allow for further movement, although much of the hand movement is the result of contraction of the forearm muscles. The hand muscles are grouped into lumbrical, interosseous, thenar, and hypothenar muscles. The thenar muscles act to effect thumb movement, and the three hypothenar muscles control the movements of the little finger. Lumbrical muscles supply the second to fifth fingers. The interosseous muscles are between the metacarpals, causing adduction and abduction.

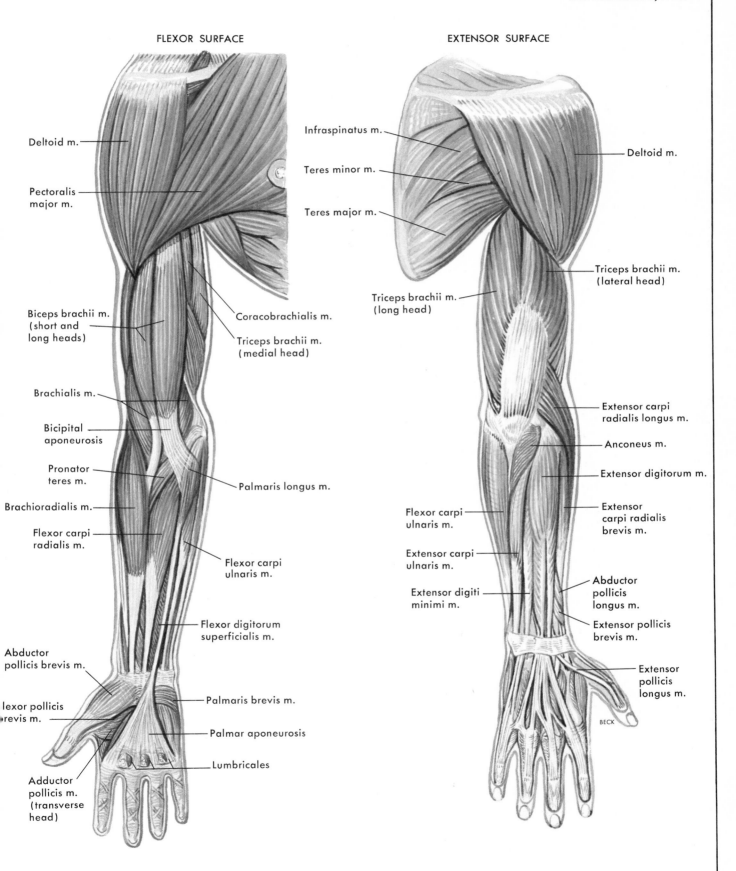

The muscular system

FLEXOR SURFACE

EXTENSOR SURFACE

Deltoid m.

Pectoralis major m.

Biceps brachii m. (short and long heads)

Brachialis m.

Bicipital aponeurosis

Pronator teres m.

Brachioradialis m.

Flexor carpi radialis m.

Abductor pollicis brevis m.

Flexor pollicis brevis m.

Adductor pollicis m. (transverse head)

Coracobrachialis m.

Triceps brachii m. (medial head)

Palmaris longus m.

Flexor carpi ulnaris m.

Flexor digitorum superficialis m.

Palmaris brevis m.

Palmar aponeurosis

Lumbricales

Infraspinatus m.

Teres minor m.

Teres major m.

Triceps brachii m. (long head)

Flexor carpi ulnaris m.

Extensor carpi ulnaris m.

Extensor digiti minimi m.

Deltoid m.

Triceps brachii m. (lateral head)

Extensor carpi radialis longus m.

Anconeus m.

Extensor digitorum m.

Extensor carpi radialis brevis m.

Abductor pollicis longus m.

Extensor pollicis brevis m.

Extensor pollicis longus m.

BECK

89

4|4

Muscles of the trunk

The muscles of the trunk are involved in movement, protection, and posture. The heavy muscles of the shoulder girdle, for example, participate in the multiple movements that the shoulder and upper arm are capable of performing. The abdominal muscles act to protect the underlying viscera and to elevate the pelvis upward and thus flatten the lumbar curve of the spinal column. When we try to stand straight and with correct posture, we are contracting the external and internal obliques and the transversus and rectus abdominis muscles. The rectus abdominis is a broad, flat muscle that originates from the pubic crest and inserts along the fifth, sixth, and seventh ribs and the xiphoid process of the sternum. We contract this muscle during straining, defecation, and childbirth. The muscles of the back are important in the maintenance of posture, flexion of the trunk, and extension and abduction of the spine. The back muscles are very susceptible to strain, especially those in the lumbar area.

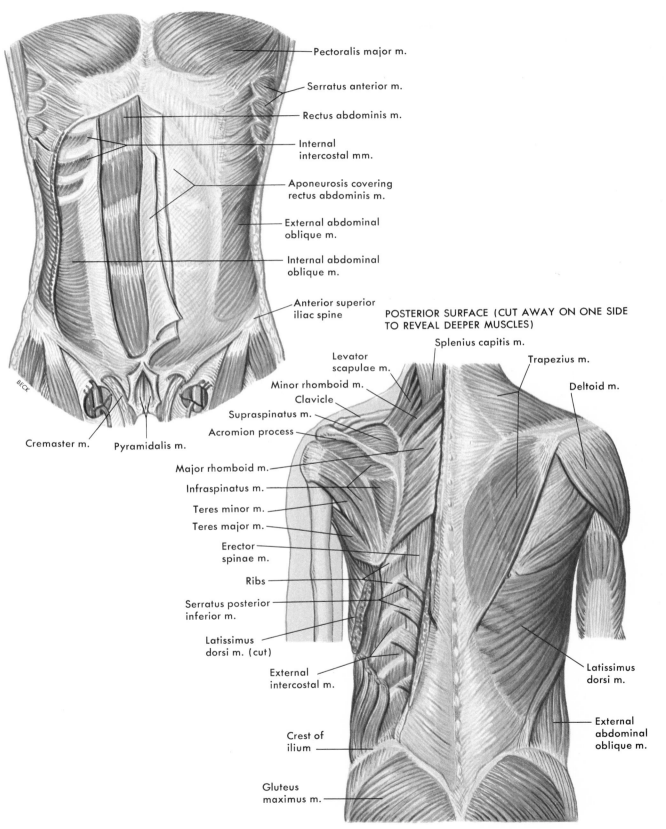

ANTERIOR SURFACE (CUT AWAY ON ONE SIDE TO REVEAL DEEPER MUSCLES)

Pectoralis major m.

Serratus anterior m.

Rectus abdominis m.

Internal intercostal mm.

Aponeurosis covering rectus abdominis m.

External abdominal oblique m.

Internal abdominal oblique m.

Anterior superior iliac spine

Cremaster m.

Pyramidalis m.

BECK

POSTERIOR SURFACE (CUT AWAY ON ONE SIDE TO REVEAL DEEPER MUSCLES)

Splenius capitis m.

Trapezius m.

Levator scapulae m.

Deltoid m.

Minor rhomboid m.

Clavicle

Supraspinatus m.

Acromion process

Major rhomboid m.

Infraspinatus m.

Teres minor m.

Teres major m.

Erector spinae m.

Ribs

Serratus posterior inferior m.

Latissimus dorsi m. (cut)

External intercostal m.

Crest of ilium

Gluteus maximus m.

Latissimus dorsi m.

External abdominal oblique m.

91

4|5

Muscles of the lower limb

Movement of the lower limb is the result of the action of the thigh muscles and the hip girdle muscles. For example, the iliopsoas muscle originates on several vertebral bodies (T12 through L5) and inserts on the lesser trochanter of the femur. This muscle functions largely in flexion of the thigh. Another major anterior thigh flexor muscle is the rectus femoris. Extension of the thigh is accomplished by the gluteus maximus and the hamstring muscles, the biceps femoris, the semitendinosus, and the semimembranosus. Leg extension is the result of the actions of the rectus femoris and vastus lateralis, medialis, and intermedius muscles. Abductors of the thigh include the gluteus medius and minimus, whereas the major adductors are the adductor brevis, longus, and magnus muscles. The gracilis and the sartorius muscles also participate in adduction.

ANTERIOR VIEW   POSTERIOR VIEW

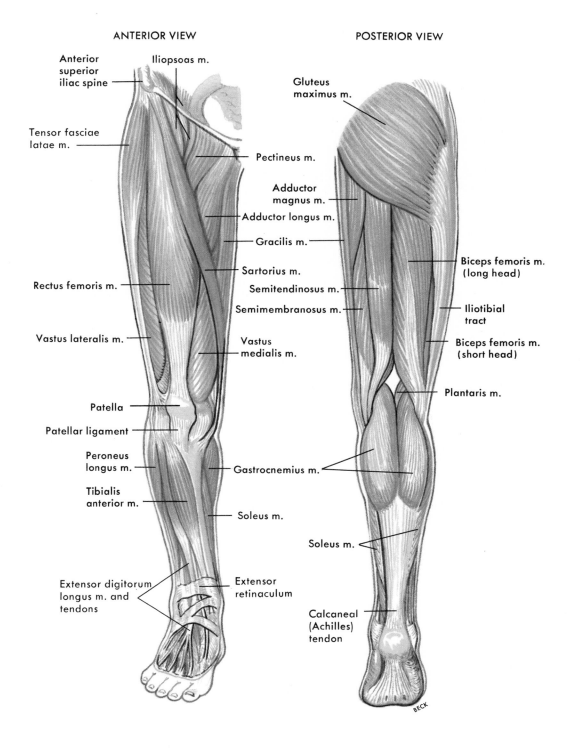

Anterior superior iliac spine

Iliopsoas m.

Tensor fasciae latae m.

Gluteus maximus m.

Pectineus m.

Adductor magnus m.

Adductor longus m.

Gracilis m.

Rectus femoris m.

Sartorius m.

Semitendinosus m.

Semimembranosus m.

Biceps femoris m. (long head)

Iliotibial tract

Biceps femoris m. (short head)

Vastus lateralis m.

Vastus medialis m.

Plantaris m.

Patella

Patellar ligament

Peroneus longus m.

Tibialis anterior m.

Gastrocnemius m.

Soleus m.

Soleus m.

Extensor digitorum longus m. and tendons

Extensor retinaculum

Calcaneal (Achilles) tendon

BECK

93

4|6

Intramuscular injections

The deltoid muscle. The deltoid is selected when the amount of fluid to be injected is less than 5 ml of solution. The patient may be in a sitting, standing, or supine position. The correct injection site is located two-fingers breadth below the acromion process of the scapula and lateral to the tip of the acromion. Usually a 2.5-cm (1-inch) needle is used to reach well into the deltoid muscle.

The gluteal region. If more than 5 ml of solution must be administered, the gluteal area is preferred as the injection site to facilitate absorption and to avoid discomfort and tenderness. With the patient lying face down, the injection is administered near the center of the upper outer quadrant (*A*) in the gluteus medius muscle. This site avoids striking the sciatic nerve or superior gluteal vessels. Another way of locating the correct injection site is to imagine a diagonal line (*B*) extending from the greater trochanter of the femur to the posterior superior iliac spine. The injection is given above and about three-fingers breadth outside of a point one third of the way down the diagonal line.

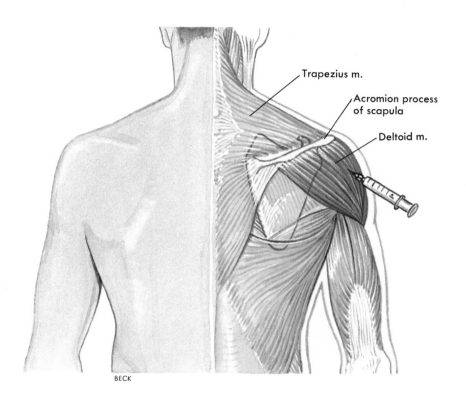

Trapezius m.

Acromion process
of scapula

Deltoid m.

BECK

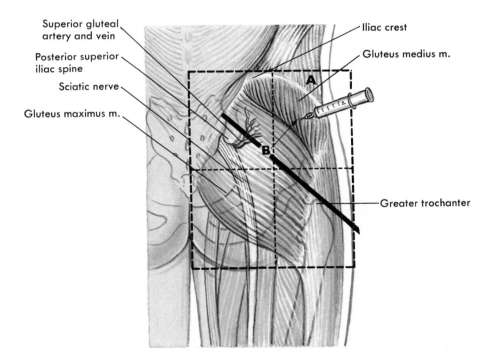

Superior gluteal
artery and vein

Posterior superior
iliac spine

Sciatic nerve

Gluteus maximus m.

Iliac crest

Gluteus medius m.

A

B

Greater trochanter

5 | The nervous system

5|1

The central and peripheral nervous systems

The central nervous system (CNS) consists of the brain and spinal cord. The peripheral nervous system (PNS) is composed of the cranial and spinal nerves that supply the periphery of the body. The peripheral nerves may contain sensory fibers, motor fibers, and autonomic (sympathetic and parasympathetic) nerves. Whereas the separate fibers run together in the peripheral nerves, the sensory and motor fibers separate into posterior (sensory) and anterior (motor) roots before joining the spinal cord.
The autonomic fibers pass through ganglia outside of the spinal cord before entering the cord.

The peripheral cutaneous nerves innervate specific areas of the body called "dermatomes."

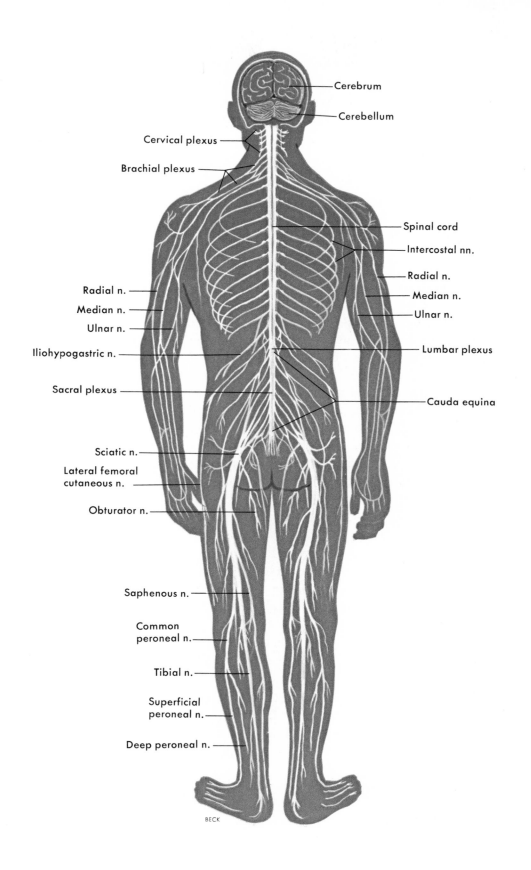

Cerebrum

Cerebellum

Cervical plexus

Brachial plexus

Spinal cord

Intercostal nn.

Radial n.

Radial n.

Median n.

Median n.

Ulnar n.

Ulnar n.

Iliohypogastric n.

Lumbar plexus

Sacral plexus

Cauda equina

Sciatic n.

Lateral femoral
cutaneous n.

Obturator n.

Saphenous n.

Common
peroneal n.

Tibial n.

Superficial
peroneal n.

Deep peroneal n.

BECK

5|2

The autonomic nervous system (schematic diagram)

The autonomic nervous system, which comprises the sympathetic (SNS) and the parasympathetic (PNS) systems, is a specialized control system that regulates visceral responses and maintains the constancy of the internal environment. Many organs receive a dual supply of SNS and PNS fibers. In general, when dual innervation is present, the effects of the two divisions are antagonistic. The autonomic nervous system is regulated by neurological centers, most of which are in the hypothalamus or medulla. Descending autonomic fibers course to the spinal cord. The autonomic nerves consist of preganglionic and postganglionic cells. The PNS, drawn in blue, arises from the CNS in the cranial and sacral areas. The preganglionic fibers are long and travel to sites near the organs to be innervated and synapse in ganglia, such as the ciliary, pterygopalatine, submandibular, and otic. The ganglia contain the cell bodies of the short postganglionic fibers, which leave the ganglia and innervate nearby organs. In contrast to this, the SNS leaves the spinal cord in the thoracolumbar areas and consists of very short preganglionic and long postganglionic fibers. The sympathetic ganglia form a chain that runs next to the vertebral column. Many postganglionic fibers leave the sympathetic chain and course to the parts to be innervated. Generally, because of the arrangement whereby one preganglionic fiber synapses with many postganglionic cells, the SNS causes a diffuse, widespread response when activated. The PNS is arranged with a 1:1 ratio of preganglionic and postganglionic fibers, and therefore its activation results in discrete and localized responses.

The SNS differs from the PNS in another way. The neurotransmitter released from the postganglionic sympathetic fibers at the site of the effector is norepinephrine, whereas acetylcholine is released by the parasympathetic postganglionic fibers. Thus the SNS is sometimes referred to as adrenergic, and the PNS as cholinergic.

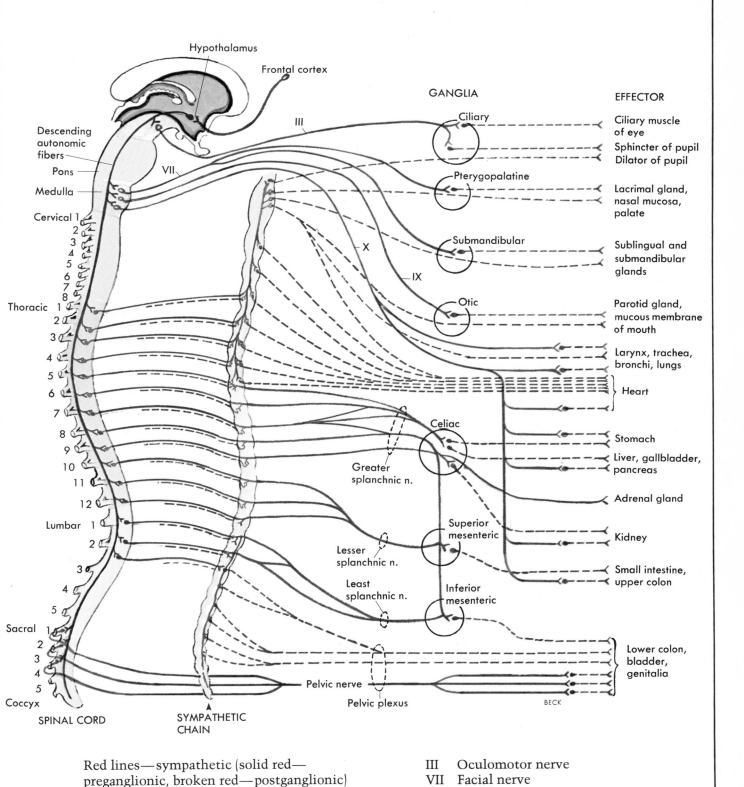

GANGLIA

EFFECTOR

Hypothalamus

Frontal cortex

Descending
autonomic
fibers

Pons

Medulla

Cervical 1
2
3
4
5
6
7
8

Thoracic 1
2
3
4
5
6
7
8
9
10
11
12

Lumbar 1
2
3
4
5

Sacral 1
2
3
4
5

Coccyx

SPINAL CORD

SYMPATHETIC
CHAIN

III

VII

X

IX

Ciliary

Pterygopalatine

Submandibular

Otic

Celiac

Greater
splanchnic n.

Lesser
splanchnic n.

Least
splanchnic n.

Superior
mesenteric

Inferior
mesenteric

Pelvic nerve

Pelvic plexus

Ciliary muscle
of eye

Sphincter of pupil
Dilator of pupil

Lacrimal gland,
nasal mucosa,
palate

Sublingual and
submandibular
glands

Parotid gland,
mucous membrane
of mouth

Larynx, trachea,
bronchi, lungs

Heart

Stomach

Liver, gallbladder,
pancreas

Adrenal gland

Kidney

Small intestine,
upper colon

Lower colon,
bladder,
genitalia

BECK

Red lines—sympathetic (solid red—
preganglionic, broken red—postganglionic)
Green—parasympathetic
Blue—central conduction paths

III   Oculomotor nerve
VII Facial nerve
IX   Glossopharyngeal nerve
X   Vagus nerve

5|3

The brain

The brain's nervous tissue consists of millions of nerve fibers interconnecting and crossing in an intricate pattern that ultimately somehow determines man's behavior activity and ability to learn. Along with neurons, there are supporting cells that help give the brain its form and substance. The cerebral cortex is that part of the brain involved in higher activities, such as thought and association, and contains the centers for motor and sensory control of the body.

The medial view of the right hemisphere shows the large corpus callosum, which connects the two cerebral hemispheres. The middle part of the brain contains the thalamus and hypothalamus. The ventricular system is also indicated. The cerebellum extends off the posterior part of the midbrain and is involved in equilibrium and coordination. The brainstem, consisting of pons and medulla, contains centers for the control of respiratory and cardiac functions.

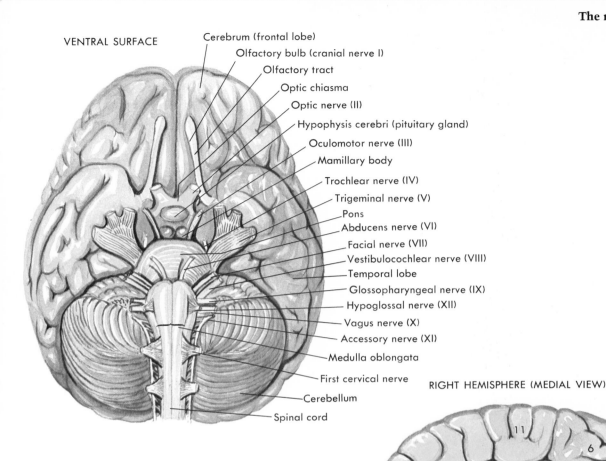

VENTRAL SURFACE

Cerebrum (frontal lobe)
Olfactory bulb (cranial nerve I)
Olfactory tract
Optic chiasma
Optic nerve (II)
Hypophysis cerebri (pituitary gland)
Oculomotor nerve (III)
Mamillary body
Trochlear nerve (IV)
Trigeminal nerve (V)
Pons
Abducens nerve (VI)
Facial nerve (VII)
Vestibulocochlear nerve (VIII)
Temporal lobe
Glossopharyngeal nerve (IX)
Hypoglossal nerve (XII)
Vagus nerve (X)
Accessory nerve (XI)
Medulla oblongata
First cervical nerve
Cerebellum
Spinal cord

RIGHT HEMISPHERE (MEDIAL VIEW)

MOTOR CONTROL AREAS OF THE BRAIN

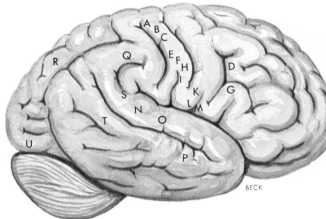

BECK

1	Cerebellum		
2	Medulla oblongata	8	Corpus callosum
3	Spinal cord	9	Thalamus
4	Pituitary gland	10	Pons
	a. Anterior lobe	11	Cerebrum
	b. Posterior lobe	12	Pineal body
5	Frontal lobe	13	Fornix
6	Parietal lobe	14	Third ventricle
7	Occipital lobe	15	Fourth ventricle

A	Ankle	L	Pharynx
B	Knee	M	Larynx
C	Trunk	N	Speech
D	Head and eyes	O	Hearing
E	Shoulder	P	Word understanding
F	Elbow	Q	Cutaneous and muscle sense
G	Motor speech	R	Touch sensation
H	Hand	S	Auditory speech
I	Face	T	Visual speech
J	Lips	U	Visual area
K	Mastication		

103

5|4

Hydrocephalus and the ventricular system

Hydrocephalus is a condition caused by an excessive accumulation of cerebrospinal fluid (CSF) within the ventricles of the brain. In the first drawing, arrows indicate how the fluid originates at various sites within the ventricles and circulates to bathe the surfaces of the brain, the walls of the ventricles, and the spinal cord. If flow through the ventricles is blocked by narrowing or constriction (obstructive hydrocephalus), or if absorption is faulty (communicating hydrocephalus), CSF production continues but its escape is prevented, ultimately causing extreme enlargement of the ventricles, enlargement of the head, and pressure on the brain.

When the aqueduct of Sylvius is blocked, CSF backs up in the ventricles behind the block and causes the brain to enlarge. In some cases pressure may be so great as to prevent the closure of the fontanels and sutures of the skull. Thus the infant's head circumference becomes disproportionately large. The child may have signs of increased intracranial pressure (headaches, vomiting, irritability, seizures).

The third and fourth ventricles of a child with hydrocephalus are also shown as projected on the surface.

Hydrocephalus is generally believed to be the result of a developmental defect in the embryo occurring during the time that the brain's ventricular system is forming. Other causes, especially in older children or adults, include tumors, infections, and head injuries. CSF from the ventricles may be shunted by a plastic tube to drain into another location in the child's body. This is done to prevent continuing increased intracranial pressure with fluid accumulation. The child's future neurological capacity is difficult to predict, but early diagnosis and successful shunting may completely prevent the probable development of mental retardation, optic nerve atrophy, and other serious neurological sequelae.

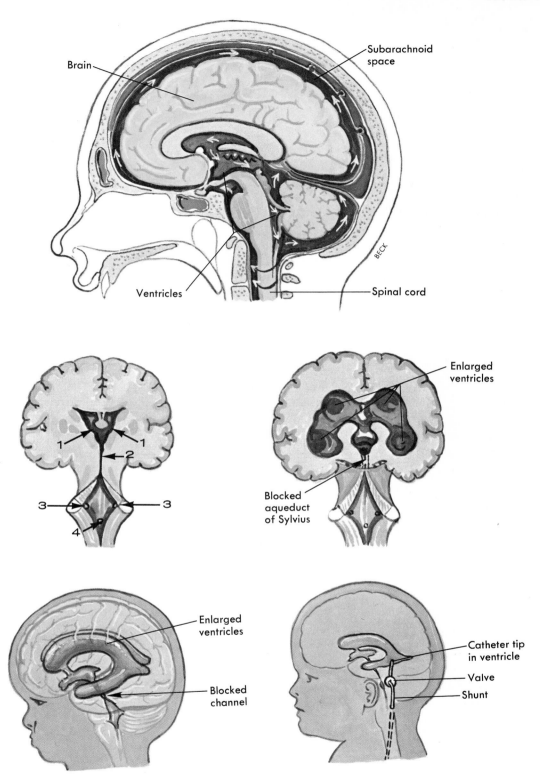

Arrows in the second illustration indicate possible sites of involvement in obstructive hydrocephalus. 1—Interventricular foramina (Monro); 2—aqueduct of Sylvius; 3—foramina of Luschka; 4—foramen of Magendie.

5|5

The spinal cord (schematic view)

The spinal cord is presented here in cross section, and two spinal nerves are illustrated. Both the vascular supply and the nerve roots are diagrammed.

The internal H-shaped core of the spinal column is penetrated by the central canal, which is an extension of the ventricles of the brain. The "H" is mainly composed of unmyelinated nerve cells. The white matter surrounding the gray matter is made up of myelinated nerve tracts, which contain neurons carrying messages from the brain to the spinal cord, or vice versa. The spinal nerve origins, also illustrated, consist of posterior and anterior roots. Swellings along the posterior roots are the sensory ganglia, in which the sensory nerve cell bodies are located. The anterior root is the route for motor nerves that pass from the spinal cord into the spinal nerves. Each spinal nerve contains sensory and motor fibers and supplies a particular area or structure of one side of the body. Although shown reflected, the pia mater cannot be "peeled" from the white matter of the spinal cord.

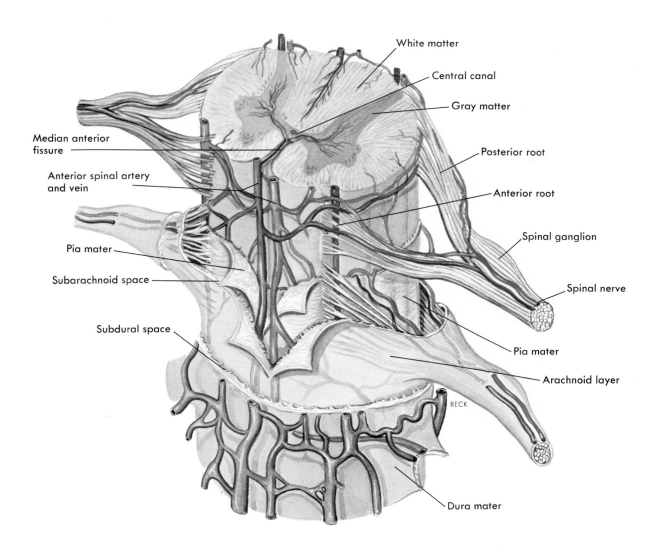

White matter

Central canal

Gray matter

Median anterior fissure

Posterior root

Anterior spinal artery and vein

Anterior root

Spinal ganglion

Pia mater

Spinal nerve

Subarachnoid space

Subdural space

Pia mater

Arachnoid layer

BECK

Dura mater

5|6

Branchings of a spinal nerve; cross section of nerve trunk

The spinal cord is illustrated in cross section; note the anterior and posterior roots of the nerve within the intervertebral foramen and the anterior and posterior rami outside of it. The posterior ramus branches into nerves that innervate the posterior part of the body; the anterior ramus innervates the anterior aspect of the body.

A cross section of a nerve trunk is also illustrated. The fiber bundles are myelinated and separated by a connective tissue, perineural sheath. Endoneurium is an extension of the perineurium, which wraps around the individual nerve fibers of the bundles.

BRANCHINGS OF A SPINAL NERVE

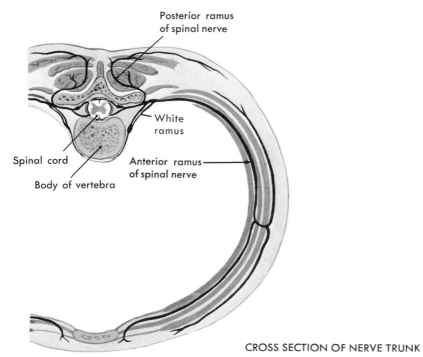

Posterior ramus
of spinal nerve

White
ramus

Spinal cord

Anterior ramus
of spinal nerve

Body of vertebra

CROSS SECTION OF NERVE TRUNK

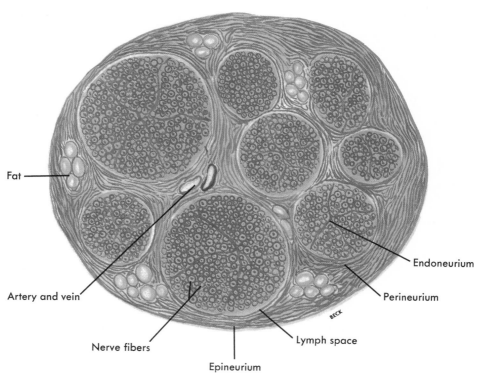

Fat

Artery and vein

Nerve fibers

Epineurium

Endoneurium

Perineurium

Lymph space

BECK

5|7

The brachial and lumbosacral plexus

The brachial plexus is a network of nerve fibers, consisting of roots, trunks, cords, and terminal and collateral branches, which provide innervation to the skin and muscles of the arms as well as to the muscles of the trunk that move the arms. There is an intimate relationship of the subclavian and axillary arteries with the brachial plexus. Injuries to the plexus are quite common and can involve both the nerves and the adjacent blood vessels. Anomalous cervical ribs may also produce damage to the brachial plexus. These are extra ribs attached to the seventh cervical vertebra (C7). They are able to exert continuous pressure on the plexus or may cause acute damage if the shoulder is injured or forcibly twisted. The symptoms usually are abnormal sensations and pain in the hand and arm, and eventually there can be muscular wasting and weakness. Continuous pressure leads to pallor, swelling, and coldness of the hand. There may be diminished arterial pulses as well.

The lumbar plexus is composed of nerves from the first four lumbar nerve roots; the sacral plexus is made up of nerves from the fourth and fifth lumbar nerves and first, second, third, and part of the fourth sacral nerves. Sacral plexus damage is extremely common in lower back injuries. Notice the origin of the large sciatic nerve. The fifth lumbar spinal root of this nerve is the most commonly affected by mechanical compression or edema because it is so large and passes through a comparatively small foramen. Back injury can result in lower back pain, as well as "sciatica." There is a characteristic pain associated with sciatica that shoots down the buttock and lower limb. Pressure on the sciatic nerve is also caused by a ruptured intervertebral disk. Principal nerves of the lumbosacral plexus are the sciatic, obturator, femoral, and pudendal. The psoas muscle (indicated in red) covers most of the nerve roots and trunks of the lumbar plexus.

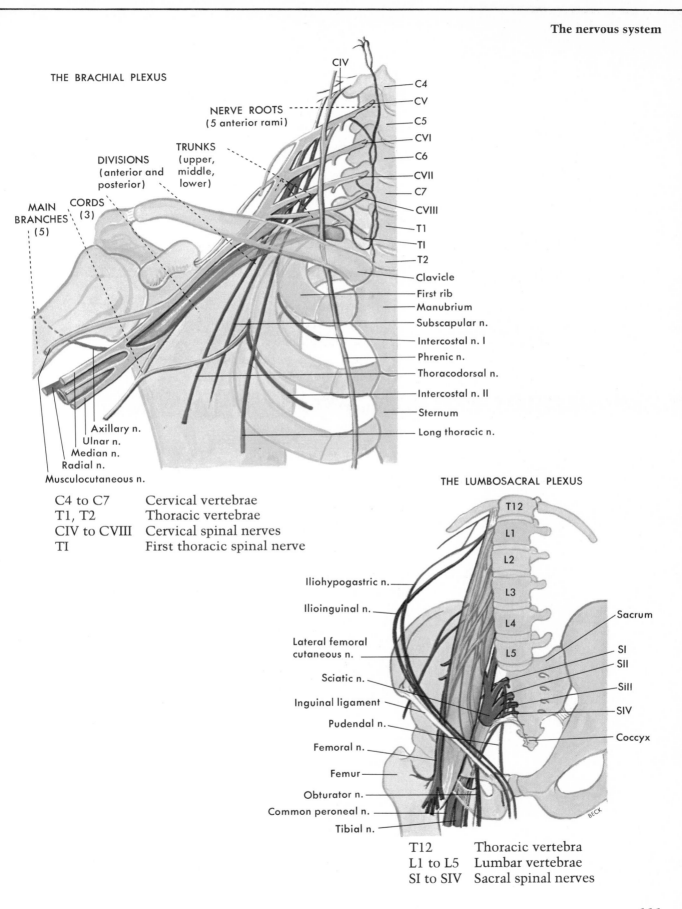

THE BRACHIAL PLEXUS

CIV

C4

CV

NERVE ROOTS
(5 anterior rami)

C5

CVI

C6

CVII

TRUNKS
(upper,
middle,
lower)

C7

DIVISIONS
(anterior and
posterior)

CVIII

T1

TI

CORDS
(3)

T2

Clavicle

MAIN
BRANCHES
(5)

First rib

Manubrium

Subscapular n.

Intercostal n. I

Phrenic n.

Thoracodorsal n.

Intercostal n. II

Sternum

Long thoracic n.

Axillary n.
Ulnar n.
Median n.
Radial n.
Musculocutaneous n.

C4 to C7   Cervical vertebrae
T1, T2   Thoracic vertebrae
CIV to CVIII Cervical spinal nerves
TI   First thoracic spinal nerve

THE LUMBOSACRAL PLEXUS

T12

L1

L2

L3

L4

Sacrum

Iliohypogastric n.

Ilioinguinal n.

L5

SI

SII

Lateral femoral
cutaneous n.

SIII

Sciatic n.

SIV

Inguinal ligament

Pudendal n.

Coccyx

Femoral n.

Femur

Obturator n.

Common peroneal n.

Tibial n.

BECK

T12   Thoracic vertebra
L1 to L5   Lumbar vertebrae
SI to SIV   Sacral spinal nerves

5|8

Spina bifida

Spina bifida results from defective closure of the vertebral column during embryogenesis and varies in severity. The most common and least symptomatic form is known as spina bifida occulta. This form may never be detected, occasionally marked only by a small dimple in the midline lumbar region. It is a defect only of the bony vertebral column and not of the underlying spinal cord. Some estimates of the incidence of spina bifida occulta are as high as 25% of all children, with the majority of the bony defects eventually fusing and disappearing by adulthood.

The more rare forms of spina bifida involve protrusion of spinal cord contents into the defect. Meningocele is a defect in which the outer coverings of the spinal cord, the meninges, and occasionally some nervous tissue protrude through the bony defect and are covered by skin. Usually paralysis of the lower limbs does not occur, but hydrocephalus (Plate 5-4) is common. In syringomyelocele portions of the spinal cord and meninges herniate into the sac accompanied with a dilation of the central canal. The myelocele form involves a complete or incomplete protrusion of the spinal cord into the defect, filling the sac. Myelomeningocele is the most devastating condition. The spinal cord, malformed nerve roots, and meninges all protrude through the defect, and often the sac is directly exposed to the outside of the body, being covered only by a thin membrane. This type is associated with severe neurological deficit below the level of the myelomeningocele, which is usually in the lumbosacral region, but may be located at any point along the spinal column.

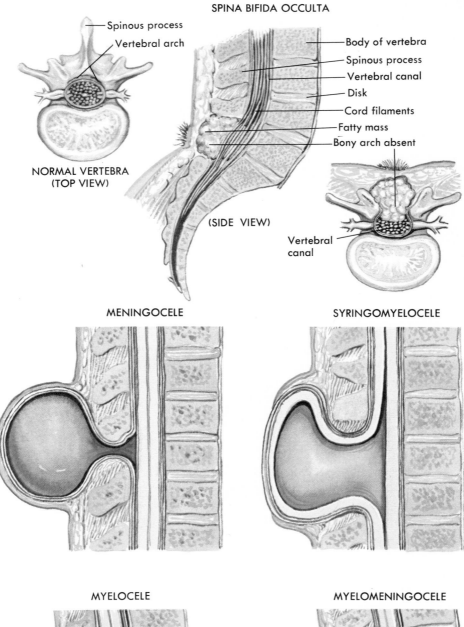

SPINA BIFIDA OCCULTA

Spinous process
Vertebral arch

NORMAL VERTEBRA
(TOP VIEW)

Body of vertebra
Spinous process
Vertebral canal
Disk
Cord filaments
Fatty mass
Bony arch absent

(SIDE VIEW)

Vertebral canal

MENINGOCELE

SYRINGOMYELOCELE

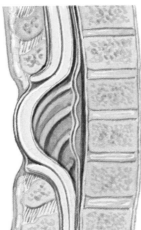

MYELOCELE

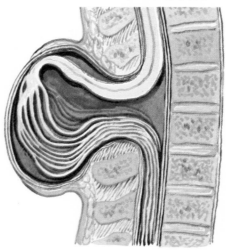

MYELOMENINGOCELE

BECK

5|9

The trigeminal nerve

The trigeminal (fifth cranial) nerve consists of large sensory branches and a small motor branch. There are three sensory branches: the ophthalmic, the maxillary, and the mandibular. These fibers transmit sensory information from the conjunctiva, skin, lips, teeth, and mucosa of the nasal and oral cavities. The cell bodies of these fibers are located in the trigeminal (gasserian) ganglion, and central processes terminate in the pons and medulla. Herpes simplex usually occurs in the area of distribution of the trigeminal nerve and is caused by a virus believed to remain in a latent state within either the trigeminal nerve, perineural sheath, or gasserian ganglion. Reactivation of the virus occurs in response to a variety of stressors, the most common being exposure to ultraviolet light (sunlight) and high fever. Most individuals have antibodies to herpes simplex, which means that they have been exposed at one time to the virus. The presence of a potent living virus coexisting with high antibody titers against it remains one of the major mysteries of virology, as does the actual mechanism of reactivation.

Another interesting condition involving the trigeminal nerve is tic douloureux. This is an inflammation of the nerve (neuralgia), which is considered by many to produce the most excruciating pain of any human disease. People suffering from tic douloureux have recurrent attacks of facial pain that can be only partially alleviated by analgesic drugs. The only cure is surgical removal of the gasserian ganglion.

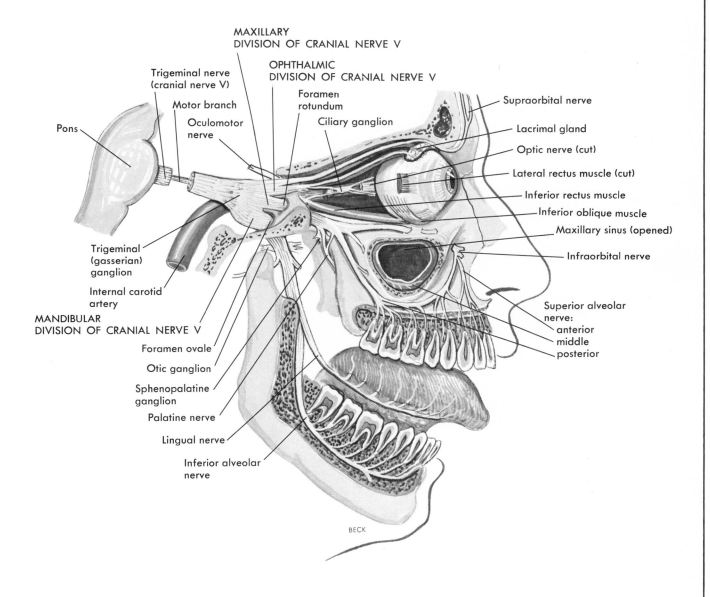

MAXILLARY
DIVISION OF CRANIAL NERVE V

OPHTHALMIC
DIVISION OF CRANIAL NERVE V

Trigeminal nerve
(cranial nerve V)

Motor branch

Oculomotor
nerve

Foramen
rotundum

Ciliary ganglion

Pons

Supraorbital nerve

Lacrimal gland

Optic nerve (cut)

Lateral rectus muscle (cut)

Inferior rectus muscle

Inferior oblique muscle

Maxillary sinus (opened)

Infraorbital nerve

Trigeminal
(gasserian)
ganglion

Internal carotid
artery

MANDIBULAR
DIVISION OF CRANIAL NERVE V

Foramen ovale

Otic ganglion

Sphenopalatine
ganglion

Palatine nerve

Lingual nerve

Inferior alveolar
nerve

Superior alveolar
nerve:
anterior
middle
posterior

BECK

115

5|10

A synapse (diagrammatic view)

Synapse is the name of the anatomical connection between individual neurons or between a neuron and the structure that it innervates, such as a muscle cell. In the illustration it can be seen that the synaptic cleft is a very tiny space between the presynaptic and postsynaptic neurons. The presynaptic axon terminal is filled with vesicles containing neurotransmitter molecules, such as acetylcholine or norepinephrine. When a nerve action potential excites the axon terminals, the vesicles are released from the axon and the neurotransmitter molecules spill into the synaptic cleft. The neurotransmitter then excites the postsynaptic membrane by causing sodium to enter the cell. Depolarization occurs when enough sodium has entered to initiate an action potential. The impulse is then conducted down the postsynaptic neuron without any decrement.

Hundreds of synaptic knobs from many different neurons may converge on a postsynaptic cell. Some of the presynaptic neurons may have an excitatory neurotransmitter. Others release an inhibitor. The further propagation of a message in a postsynaptic cell would therefore depend on the summation of all the stimulatory and inhibitory signals.

Many drugs act at the synapse by either depleting the neurotransmitter vesicles, altering the release or removal of the neurotransmitter, or affecting the permeability state of the postsynaptic membrane.

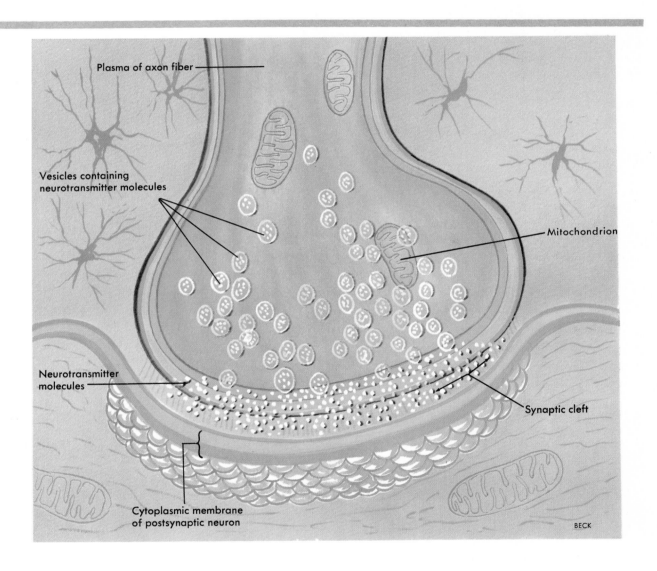

Plasma of axon fiber

Vesicles containing
neurotransmitter molecules

Mitochondrion

Neurotransmitter
molecules

Synaptic cleft

Cytoplasmic membrane
of postsynaptic neuron

BECK

6 | Special senses

6|1

The right eye (horizontal section)

The eye is a complex structure that can be regarded as an extension of the central nervous system and a window of the brain. The entire ocular apparatus is designed to allow light and visual stimuli to fall on the retina, which then transmits color, light, and other visual information to the optic nerve. The amount of light entering the eye is dependent on the pupil, an aperture whose size is controlled by the ciliary muscle that forms the iris. Light constricts, whereas darkness dilates the pupil. The diffusion and bending of light between the pupil and the retinal epithelium is caused by the refractive powers of the lens, the shape of which is controlled by the ciliary muscle. A common condition eventually resulting in blindness is cataract, which is an opacity of the lens.

The aqueous humor is produced by filtration of plasma from the vessels of the iris and ciliary body and is present in the anterior chamber in front of the lens. If the pressure is increased in this chamber of the eye, glaucoma may result. The aqueous humor is continually formed and reabsorbed, and if the reabsorption of fluid is blocked, the intraocular pressure rises and results in damage.

The optic nerve's entrance into the eye can be visualized with an ophthalmoscope and is known as the optic disc (or blind spot). When intracranial pressure is increased, the optic disc may become edematous, a condition known as papilledema.

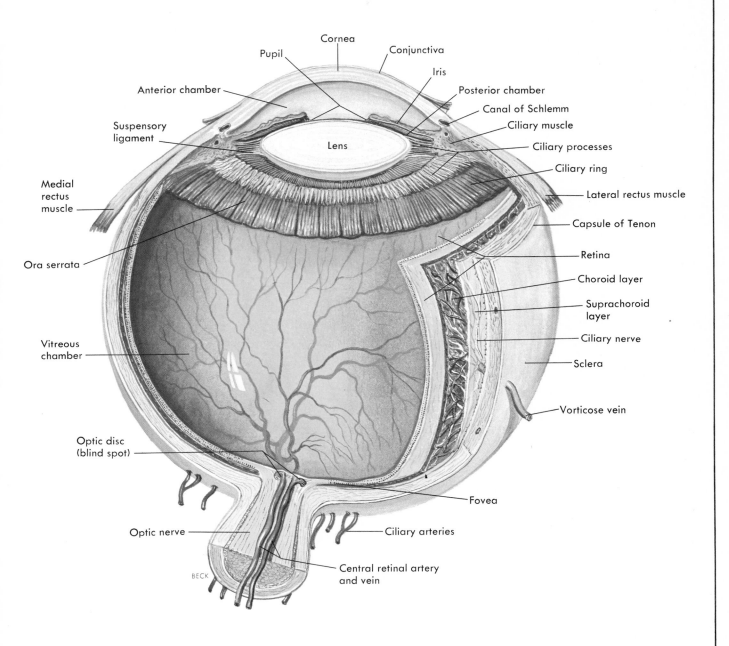

Cornea

Pupil

Conjunctiva

Iris

Anterior chamber

Posterior chamber

Canal of Schlemm

Suspensory ligament

Ciliary muscle

Lens

Ciliary processes

Ciliary ring

Medial rectus muscle

Lateral rectus muscle

Capsule of Tenon

Ora serrata

Retina

Choroid layer

Suprachoroid layer

Ciliary nerve

Vitreous chamber

Sclera

Vorticose vein

Optic disc (blind spot)

Fovea

Optic nerve

Ciliary arteries

BECK

Central retinal artery and vein

6|2

Exterior of the eye; muscles that move the eye

The eye is contained within a bony orbit that helps protect it from injury. Other external eye structures further protect the eye. These include the fleshy lids and the blink reflex; the lashes, which screen the eye from foreign bodies; and the lacrimal apparatus, which forms and reabsorbs the tears. The sclera of the eye, along with the cornea, secretes an external fibrous lining. Minute blood vessels are usually visible on the white sclera. The iris is the colored part of the eye, with the amount of pigment genetically determined. In albinism no pigment is present and the iris is pink because blood vessels are readily visible. The iris is made up of muscle fibers that regulate the dilation or constriction of the pupil. This in turn controls the amount of light that enters the eye and falls on the retina. The lacrimal glands continuously produce tears that wash across the eye and are then reabsorbed through the punctae, which transport the tears into the lacrimal canaliculi and sacs. Along the superior and inferior tarsus are the tiny openings of the tarsal or ciliary glands. These are modified sweat glands that can easily become inflamed, producing a sty.

The eye muscles are innervated by motor fibers from several cranial nerves. There is a constant balance of eye muscle contraction and relaxation, which permits the eyes to move appropriately and symmetrically. Muscles that adduct the eye are the medial, inferior, and superior recti. Abduction is accomplished by the lateral rectus and superior and inferior oblique muscles. Downward gaze is the result of contraction of the superior oblique and inferior rectus; elevation of the eye is caused by the superior rectus and inferior oblique. Rotational movements result from contraction of the superior rectus and oblique (medial rotation) or inferior rectus and oblique (lateral rotation).

Eye muscle weakness is quite common in children and must be diagnosed and treated early in life. If it is not, a "lazy eye" may develop, and blindness can result with time.

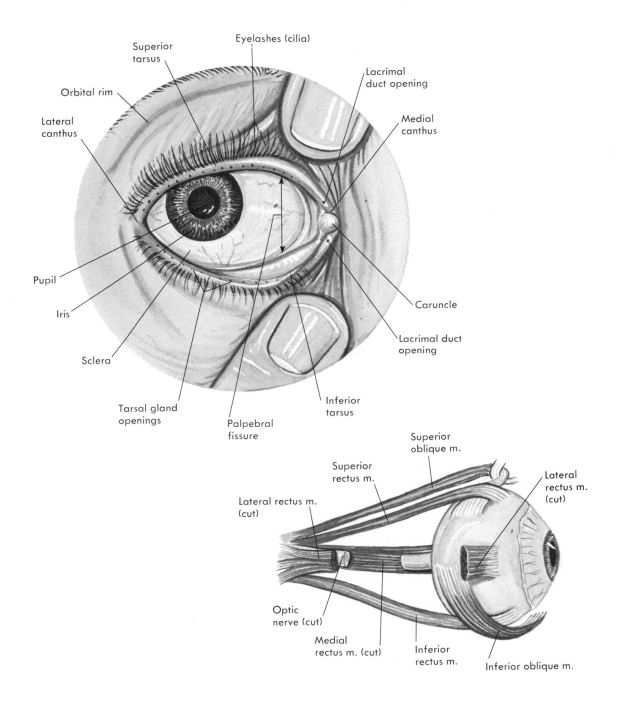

Superior tarsus

Orbital rim

Lateral canthus

Eyelashes (cilia)

Lacrimal duct opening

Medial canthus

Pupil

Iris

Sclera

Caruncle

Lacrimal duct opening

Tarsal gland openings

Palpebral fissure

Inferior tarsus

Superior oblique m.

Superior rectus m.

Lateral rectus m. (cut)

Lateral rectus m. (cut)

Optic nerve (cut)

Medial rectus m. (cut)

Inferior rectus m.

Inferior oblique m.

6|3

Aqueous humor; acute glaucoma; astigmatism

Aqueous humor is a fluid that is formed mainly through secretion by the ciliary body into the posterior chamber. From there it drains into the anterior chamber through the pupil, exits by way of the ring-shaped canal of Schlemm, and finally flows into the anterior ciliary veins. The small arrows indicate the direction of the pressure exerted by the aqueous humor; the heavy arrows show the direction of flow of aqueous humor.

Acute glaucoma is a serious condition in which the pressure of the aqueous humor in the anterior chamber rises. This forces the iris forward and the canal of Schlemm is blocked, so that the fluid does not drain from the anterior chamber. The eyeball becomes hard and painful when the condition develops acutely, and treatment is required immediately. Medications that dilate the outflow duct may be instilled into the eye. If this fails, surgical creation of a new outflow duct is necessary.

Astigmatism results when the cornea becomes irregular. The cornea may be only slightly flattened horizontally, vertically, or diagonally to produce distortion of vision. The compensating shape of the lens largely nullifies the irregularities of the cornea. An irregular lens causes light to be bent in such a way that it does not focus the image on the sharpest area of vision on the retina. An astigmatic eye with this defect causes distorted or blurred vision.

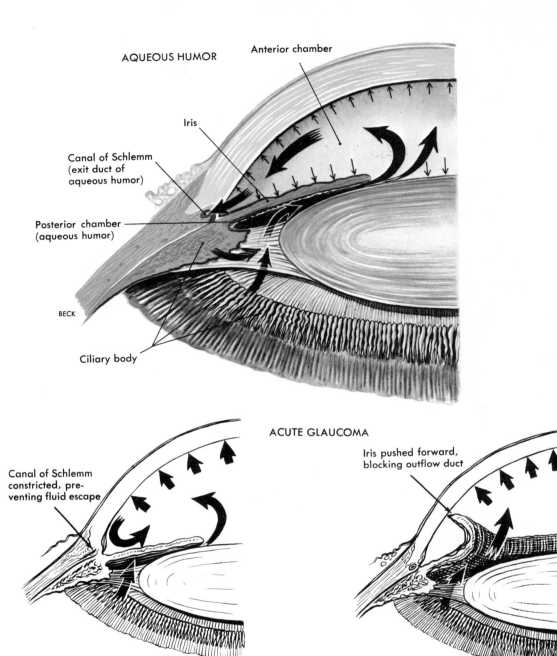

AQUEOUS HUMOR

Anterior chamber

Iris

Canal of Schlemm
(exit duct of
aqueous humor)

Posterior chamber
(aqueous humor)

Ciliary body

BECK

ACUTE GLAUCOMA

Canal of Schlemm
constricted, pre-
venting fluid escape

Iris pushed forward,
blocking outflow duct

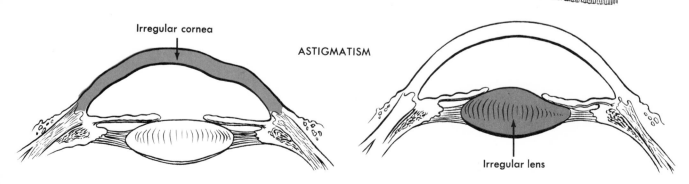

Irregular cornea

ASTIGMATISM

Irregular lens

6|4

Retina of the eye (ophthalmoscopic view)

Examination of the posterior part of the eye is done with an ophthalmoscope, with the examiner looking through a dilated pupil, through the lens, and to the retina. Shown is the appearance of the retina of a normal right eye. The orange-red appearance of the eyeground is caused by the pigment and large abundance of blood vessels in the choroid layer visible through the normally transparent retina.

The central retinal artery is a branch of the ophthalmic artery, entering the optic nerve about 2 cm (⁴/₅ inch) from the eyeball and running in the center of it as far as the retina, which it enters about the middle of the optic disc. After emerging through the disc, the central artery divides into the superior and inferior branches, each of which subdivides into nasal and temporal branches. Veins follow the same distribution as the arteries. The artery-vein size ratio is about 5:2.

The retina is the innermost coat of the eye and is the expanded portion of the optic nerve. It consists mainly of nervous tissue. When an image is focused on the retina, the rods and cones (photosensitive cells) translate the light energy into nervous impulses. Numerous vascular changes as well as optic nerve pathology can actually be visualized in the retina. Hemorrhages, exudates, and artery-vein ratio alterations are readily observed eye conditions. Diabetic and arteriosclerotic processes are the most common causes of retinal vascular disease.

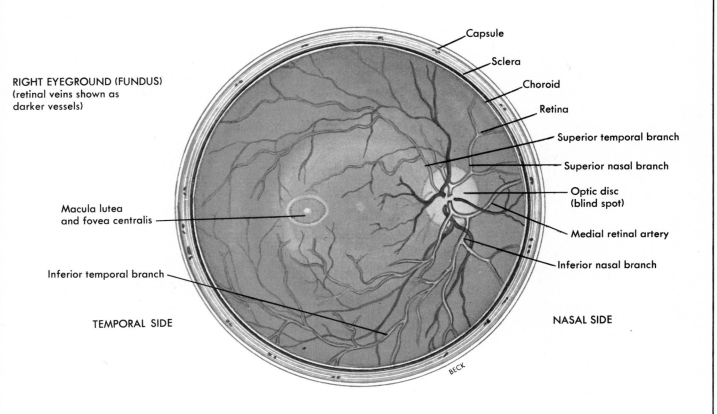

Capsule

Sclera

Choroid

Retina

Superior temporal branch

Superior nasal branch

Optic disc (blind spot)

Medial retinal artery

Inferior nasal branch

RIGHT EYEGROUND (FUNDUS) (retinal veins shown as darker vessels)

Macula lutea and fovea centralis

Inferior temporal branch

TEMPORAL SIDE

NASAL SIDE

BECK

6|5

The lacrimal apparatus

The conjunctiva of the eye is protected by a fluid film produced by the lacrimal (tear) gland, which is situated in the upper outer margin of each orbit. Ten to twelve small ducts lead from each gland, draining the tears diagonally across the front of the eye and into the superior and inferior lacrimal canaliculi, which lead to a larger sac and duct. The duct is contained in an osseous canal formed by the inferior nasal concha (turbinate), the maxilla, and lacrimal bone. The opening of the duct into the nasal cavity is under the inferior concha.

All the tear ducts are lined with mucous membrane and epithelium. When this membrane becomes engorged and inflamed, the nasolacrimal ducts become plugged, causing the tears to well up in the eyes instead of draining into the nose as they normally do. Tears contain various salts and an enzyme (lysozyme) that is bactericidal.

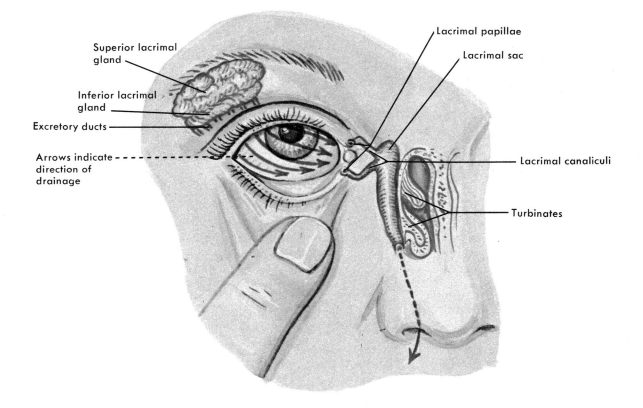

Superior lacrimal gland

Inferior lacrimal gland

Excretory ducts

Arrows indicate direction of drainage

Lacrimal papillae

Lacrimal sac

Lacrimal canaliculi

Turbinates

6|6

Layers of the retina

The total number of rods in the human retina has been estimated at 110 to 125 million and the number of cones at 6.3 to 6.8 million; the rods outnumber the cones 18 to 20:1. Cones contain a photosensitive chemical known as iodopsin (visual violet) and are considered to be the receptors responsible for daylight and color vision. They have their densest arrangement at the fovea centralis. The number of cones in the retina diminishes sharply with distance from the fovea.

Rods contain rhodopsin (visual purple), a pigmented compound that is highly light-sensitive. When light strikes a rod, rhodopsin rapidly breaks down. Rods are considered to be receptors for night or relatively "dark" vision, since the rhodopsin quickly becomes depleted in bright light because of the rapid breakdown and slow regeneration. This explains the momentary lag in sharp vision after one goes from bright light to darkness. As rhodopsin reforms, the rods start functioning again and the eye is said to adapt. When exposed to light, visual purple bleaches out to visual yellow (retinene). In the absence of light the reaction is reversed and rhodopsin is reformed. Vitamin A is essential in the rhodopsin cycle as an intermediary in the conversion of retinene to rhodopsin. When vitamin A is lacking or diminished, the cycle is slowed and a much slower rate of dark adaptation results, a condition known as "night blindness."

Color vision. It is believed that there are only three different kinds of cones, each containing a different visual pigment. When stimulated, they elicit sensations of red, green, and blue-violet, according to the theories of Helmholtz (1802) and Young (1862). Each pigment is affected by light of a specific wave length. Visible color is perceived by the brain as a mixture in varying amounts of the primary hues, a result of mixing stimulation of the cones in proper proportions. When all three are stimulated equally, the result is white light.

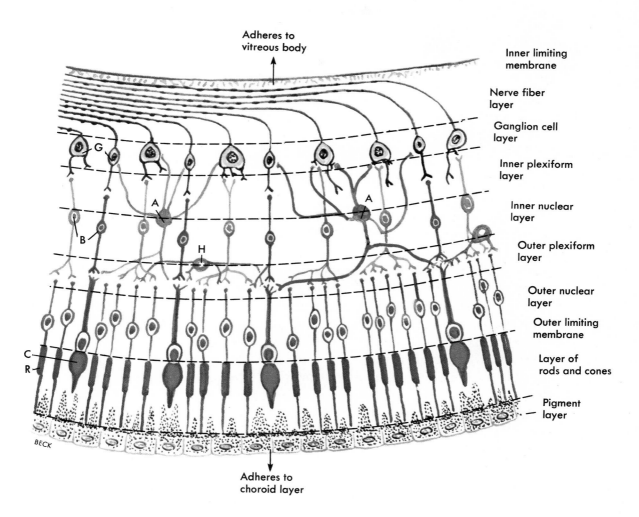

Adheres to
vitreous body

Inner limiting
membrane

Nerve fiber
layer

Ganglion cell
layer

Inner plexiform
layer

Inner nuclear
layer

Outer plexiform
layer

Outer nuclear
layer

Outer limiting
membrane

Layer of
rods and cones

Pigment
layer

BECK

Adheres to
choroid layer

A	Amacrine cell	R	Rod
B	Bipolar cell	H	Horizontal cell
C	Cone	G	Ganglion cell

Color blindness. This problem is much more prevalent in males (8%) than in females (0.4%), since the presence of each type of cone is controlled by sex-linked recessive genes. All three kinds of cones must be present in proper proportion for perfect color vision. In most cases of color blindness there is not complete absence of cones, but rather a diminished number of one kind. Those with difficulty in seeing red are protanopes; they are insensitive to deep red light. Deuteranopes confuse shades of red, green, and yellow. Tritanopes are "blue-blind," confusing blue and green shades and usually orange and pink shades.

6|7

Sense of hearing

Hearing results when sound waves are conducted through air, bone, and fluid to nerves reaching the cerebral cortex in the temporal lobes of the brain.

The specific steps in the transmission of sound waves follow. (1) Sound vibrations enter the external acoustic meatus (auditory tube) and strike against the tympanic membrane (eardrum). (2) The vibrating membrane transmits the sound to the handle of the malleus (hammer), which is attached to the medial aspect of the eardrum at about its midpoint. (3) Bone conduction of sound waves proceeds through the three tiny connected ear bones—from malleus to incus to stapes. (4) Sound is then transmitted from the footplate of the stapes through the oval window of the vestibule of the inner ear structure. Pressure is thus exerted by the footplate inward into the perilymph (fluid) in the scala vestibuli of the cochlea. (5) The sound ripple passes through this fluid to Reissner's membrane, which is the roof of the cochlear duct, to endolymph inside the cochlear duct, and to the basilar membrane that supports the organ of Corti. (6) From the basilar membrane the wave is next transmitted to and through the perilymph in the scala tympani, and finally is expended against the round window.

The cochlea in the inner ear is a bony tube consisting of 2½ spirals. The cochlear duct runs the length of the cochlea, and it is this structure's mechanical vibrations that are essential for normal hearing. The hair cells of the organ of Corti are located along the cochlear duct, which is filled with endolymph. A gelatinous membrane lies atop the organ of Corti, and the hair cells project into it. The sensory endings of the cochlear nerve lie on the hair cells; the movement of hair cells causes these neurons to fire. The sound message is transmitted by nerve relays to the spiral ganglion. From this structure the nerve fibers gather in three strands, and the impulse travels through centers in the medulla, pons, midbrain, and thalamus. Some fibers cross over in the brain, and thus both sides of the cortex receive messages from both ears.

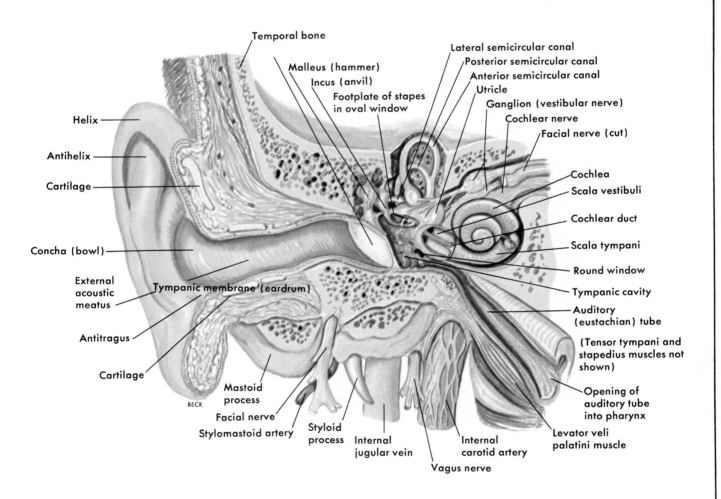

Temporal bone

Malleus (hammer)
Incus (anvil)
Footplate of stapes
in oval window

Lateral semicircular canal
Posterior semicircular canal
Anterior semicircular canal
Utricle
Ganglion (vestibular nerve)
Cochlear nerve
Facial nerve (cut)

Helix

Antihelix

Cartilage

Cochlea
Scala vestibuli
Cochlear duct
Scala tympani
Round window
Tympanic cavity
Auditory
(eustachian) tube

Concha (bowl)

External
acoustic
meatus

Tympanic membrane (eardrum)

Antitragus

Cartilage

(Tensor tympani and
stapedius muscles not
shown)

Opening of
auditory tube
into pharynx

Mastoid
process
Facial nerve
Stylomastoid artery

BECK

Styloid
process
Internal
jugular vein

Internal
carotid artery

Vagus nerve

Levator veli
palatini muscle

6|8

Auditory tube in child and adult (compared)

The auditory, or eustachian, tube is the channel through which the middle ear chamber communicates with the nasal part of the pharynx. Through this tube air passes between the pharynx and tympanic cavity, equalizing the air pressure on the lateral and medial surfaces of the eardrum. In the child the auditory tube inclines downward only about 10 degrees; in the adult the angle is 40 degrees. The length of the child's tube is only half that of the adult, but the diameter is as large and most often wider. The tympanic membrane (eardrum) in the child is slanted more horizontally and is thicker and more elastic. The external ear canal is also narrower.

When the narrow, slitlike pharyngeal opening of the auditory tube is blocked by a congested mucous membrane or overgrowth of lymphoid (tonsillar or adenoid) tissue, normal drainage is prevented. The organisms of the middle ear are those of the normal flora of the nasopharynx. When the auditory tube is blocked, some pathogenic organisms thrive because of the altered pH and oxygenation status. Infection results, leading to acute otitis media.

As the child grows to adulthood, the auditory tube lengthens and descends considerably below the level of the external ear canal. Its opening in the pharynx is surrounded by less lymphoid tissue than in childhood. Ear complications as a result of throat infections are fewer. Adults and children are susceptible to serous otitis media, which results from accumulation of serous fluid within the middle ear. This condition may follow an acute infection and is characterized by a sensation of fullness and pressure. There may also be a hearing loss.

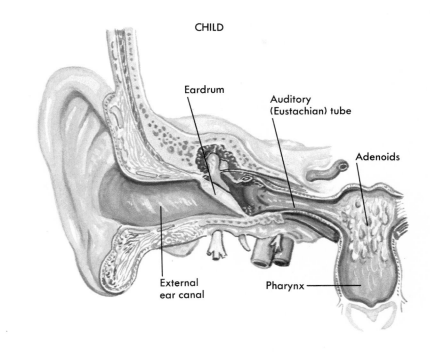

CHILD

Eardrum

Auditory (Eustachian) tube

Adenoids

External ear canal

Pharynx

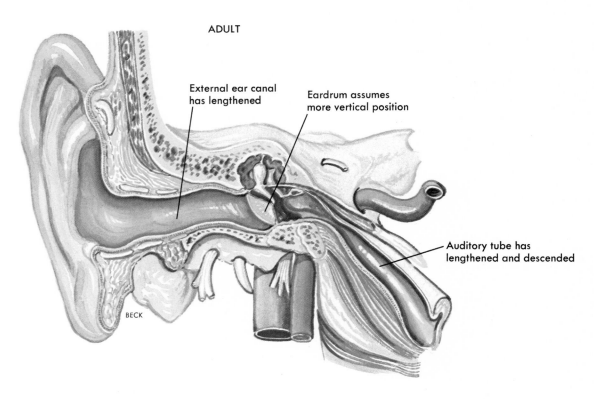

ADULT

External ear canal has lengthened

Eardrum assumes more vertical position

Auditory tube has lengthened and descended

BECK

6|9

Membranous labyrinth of the ear

The inner ear comprises the organ of balance (semicircular canals and utricle) and the organ of hearing (cochlea, ducts, and saccule).

The membranous semicircular canals are similar in shape to their surrounding osseous channels. The principal function of the semicircular canals is to register motion (acceleration or deceleration) or a change in the direction of motion.

The receptor organ of the semicircular canals lies in the ampulla of each canal and is called the crista. It consists of nonsensory supporting cells and sensory hair cells, which are the sensory endings of the vestibular nerve. Currents in the endolymph displace the cupulae of the hair cells, which results in excitation of nerve endings at the base of the crista. Impulses are transmitted through a series of ganglia and relays to the temporal lobe of the brain.

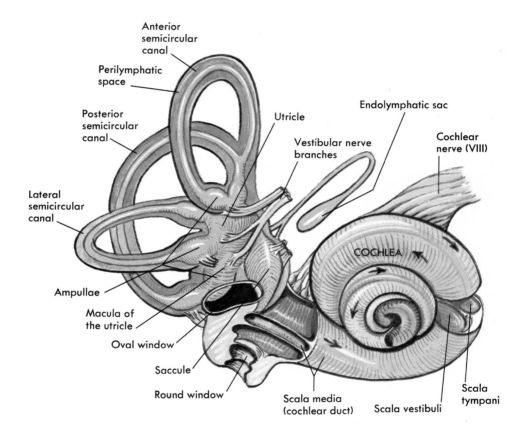

Anterior semicircular canal

Perilymphatic space

Posterior semicircular canal

Lateral semicircular canal

Ampullae

Macula of the utricle

Oval window

Saccule

Round window

Utricle

Vestibular nerve branches

Endolymphatic sac

Cochlear nerve (VIII)

COCHLEA

Scala media (cochlear duct)

Scala vestibuli

Scala tympani

6|10

Internal structures of the ear—cochlea and organ of Corti

Transverse section through the middle coil of the cochlea shows the three compartments and the organ of Corti. The cochlear nerve originates within the scala media at the bases of specialized hair cells that communicate with the tectorial membrane.

The organ of Corti is the most highly developed and complex component of the hearing system. It serves two vital functions: conversion of mechanical energy into electrical energy and transmission to the brain of a coded version of the original sound. It conveys information not only about the frequency of sound waves but about the timbre and intensity as well.

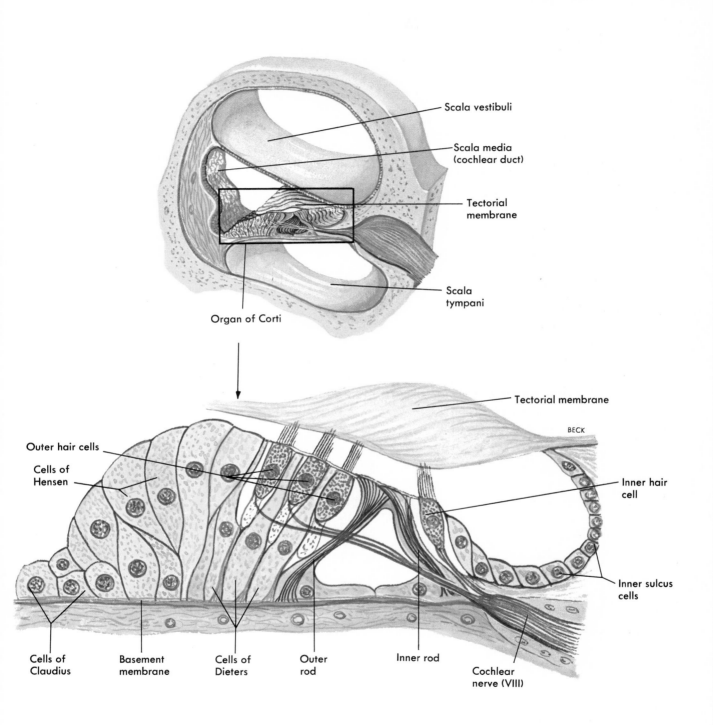

Scala vestibuli

Scala media (cochlear duct)

Tectorial membrane

Scala tympani

Organ of Corti

Tectorial membrane

BECK

Outer hair cells

Cells of Hensen

Inner hair cell

Inner sulcus cells

Cells of Claudius

Basement membrane

Cells of Dieters

Outer rod

Inner rod

Cochlear nerve (VIII)

6|11

Sense of smell

The total area of olfactory epithelium in the interior of the nose is only about 2.5 cm² (0.4 square inches) on each side. It includes the medial wall of the superior conchas (turbinate) and the adjacent lateral surface of the nasal septum. It can be distinguished by its dark yellow color.

The olfactory epithelium consists of supporting cells, basal cells, and the olfactory receptor cells. Cilia project from the top of these cells into the mucus of the nose. At the basal end of each cell an axon projects upward with millions of other olfactory axons to the olfactory bulb, where they continue in nerve tracts to the olfactory area of the cortex. There is an interrelationship between smell and taste sensations, and most people complain of impaired taste when they have nasal congestion.

The sensation of smell depends on diffusion of respiratory air into the still air of the upper olfactory portion of the nasal cavity. The act of sniffing causes the nostril to dilate and the direction of the anterior part of the nasal respiratory chamber to be altered, so that the stream of inspired air is directed toward the upper olfactory area of the cavity. Odors can be perceived in very minute quantities and can be finely discriminated.

Just how the receptors are stimulated and how discrimination between odors is achieved is not understood. Attempts to classify odors fall short, since there is not one kind of receptor for each kind of odor. It seems safe to assume that we are able to distinguish among the several thousand odors as the result of some sort of mixing process, as occurs in color perception. One classification attempt on the basis of similarities of molecular structure and odor names the following as seven primary classes of odors: camphoraceous, musky, floral, pepperminty, ethereal, pungent, and putrid.

SCHEME OF CELL AND FIBER ARRANGEMENT
IN OLFACTORY EPITHELIUM

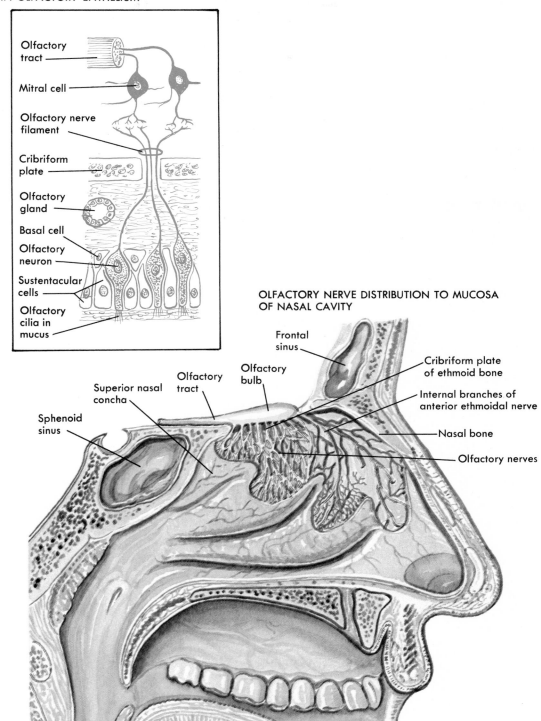

Olfactory tract
Mitral cell
Olfactory nerve filament
Cribriform plate
Olfactory gland
Basal cell
Olfactory neuron
Sustentacular cells
Olfactory cilia in mucus

OLFACTORY NERVE DISTRIBUTION TO MUCOSA
OF NASAL CAVITY

Frontal sinus
Olfactory bulb
Cribriform plate of ethmoid bone
Internal branches of anterior ethmoidal nerve
Nasal bone
Olfactory nerves
Olfactory tract
Superior nasal concha
Sphenoid sinus

7 | The endocrine system

The thyroid gland
The parathyroid glands (rear view)
The pancreas
The adrenal glands

7|1

The thyroid gland

The thyroid gland is a highly vascular endocrine organ situated in front of and to the sides of the upper part of the trachea at the level of the fifth, sixth, and seventh cervical and first thoracic vertebrae. It is horseshoe-shaped, consisting of two lateral lobes connected by a narrow central portion, the isthmus, and occasionally by an elongated portion, the pyramidal lobe. It is normally not palpable unless enlarged.

The functions of the thyroid gland are to produce, store, and release thyroxine, or tetraiodothyronine (T_4), and triiodothyronine (T_3). Thyroxine and triiodothyronine control growth and metabolism. These hormones require thyroid-stimulating hormone (TSH) from the anterior pituitary gland for synthesis and secretion. Iodine is also necessary and is efficiently trapped by the thyroid gland, a process that requires both TSH and adequate dietary iodine intake. Individuals born with deficient thyroid gland function are classified as congenital cretins and have stunted growths and are mentally retarded. Adults who develop hypothyroidism are often lethargic, dull, and tired, while those with hyperthyroidism usually exhibit nervous irritability, restlessness, and tremors.

The important metabolic effect of the thyroid hormones on cellular metabolism is also exemplified through hyperthyroidism and hypothyroidism. In the latter condition, general metabolism is described as sluggish and weight gain is common. Hyperthyroidism is associated with increased metabolism and oxygen consumption; the hyperthyroid individual has increased appetite, heart rate, respiratory rate, and temperature and often loses weight.

Another thyroid hormone, thyrocalcitonin, causes a lowering of the calcium level in the blood when serum calcium is high. Thyroid diseases may be divided into four main categories: (1) deficient hormones—hypothyroidism (endemic goiter, cretinism, myxedema); (2) excess hormones—hyperthyroidism (thyrotoxicosis, exophthalmic goiter); (3) nodular—adenomatous goiters and carcinomas without recognizable effect on hormone production; and (4) acute and chronic thyroid gland inflammation.

144

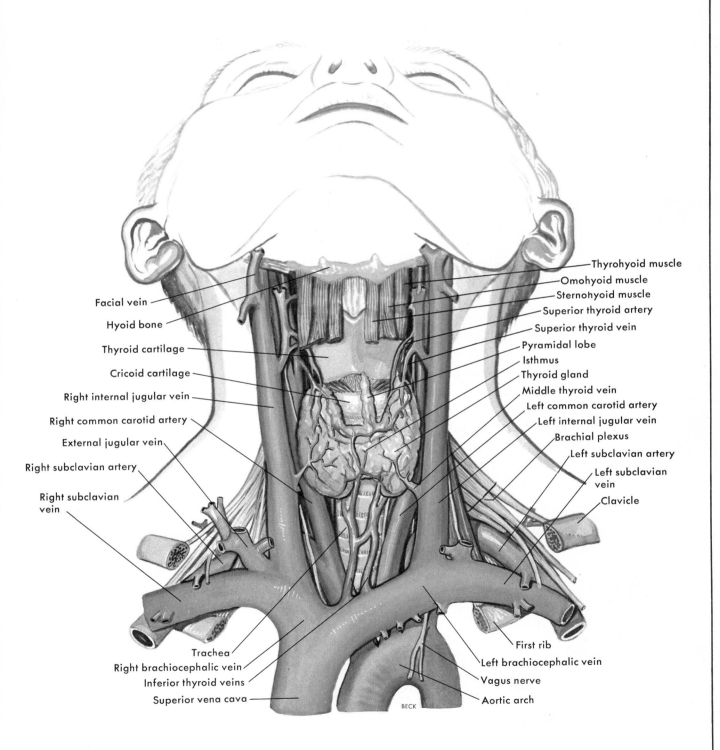

Thyrohyoid muscle
Omohyoid muscle
Sternohyoid muscle
Superior thyroid artery
Superior thyroid vein
Pyramidal lobe
Isthmus
Thyroid gland
Middle thyroid vein
Left common carotid artery
Left internal jugular vein
Brachial plexus
Left subclavian artery
Left subclavian vein
Clavicle

Facial vein
Hyoid bone
Thyroid cartilage
Cricoid cartilage
Right internal jugular vein
Right common carotid artery
External jugular vein
Right subclavian artery
Right subclavian vein

First rib
Left brachiocephalic vein
Vagus nerve
Aortic arch

Trachea
Right brachiocephalic vein
Inferior thyroid veins
Superior vena cava

BECK

7|2

The parathyroid glands (rear view)

The parathyroid glands, usually four in number, lie immediately behind the thyroid gland and are frequently imbedded in thyroid tissue. Their function is to secrete a hormone known as parathormone (parathyroid hormone), which controls the homeostasis of calcium absorption from bone, digestive organs, and the kidneys into the blood.

Of the body's 1200 g (42 ounces) of calcium, only about 1 g is in the blood; the rest is in the teeth and bones, extracellular fluid, and soft tissues. Serum calcium is essential for normal contraction of cardiac and skeletal muscle, for normal nerve function, for blood coagulation, and for cell permeability. Too much calcium depresses muscle excitability and causes cardiac irregularities. Too little calcium elevates nerve and muscle excitability and results in muscle twitches that may progress to convulsions and tonic spasms (tetany).

Parathormone also affects the metabolism of phosphorus, a mineral present in bone with calcium as a complex salt. There is a reciprocal relationship between serum calcium and serum phosphorus levels. As serum calcium level decreases, serum phosphorus level rises, and vice versa. Parathormone regulates this delicate balance.

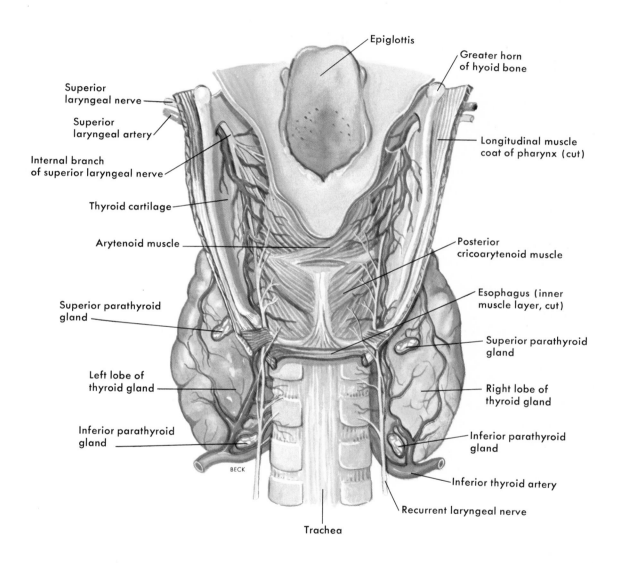

Epiglottis

Greater horn
of hyoid bone

Superior
laryngeal nerve

Superior
laryngeal artery

Internal branch
of superior laryngeal nerve

Longitudinal muscle
coat of pharynx (cut)

Thyroid cartilage

Arytenoid muscle

Posterior
cricoarytenoid muscle

Superior parathyroid
gland

Esophagus (inner
muscle layer, cut)

Superior parathyroid
gland

Left lobe of
thyroid gland

Right lobe of
thyroid gland

Inferior parathyroid
gland

Inferior parathyroid
gland

BECK

Inferior thyroid artery

Recurrent laryngeal nerve

Trachea

7|3

The pancreas

The pancreas is composed of both exocrine and endocrine cells. The acini that make up the exocrine portion send their secretions through ducts to the duodenum to aid in digestion. The components of the pancreatic juice are the enzymes amylase, carboxypeptidase, lipase, trypsin, chymotrypsin, and others. Amylase acts on glycogen and starch in the intestine to form fermentable sugars, chiefly maltose. Carboxypeptidase acts on polypeptides at the final stage to reduce these large protein molecules into their constituent amino acids. Lipase hydrolyzes the ester linkages of triglycerides into component fatty acids and glycerol. Trypsin and chymotrypsin are proteolytic enzymes that split peptide bonds.

The endocrine portion of the pancreas, scattered in islands (of Langerhans), consists of several different kinds of cells, including the alpha cells that secrete glucagon. Glucagon facilitates the breakdown of glycogen to glucose by stimulating the formation of cyclic AMP (adenosine 3':5'-cyclic phosphate) in liver cells. Cyclic AMP then participates in the formation of an enzyme that splits glycogen.

The beta cells produce the hormone insulin, which plays a central role in carbohydrate and fat metabolism. Insulin acts as a lipid storage hormone and also facilitates glucose entry into certain cells (muscle, brain, adipose tissue). Insulin also increases glucose oxidation and the formation of liver glycogen from glucose.

Diabetes mellitus is a disease in which insulin secretion is deficient or even absent, or in which insulin is present but cells are resistant to the hormone. In either case, hyperglycemia (a rise in blood glucose) develops. Energy needs are met by the utilization of fat and amino acids. Diabetes mellitus can result in long-term damage to the liver, kidneys, eyes, heart, and nervous system. Vascular changes are characteristic and lead to most of the damaging

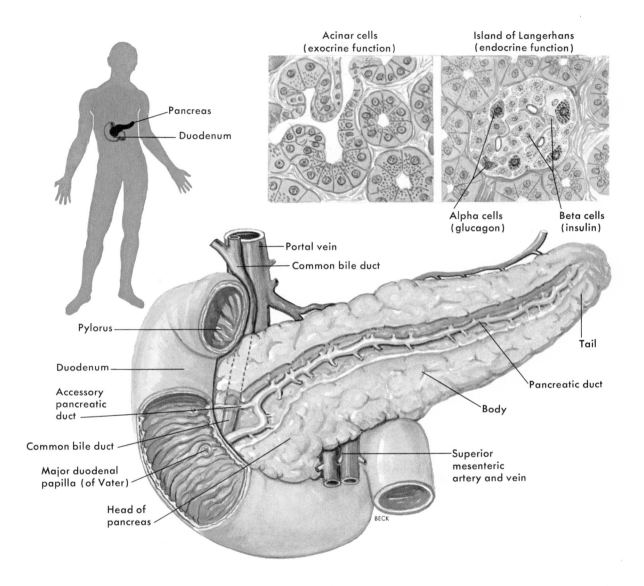

Acinar cells (exocrine function)

Island of Langerhans (endocrine function)

Pancreas

Duodenum

Alpha cells (glucagon)

Beta cells (insulin)

Portal vein

Common bile duct

Pylorus

Tail

Duodenum

Accessory pancreatic duct

Pancreatic duct

Common bile duct

Body

Major duodenal papilla (of Vater)

Superior mesenteric artery and vein

Head of pancreas

BECK

consequences in the various organs involved. The cause of diabetes mellitus is not known, although there is a definite genetic background. However, the pattern of inheritance is variable and difficult to predict. There is a proven interplay of genetic and environmental factors in the etiology of the disease. In adults, obesity predisposes to diabetes. Some evidence for a viral origin for juvenile diabetes also exists.

7|4

The adrenal glands

The adrenal glands are located on top of each kidney and are sometimes referred to as the "caps" of the kidneys. They are endocrine glands that provide hormones in states of acute or chronic stress. The medulla of the adrenal gland functions in a sense like a giant postganglionic neuron, responding to nervous excitation of the sympathetic nervous system. Preganglionic fibers supply the medulla and cause it to secrete epinephrine. This hormone is sometimes known as the "fight-or-flight" hormone, since it arouses the body in states of extreme emergency. The activation of the sympathetic nervous system and the secretions released from the adrenal medulla result in a flooding of the body fluids with catecholamines (mainly epinephrine and norepinephrine). These are chemicals that increase the heart rate and blood pressure, widen the pupils, increase the blood supply of the muscles, and cause the individual to react quickly to the danger that has aroused him. The stimulation of the adrenal medulla and the release of the hormones is virtually instantaneous.

The adrenal cortex, on the other hand, is an entirely different endocrine organ. It releases hormones called corticosteroids that allow long-term adaptation to chronic stress. Even in many acute stress situations, however, these hormone levels rise, but they generally are present in the body fluids much longer than catecholamines. The three major secretions of the adrenal cortex are cortisol, corticosterone, and aldosterone. The first two are considered glucocorticoids, since their major action is on glucose metabolism. Aldosterone is a mineralocorticoid, since it acts on sodium and potassium balance. Androgens are also secreted in small amounts in both males and females. The general actions of glucocorticoids are (1) implementation of anti-inflammatory reactions, (2) stimulation of gluconeogenesis and protein catabolism, (3) maintenance of blood pressure by acting synergistically with catecholamines, (4) mobilization of fatty acids from fat stores to the liver, and (5) immunological depression. Mineralocorticoids act by stimulation of sodium reabsorption and potassium and hydrogen ion secretion in the distal tubule and across other epithelial tissues as well.

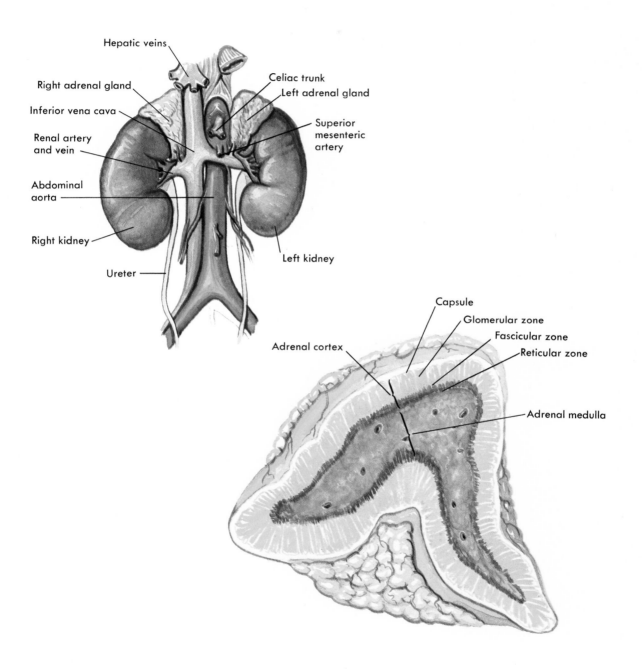

Hepatic veins

Right adrenal gland

Inferior vena cava

Renal artery and vein

Abdominal aorta

Right kidney

Ureter

Celiac trunk

Left adrenal gland

Superior mesenteric artery

Left kidney

Capsule

Glomerular zone

Fascicular zone

Reticular zone

Adrenal cortex

Adrenal medulla

8 | The respiratory system

8|1

Nasal cavity and related structures

The nasal cavity is a space lined by a mucous membrane continuous with the nasopharynx. The mucosa extends into the facial sinuses and into the middle ear via the eustachian tubes. The nature of these anatomical connections is such that an infection of the nasal cavity or nasopharynx often spreads into the sinuses, particularly the frontal sinuses, or into the middle ear cavity. Tears drain from the eye through the nasolacrimal duct into the nasal cavity. The nose and nasopharynx are the sites of our most common health problem—the common cold. Invasion of the rich, vascular mucosa by cold viruses results in inflammation, capillary enlargement, and excessive mucous secretion.

FRONTAL SECTION THROUGH THE FACE VIEWED FROM BEHIND

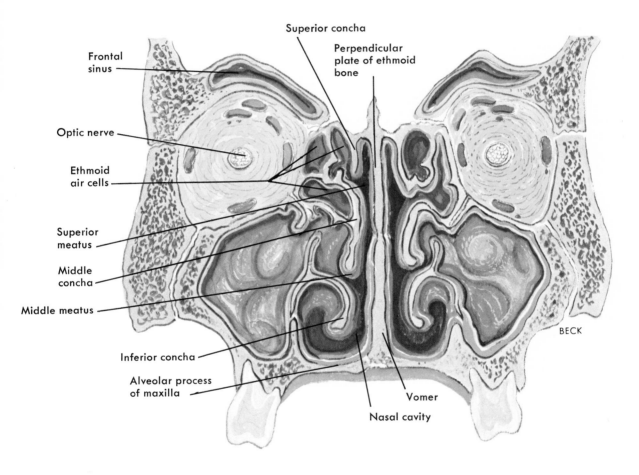

Frontal sinus

Optic nerve

Ethmoid air cells

Superior meatus

Middle concha

Middle meatus

Inferior concha

Alveolar process of maxilla

Superior concha

Perpendicular plate of ethmoid bone

BECK

Vomer

Nasal cavity

8|2

Gas exchange between air and blood

Oxygen and carbon dioxide exchange occurs across the membranes of the alveoli and capillaries. The laws of physics determine the direction of gas flow. Carbon dioxide is present at a higher pressure in the pulmonary capillary blood than in the alveolar air and therefore moves out of the blood and into the alveoli. Oxygen, on the other hand, has a pressure gradient in the opposite direction, moving into the capillary blood and eventually to the left side of the heart for distribution to the body tissues.

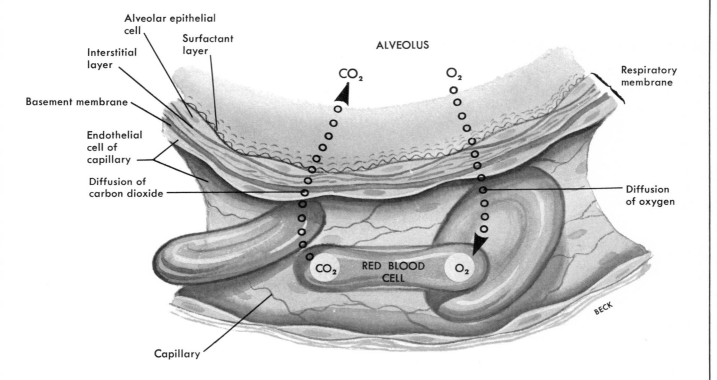

Alveolar epithelial cell

Surfactant layer

Interstitial layer

Basement membrane

Endothelial cell of capillary

Diffusion of carbon dioxide

ALVEOLUS

CO_2

O_2

Respiratory membrane

Diffusion of oxygen

CO_2 RED BLOOD CELL O_2

BECK

Capillary

8|3

Segmental anatomy of the lungs

Air is conducted to and from the lungs via the bronchial tree, which is a system of increasingly smaller tubes that culminate in alveolar sacs. The sacs are epithelium-lined outpouchings of the alveolar ducts. It is across the walls of these epithelial sacs that oxygen and carbon dioxide exchange takes place. This diagram shows the anatomical segments of the right and left lungs. There are three lobes in the right lung, two in the left. The base of the lung is that part close to the diaphragm, whereas the apex is the upper area, the top border of which is above the clavicle.

The lungs are divided into segments for descriptive purposes. Identification of pathological processes in these segments is commonly done by means of chest roentgenograms. (See also Plate 1/8.)

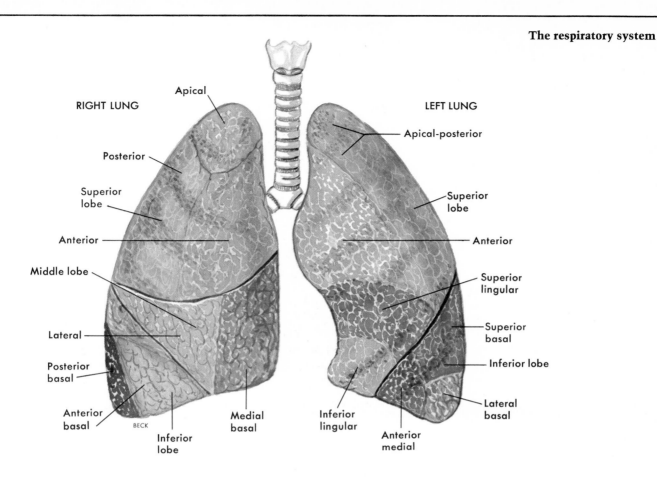

RIGHT LUNG

Apical

Posterior

Superior lobe

Anterior

Middle lobe

Lateral

Posterior basal

Anterior basal

BECK

Inferior lobe

Medial basal

LEFT LUNG

Apical-posterior

Superior lobe

Anterior

Superior lingular

Superior basal

Inferior lobe

Lateral basal

Inferior lingular

Anterior medial

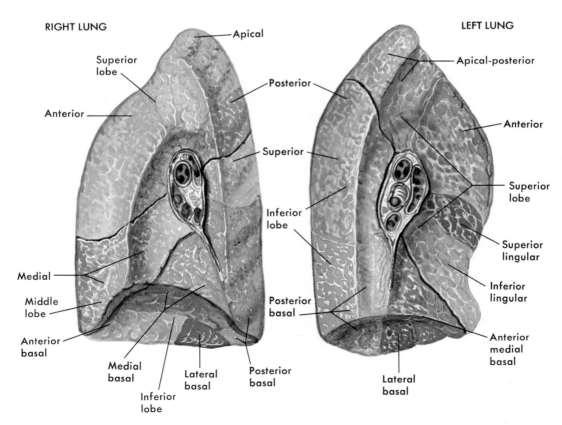

RIGHT LUNG

Superior lobe

Anterior

Medial

Middle lobe

Anterior basal

Medial basal

Inferior lobe

Apical

Posterior

Superior

Inferior lobe

Posterior basal

Lateral basal

Posterior basal

LEFT LUNG

Apical-posterior

Anterior

Superior lobe

Superior lingular

Inferior lingular

Anterior medial basal

Lateral basal

8|4

Diseases of the respiratory system

The diseases that are illustrated represent some general aspects of altered respiratory functions. When the normal respiratory tract function is disturbed, there is an increased possibility for infections to occur. Retention of mucus, decreased ciliary function, and interrupted oxygenation and nutrition of respiratory structures are causes of these respiratory diseases. If infection occurs, the pathophysiological disease process will be further perpetuated.

The trapping of air in the lung (emphysema) and the airway collapse that occur in many respiratory diseases may be explained by a phenomenon that occurs during normal respiration. During inspiration, because of the negative intrapulmonic pressure, the tubes of the respiratory tract are dilated. However, the opposite happens during expiration, and it becomes difficult to expel the air through the narrow tubes if the airways are edematous, inflamed, or filled with obstructing mucus. When air moves through such narrowed passages, it is common to hear a whistling sound, or "wheeze," which in asthma may be heard through a stethoscope.

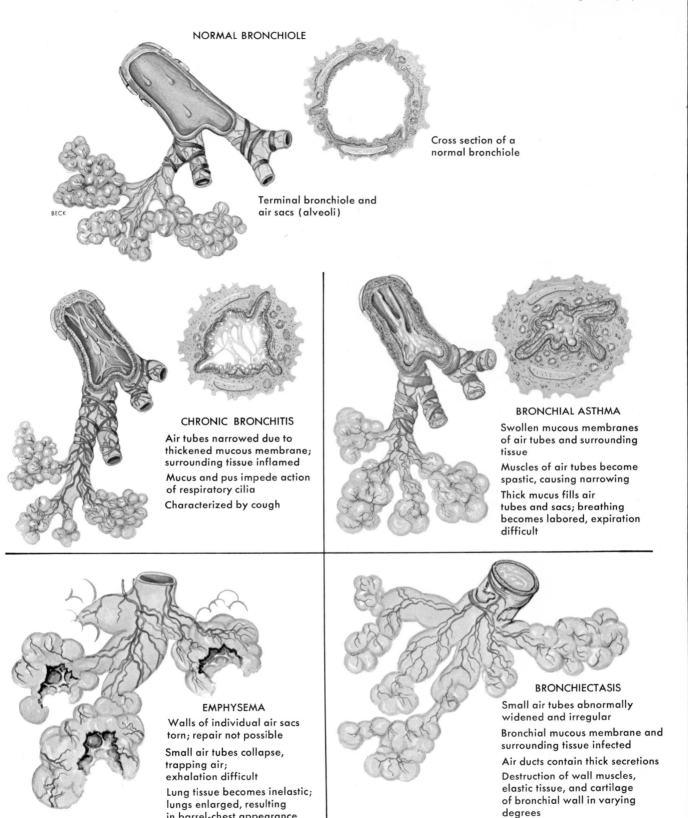

NORMAL BRONCHIOLE

Cross section of a
normal bronchiole

Terminal bronchiole and
air sacs (alveoli)

BECK

CHRONIC BRONCHITIS

Air tubes narrowed due to
thickened mucous membrane;
surrounding tissue inflamed

Mucus and pus impede action
of respiratory cilia

Characterized by cough

BRONCHIAL ASTHMA

Swollen mucous membranes
of air tubes and surrounding
tissue

Muscles of air tubes become
spastic, causing narrowing

Thick mucus fills air
tubes and sacs; breathing
becomes labored, expiration
difficult

EMPHYSEMA

Walls of individual air sacs
torn; repair not possible

Small air tubes collapse,
trapping air;
exhalation difficult

Lung tissue becomes inelastic;
lungs enlarged, resulting
in barrel-chest appearance

BRONCHIECTASIS

Small air tubes abnormally
widened and irregular

Bronchial mucous membrane and
surrounding tissue infected

Air ducts contain thick secretions

Destruction of wall muscles,
elastic tissue, and cartilage
of bronchial wall in varying
degrees

161

8|5

Cystic fibrosis

Cystic fibrosis is a genetic disorder that is transmitted in an autosomal, recessive manner and is carried by one in every 20 persons in the United States. This is a devastating disease of unknown etiology. The exocrine glands appear to be primarily involved; their secretions are extremely thick and viscous and tend to obstruct the ducts. The pathological results are numerous. The secretions of the exocrine glands are unable to exert their physiological effect, as evidenced by the digestive disturbances seen in cystic fibrosis. Since the exocrine ducts of the pancreas become obstructed, the digestive enzymes of the pancreas cannot reach their usual site of action, the small intestine. Malabsorption and malnutrition result, and the stools are characteristically bulky, greasy, and foul smelling. Children that are affected usually are small and thin. Eventually, the pancreas becomes scarred and nonfunctional, and enzymes are not produced at all. Enzyme tablets must be ingested with meals so that food molecules will be broken down and prepared for absorption.

Another major and usually chronic and debilitating result of the disease process is chronic obstructive lung disease. The production of very sticky, thick mucus throughout the respiratory tract leads to respiratory distress, poor peripheral tissue oxygenation, cyanosis and clubbing of the fingers, cough, and eventually development of fibrotic lung changes leading to right-sided congestive heart failure.

The plate illustrates a child with end-stage disease, which is characterized by right-sided heart failure. Venous pressure increases, causing ascites (fluid in the peritoneal cavity), enlargement of the liver and spleen, and edema.

Other organs that may become involved are the reproductive organs, salivary glands, and sweat glands. The observation by mothers of children with cystic fibrosis that their children tasted "salty" when kissed led to the

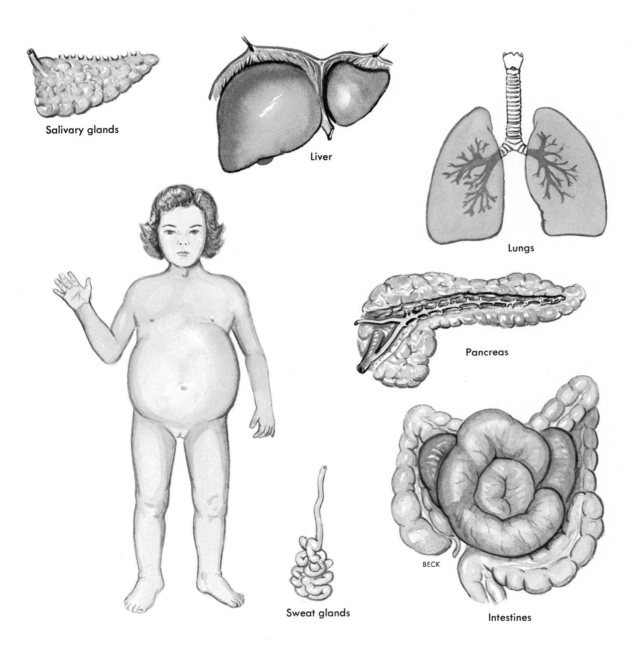

Salivary glands

Liver

Lungs

Pancreas

Sweat glands

Intestines

BECK

development of the diagnostic sweat test. There is an abnormal elevation of sweat chloride and sodium in this disease. The disease is best kept under control when diagnosis is made early in life and treatment aimed at lessening lung secretions and increasing nutritional integrity is begun. The disease is no longer universally fatal but still has a high mortality rate.

8|6

The Heimlich maneuver for dislodging aspirated foods or other foreign objects

The Heimlich maneuver is an effective intervention for use in people whose airways have become suddenly obstructed. Usually this occurs during eating, but chewing gum or balloons may be aspirated, especially in children, and produce obstruction as well. It is imperative that choking be recognized and differentiated from the other common cause of cyanosis and loss of consciousness, heart attack. The key question to ask a person who appears to be choking is "Can you talk?" The person suffering an acute airway obstruction will not be able to speak even while conscious. A universal sign for choking, the hand held to the throat, may lend further evidence. Usually the choking attack takes place during a meal. The Heimlich maneuver uses residual air in the lungs to expel the object obstructing the trachea. The thrusting upward of the rescuer's hands creates an enormous increase in intrathoracic pressure. The average expiratory air flow rises from 52.5 liters per minute to 205 liters per minute when the maneuver is performed. This creates positive pressure below the obstruction, which usually is sufficient to expel the object, even if considerable force is needed.

The Heimlich maneuver has saved thousands of lives and can be performed by children as well as adults; it has also been used as a self-saving maneuver by choking individuals.

Technique if victim can be lifted
1 Rescuer stands behind the victim and wraps his arms around the victim's chest slightly below the rib cage and above the navel. Victim is allowed to fall forward with his head, arms, and chest over the rescuer's arms.
2 Rescuer makes a fist with one hand and grasps it with the other hand, pressing thumb side of fist against victim's abdomen just below the end of the xiphoid process and above the navel.
3 The hands only are used to deliver the upward subdiaphragmatic thrusts. It is performed with sharp flexion of the elbows, in an upward rather than inward direction, and is usually repeated four times. It is very important *not* to compress the rib cage or actually press on the sternum during the Heimlich maneuver.

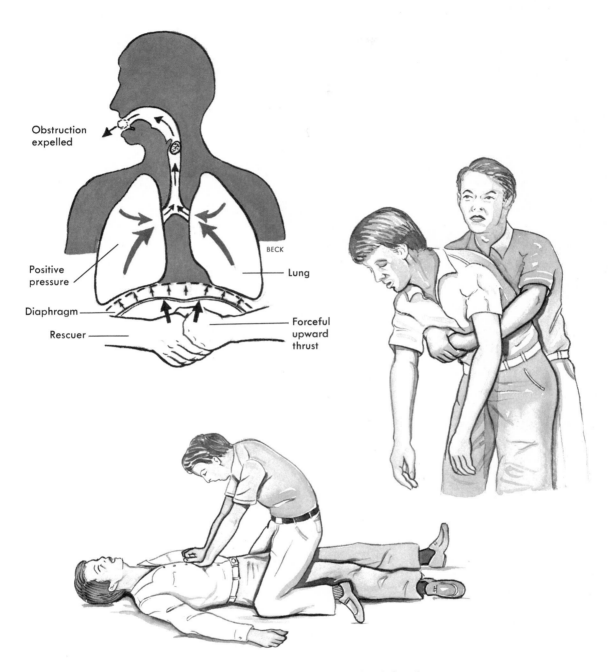

Obstruction expelled

Positive pressure

Diaphragm

Rescuer

BECK

Lung

Forceful upward thrust

Technique if victim has collapsed or cannot be lifted

1 Rescuer places victim on floor face up.
2 Facing victim, rescuer straddles the hips.
3 Rescuer places one of his hands on top of the other, with the bottom hand on the victim's abdomen slightly above the navel and below the rib cage.
4 Rescuer performs a forceful upward thrust with the heel of the bottom hand, repeating several times if necessary.

9 | The circulatory system

9│1

Principal arteries and veins

The circulatory system is a closed system of vessels that functions to provide a transport route for nutrients, gases, hormones, biochemical mediator molecules of all types, protein waste products, blood cells, and many other components of the blood. The heart serves as a double pump system, pumping deoxygenated, venous blood (blue vessels) into the capillaries of the lungs, across which oxygen and carbon dioxide freely move. The blood entering the right side of the heart comes from the veins, which carry deoxygenated blood from all the tissues of the body. Once the blood is oxygenated in the lungs, it returns to the left side of the heart, which pumps it out into the arteries (red vessels). This blood supplies oxygen to all the tissues of the body by entering the thin capillaries that eventually branch from arterial vessels. Oxygen can move out of the arterial blood across the capillary membrane, and carbon dioxide moves in (see Plate 8/2). As oxygen leaves the arterial blood, the bright red color (caused by the presence of oxyhemoglobin) disappears and the blood becomes darker and bluish and is then venous (deoxygenated) blood.

This blood leaves the capillary vessels and enters the veins, eventually to return to the right side of the heart and the lungs. The carbon dioxide it has picked up in the body's tissues will be expelled into the respiratory tract air, and new oxygen will be picked up. It is an important observation that this entire circulatory system is closed and that under normal conditions the blood itself never leaves the vessels.

(See pp. 168 and 169 for plate and names of vessels.)

Principal arteries
1 Angular
2 Anterior tibial
3 Aorta
4 Arcuate
5 Axillary
6 Brachial
7 Celiac
8 Common carotid, left
9 Common carotid, right
10 Common iliac, right
11 Coronary, left
12 Deep femoral
13 Deep medial
circumflex femoral
14 Digital
15 Dorsal metatarsal
16 Dorsalis pedis
17 External carotid
18 External iliac
19 Femoral
20 Hepatic
21 Metacarpal
22 Inferior mesenteric
23 Internal iliac
(hypogastric)
24 Palmar arch, deep
25 Palmar arch, superficial
26 Peroneal
27 Popliteal
28 Posterior tibial
29 Pulmonary
30 Radial
31 Renal
32 Splenic
33 Subclavian, left (cut)
34 Subclavian, right
35 Superficial temporal
36 Superior mesenteric
37 Ulnar

Principal veins
1 Anterior tibial
2 Axillary
3 Basilic
4 Brachial
5 Cephalic
6 Cervical plexus
7 Colic
8 Common iliac, left
9 Digital
10 Dorsal venous arch
11 External jugular
12 Femoral
13 Great saphenous
14 Hepatic
15 Inferior mesenteric
16 Inferior sagittal
sinus
17 Inferior vena cava
18 Brachiocephalic, left
19 Internal jugular, left
20 Internal jugular, right
21 Lateral thoracic
22 Median cubital
23 Peroneal
24 Popliteal
25 Portal
26 Posterior tibial
27 Pulmonary
28 Subclavian, left
29 Superior mesenteric
30 Superior sagittal sinus
31 Superior vena cava

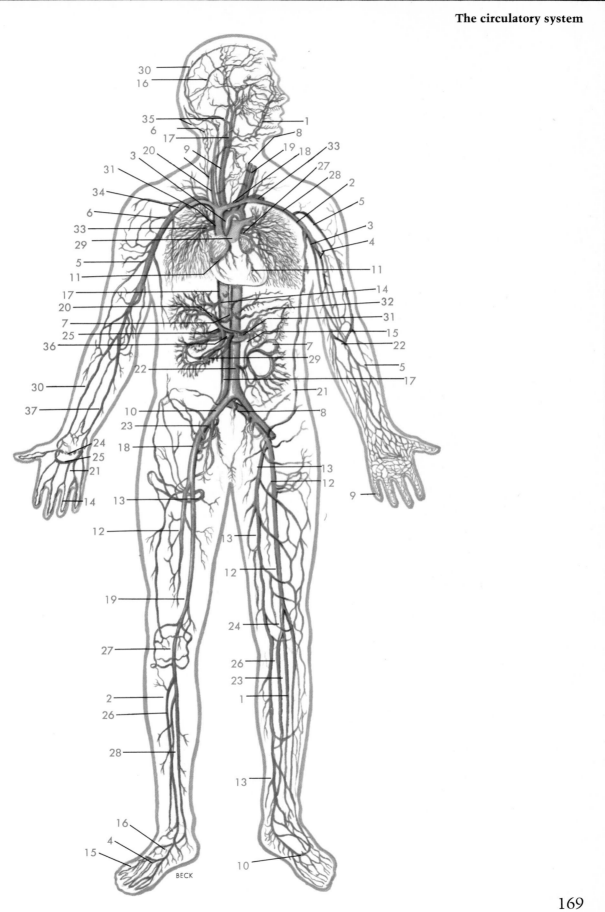

BECK

9|2

Structure of blood vessels

The microstructure of the arteries and veins is quite different. Arteries are more muscular and have thicker walls than veins. Veins are much more distensible and have valves that prevent backflow of venous blood. These anatomical differences reflect the differences in functions. Arteries must pump the blood forward and store the energy of the systolic ejection of the heart so that blood continues to flow into the arterioles after the heart's systole is finished. Veins are known as "capacitance" vessels and can hold and store large amounts of blood because of their ability to stretch. This extra volume of blood can be made available, when the body requires it, through venoconstriction by the sympathetic nervous system. This forces the vessels closed, and the blood is pushed forward. Blood moves through the veins normally through the action of skeletal muscle contraction, which produces external pressure on the walls of the vein, forcing blood forward. An additional factor is the action of respiration, which creates a pressure gradient from abdomen to thorax, so that blood in the great veins moves toward the heart.

The structure of the arterioles, capillaries, and venules is illustrated. Precapillary sphincters and the smooth muscle in the walls of the arterioles are under the control of the autonomic nervous system, with sympathetic regulation predominating. The capillaries themselves are not under nervous control but open or close depending on the state of constriction of the arterioles supplying them. The capillaries are composed of endothelium that is only one cell layer thick. It is here that gas exchange with the tissues and filtration and diffusion of fluid and nutrients from the blood into the interstitial fluid takes place. The blood flows through the vascular system from arteries to veins and through millions of capillary beds, with a gradual loss of pressure from a mean arterial pressure of 100 mm Hg to a mean central venous pressure ranging from 0 to 6 mm Hg.

MUSCULAR ARTERY

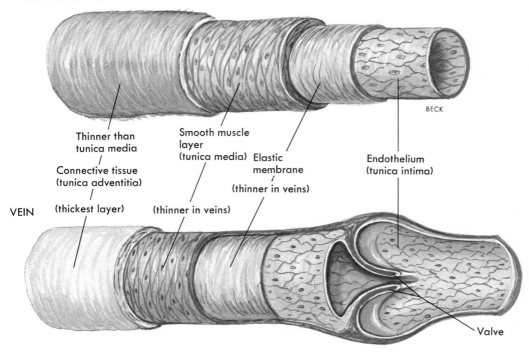

BECK

Thinner than
tunica media

Connective tissue
(tunica adventitia)

(thickest layer)

Smooth muscle
layer
(tunica media)

(thinner in veins)

Elastic
membrane

(thinner in veins)

Endothelium
(tunica intima)

VEIN

Valve

VALVE FUNCTION

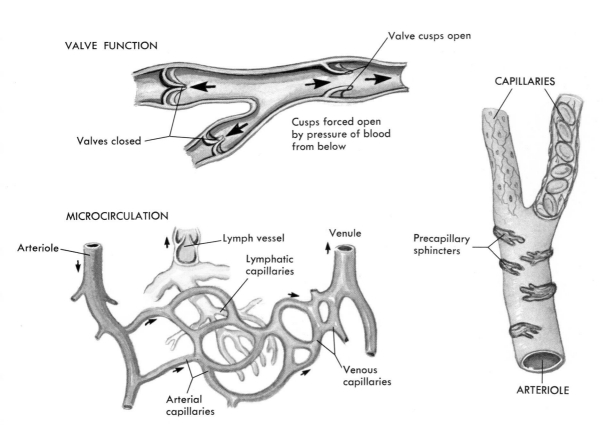

Valve cusps open

Valves closed

Cusps forced open
by pressure of blood
from below

CAPILLARIES

Precapillary
sphincters

MICROCIRCULATION

Arteriole

Lymph vessel

Lymphatic
capillaries

Venule

Arterial
capillaries

Venous
capillaries

ARTERIOLE

171

9|3

Blood flow through the heart

The pathway of blood through the heart is simple to remember if the heart is regarded as two pumps: a right pump providing blood to the lungs and a left pump pushing blood out into the systemic circulation. Of course, both pumps are operating at the same time, pushing out the same volume of blood (5 liters per minute).

Deoxygenated blood enters from the vena cavae, which drain all of the venous blood from the body into the right atrium. This blood then fills the right ventricle, where it is pumped out into the low-pressure, low-resistance pulmonary artery. This vessel has a confusing name, since it is the only artery in the body that carries deoxygenated blood. The pulmonary artery branches into right and left subdivisions that eventually subdivide into pulmonary arterioles and then capillaries. It is across the walls of these pulmonary capillaries that gas exchange takes place, with carbon dioxide moving out into the lung alveoli and oxygen moving into the blood. This oxygenated blood moves into the pulmonary venules and then to pulmonary veins that empty the blood into the left atrium. The blood fills the left ventricle, moving through the mitral valve, and is pumped out into the aorta during systolic contraction of the heart. The left side of the heart pumps against a very high-pressure, high-resistance vascular bed. Therefore, the muscular walls of the left ventricle are much thicker because of the larger amount of work required to pump the blood.

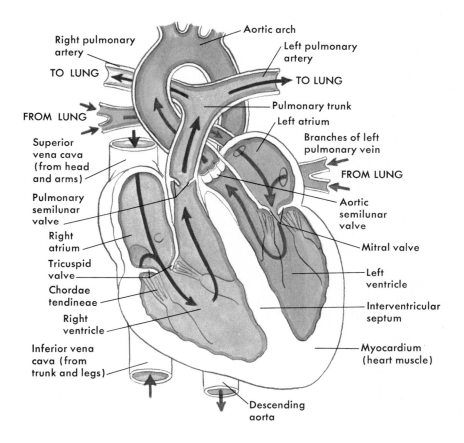

Aortic arch

Right pulmonary artery

Left pulmonary artery

TO LUNG

TO LUNG

Pulmonary trunk

FROM LUNG

Left atrium

Superior vena cava (from head and arms)

Branches of left pulmonary vein

FROM LUNG

Pulmonary semilunar valve

Aortic semilunar valve

Right atrium

Mitral valve

Tricuspid valve

Left ventricle

Chordae tendineae

Interventricular septum

Right ventricle

Myocardium (heart muscle)

Inferior vena cava (from trunk and legs)

Descending aorta

9|4

Circulatory system of the fetus

The fetal circulation is designed to bypass the fetal lungs and to provide oxygen and nutrition to the fetus from the maternal blood. The two umbilical arteries branch from the internal iliac arteries and carry blood to the placenta. The umbilical vein carries blood from the placenta and is connected to the inferior vena cava by a vessel known as the ductus venosus. Most of the blood enters the circulation through this route. The rest of the blood is carried to the liver, emptying into the hepatic vein.

Shunting of the blood away from the lungs is accomplished through the foramen ovale into the left side of the heart and from the pulmonary artery directly into the aorta via the ductus arteriosus. During fetal life both arteries and veins carry mixed blood, rather than purely arterial or purely venous blood.

At birth most of the fetal circulatory structure becomes nonfunctional. When the umbilicus is tied off and separated from the placenta, the ductus venosus closes, as does the foramen ovale and ductus arteriosus. Occasionally, a child will have a patent foramen ovale or ductus arteriosus because of incomplete closure after birth. Serious heart disease is a possibility if such defects are large and are not surgically repaired.

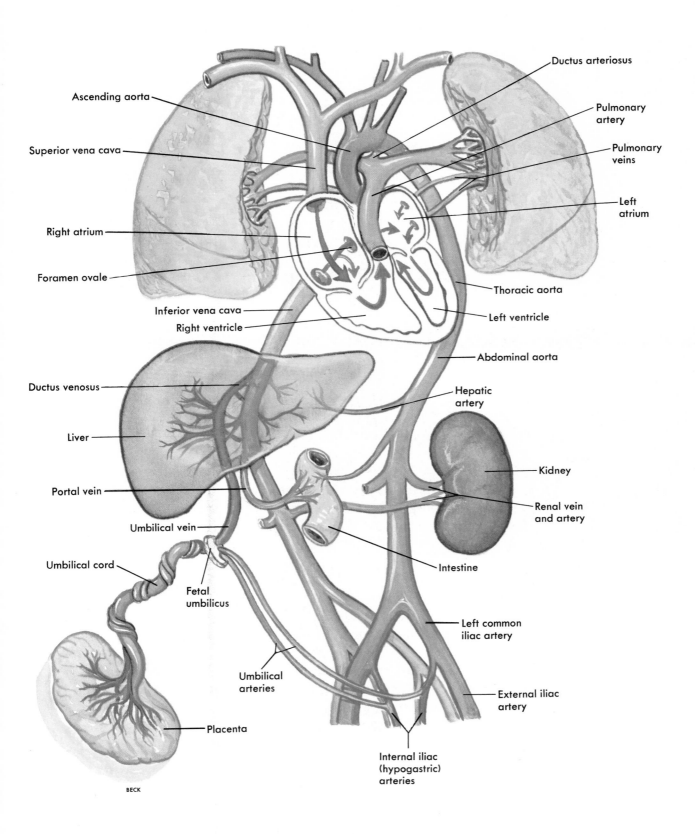

Ascending aorta

Superior vena cava

Right atrium

Foramen ovale

Inferior vena cava

Right ventricle

Ductus venosus

Liver

Portal vein

Umbilical vein

Umbilical cord

Fetal umbilicus

Umbilical arteries

Placenta

BECK

Ductus arteriosus

Pulmonary artery

Pulmonary veins

Left atrium

Thoracic aorta

Left ventricle

Abdominal aorta

Hepatic artery

Kidney

Renal vein and artery

Intestine

Left common iliac artery

External iliac artery

Internal iliac (hypogastric) arteries

9|5

Congenital heart defects—patent ductus arteriosus; coarctation of the aorta; atrial and ventricular septal defects

Patent ductus arteriosus. The ductus arteriosus, a short fetal blood vessel connecting the aorta and pulmonary artery, normally closes within 10 to 15 hours after birth. If it fails to close (about one infant in 4000), oxygenated blood in the aorta begins to seep back into the pulmonary artery through the open ductus and thus a wasteful recirculation of oxygenated blood proceeds to the lungs. The heart begins to pump hard as the rest of the body is deprived of essential oxygen. Surgery involves closing the open ductus by severing the vessel and sewing the ends tightly shut.

Coarctation of the aorta. A narrowing or constriction (coarctation) of the aorta usually occurs near the distal end of the aortic arch. Its seriousness depends on the severity of the narrowing and whether or not the left ventricle is underdeveloped. The condition is not characterized by cyanosis. It causes pathophysiological changes resulting from the production of high blood pressure above the coarctation and low pressure below it. Hypertensive heart failure and strokes may possibly develop. Correcting coarctation involves cutting out the constricted portion and sewing the aorta back together again. If the affected segment is long, a synthetic graft may be inserted or used as a bypass.

Atrial septal defect. A defect in the septum separating the right and left atria is not considered as serious as a hole in the septum separating the ventricles. A fetal opening, the foramen ovale, gradually closes during the first months of life. If it remains open, a small, sometimes asymptomatic defect is present. A true atrial septal defect is large, and considerable right-to-left shunting occurs, leading to congestive heart failure or pulmonary hypertension. Small defects apparently are well tolerated and are not incompatible with long life. The larger defects are likely to lead to congestive heart failure or pulmonary hypertension. Operative repair is accomplished by insertion of a prosthetic patch or by direct closure.

PATENT DUCTUS ARTERIOSUS

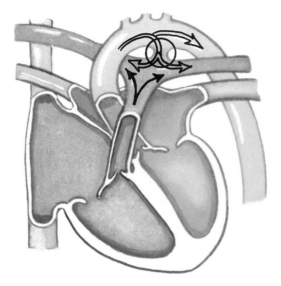

COARCTATION OF AORTA

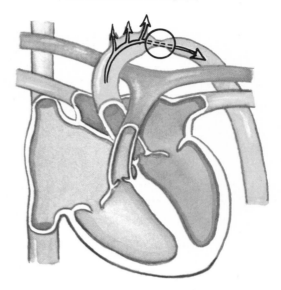

ATRIAL SEPTAL DEFECT

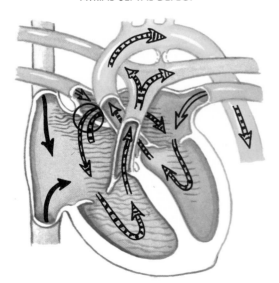

VENTRICULAR SEPTAL DEFECT

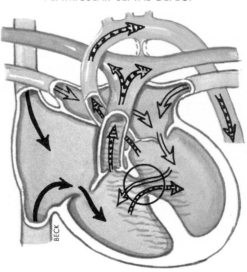

Ventricular septal defect. A hole in the septum between ventricles allows oxygenated and unoxygenated blood to mix. Symptoms vary and are related to the size of the defect, the volume of blood shunted through it, and the extent of elevation in pressure in the right ventricle and of the pulmonary circulation. A heart with this defect frequently has a small aorta, an enlarged left atrium and left ventricle, and a pulmonary artery that is larger than normal. The only treatment is surgical closure of the defect.

9|6

Congenital heart defects—tricuspid atresia; transposition of great vessels; valvular stenosis; tetralogy of Fallot

Tricuspid atresia. Blood cannot flow from the right atrium into the right ventricle because there is no opening in the tricuspid valve. Deoxygenated blood mixes with oxygenated blood in the left atrium if an atrial septal defect is present and is pumped through the heart and out to the lungs and rest of the body. The condition usually is associated with openings in the atrial and ventricular septa. Only palliative surgery is attempted in this severe condition. A connection between the superior vena cava and the right pulmonary artery may be made in infants 6 months of age or older.

Transposition of great vessels. The great vessels of the heart (aorta and pulmonary artery) exit from the opposite ventricles. Oxygenated blood from the lungs is pumped right back to the lungs. Deoxygenated blood is pumped out again to the systemic circulation. Survival is possible only if a septal defect exists or if there is a patent ductus arteriosus. This condition was universally fatal until recently. Surgical techniques have been devised that permit correction. The most popular operation is the Mustard procedure, which causes diversion of cardiac flow in the proper directions.

Valvular stenosis. This illustration shows a top view of the heart below the atria, revealing the two major blood vessels and the atrioventricular valves. When valve flaps become stiff or stuck and the opening and closing function is impaired, blood flow is decreased or shut off. For example (inset drawing), in pulmonic stenosis the three cusps of the valve are fused and blood cannot flow from the right ventricle through the pulmonary artery into the lungs.

Tetralogy of Fallot. In this condition there are four abnormalities in the heart: (1) ventricular septal defect (VSD), (2) overriding aorta, (3) pulmonic stenosis, and (4) enlarged right ventricle. Deoxygenated blood flows from the right side to the left side of the heart (right-to-left shunt) without being oxygenated through the lungs. The degree of right-to-left shunt depends

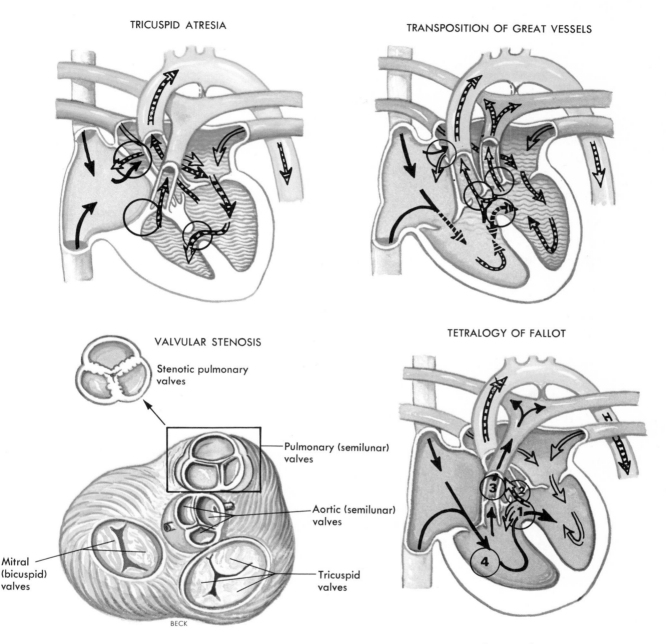

TRICUSPID ATRESIA

TRANSPOSITION OF GREAT VESSELS

VALVULAR STENOSIS

Stenotic pulmonary valves

Pulmonary (semilunar) valves

Aortic (semilunar) valves

Mitral (bicuspid) valves

Tricuspid valves

TETRALOGY OF FALLOT

BECK

on the size of the VSD and the degree of pulmonic stenosis. When pulmonary blood flow is decreased, bronchial arteries and other routes of collateral circulation are enlarged throughout the mediastinum and the chest wall. This creates a characteristic notching of the ribs on x-ray film. Cyanosis is characteristic, as are hypoxic spells, poor growth, and frequent infections. The Blalock-Taussig operation ("blue-baby operation") was previously used to increase pulmonary blood flow and consisted of joining the subclavian artery to the pulmonary artery. Now, open heart surgery is frequently performed to correct the defects in very young children.

Conduction system of the heart; the electrocardiogram

Flow of blood from the heart is produced by contraction of the ventricles. However, these muscular contractions require electrical stimulation, which is transmitted through the specialized conduction system of the heart. The impulse begins in the pacemaker, the sinoatrial (SA) node located in the right atrium at the point where the superior vena cava enters the heart. The wave of excitation spreads from the SA node throughout the right and left atria at a speed of 1 meter per second, as well as down a specialized tract of fibers that transmit the impulse to the atrioventricular (AV) node. From here the impulse is sent to the ventricles after a delay of 0.12 to 0.20 seconds that occurs through the AV node. This delay allows adequate time for filling of the ventricles from the atria, before ventricular contraction takes place. From the AV node the bundle of His transmits the message through the ventricles. The bundle bifurcates into right and left bundle branches. These specialized pathways subdivide into smaller fibers known as Purkinje's fibers, which supply the subendocardial surface of the heart. The spread of excitation through the ventricles from the AV nodes is extremely rapid, moving at 1 to 4 meters ($3^3/_{10}$ to $13^2/_{10}$ feet) per second.

Abnormalities in conduction can occur at any point along this pathway. For example, there may be abnormal rhythmicity at the SA node resulting from structural or functional disruption. The rate may be too slow to pace the heart adequately. There may be damage to the atria or ventricles, such as the result of ischemia during a myocardial infarction. This will leave a scar, and the impulse will skirt around this area, causing a delay in conduction, which may be apparent on the electrocardiogram (ECG). Characteristic changes on the ECG can be observed with a block in the left or right bundle branch. AV blocks in impulse propagation are another common site. There may be a greater delay in the impulse through the AV node, or the impulse may actually be completely blocked at the AV node.

The electrocardiogram (ECG) is a tracing of electrical cardiac events transmitted to the external surfaces of the body and recorded by deflections

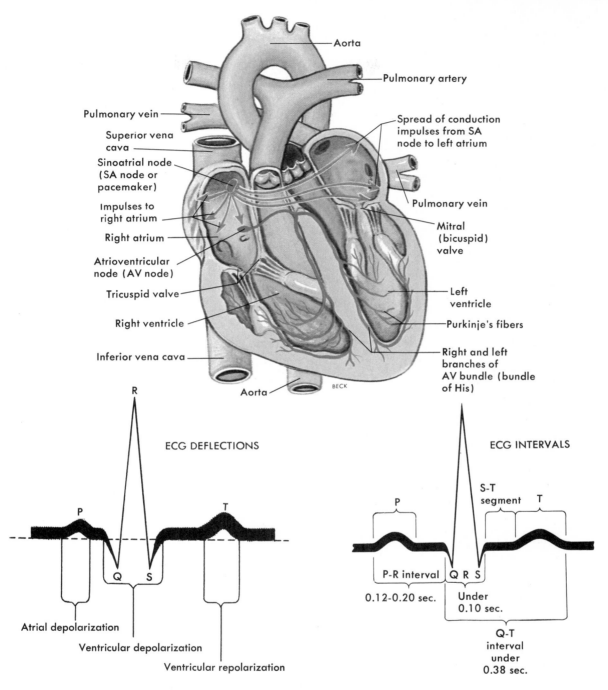

Aorta

Pulmonary artery

Pulmonary vein

Superior vena cava

Sinoatrial node (SA node or pacemaker)

Impulses to right atrium

Right atrium

Atrioventricular node (AV node)

Tricuspid valve

Right ventricle

Inferior vena cava

Aorta

BECK

Spread of conduction impulses from SA node to left atrium

Pulmonary vein

Mitral (bicuspid) valve

Left ventricle

Purkinje's fibers

Right and left branches of AV bundle (bundle of His)

ECG DEFLECTIONS

R

P

T

Q

S

Atrial depolarization

Ventricular depolarization

Ventricular repolarization

ECG INTERVALS

R

P

S-T segment

T

P-R interval

0.12-0.20 sec.

Q R S

Under 0.10 sec.

Q-T interval under 0.38 sec.

of a needle. The main parts of the ECG reflect the depolarizations and repolarizations of cardiac muscle. The P wave, for example, is the electrical depolarization of the entire atria. The wave of excitation travels from the atria to the ventricles causing the next deflection, ventricular depolarization. This is followed by ventricular recovery or repolarization. The heights of the waveforms produced and their timing can tell much about general cardiac health. Illustrated are the normal ECG deflections and principal ECG intervals.

9|8

Coronary circulation of the heart

The right and left coronary arteries originate from the base of the ascending aorta at a site where the aorta dilates as a result of the cusps of the aortic valve. The main portion of the left coronary artery is only about 2.5 cm (1 inch) long, dividing into a circumflex and an anterior interventricular branch. At its origin it is behind the pulmonary artery, shown sectioned in the first illustration. The circumflex branch follows the atrioventricular groove to the posterior of the heart, where it supplies the wall of the left ventricle. The anterior interventricular branch of the left coronary artery follows the interventricular sulcus on the anterior of the heart and supplies the myocardium of both ventricles. The right coronary artery follows the atrioventricular groove, its branches going to the right ventricle with a large marginal branch to the lower border of the right ventricle, and turns posteriorly to continue as the posterior interventricular artery. Veins accompany branches of the coronary arteries.

The great cardiac vein ascending in the anterior interventricular sulcus can be seen in the posterior aspect of the heart; it turns posteriorly to the back of the heart to become the coronary sinus. The middle cardiac vein is located in the posterior interventricular sulcus. It empties into the middle of the coronary sinus. All venous coronary blood empties into the right atrium, mostly by way of the coronary sinus. The right coronary artery usually is larger than the left but incidence of heart attack is higher in those individuals with a left coronary artery predominance.

What happens in a heart attack?
When the blood supply to the heart muscle (myocardium) is diminished or blocked, that portion of the muscle cannot contract adequately in response to the wave of electrochemical excitation that causes the heart to beat. The area of ischemic damage can cause the heart to develop abnormal rhythms and even to completely fail in its ability to pump blood. Eventually, the

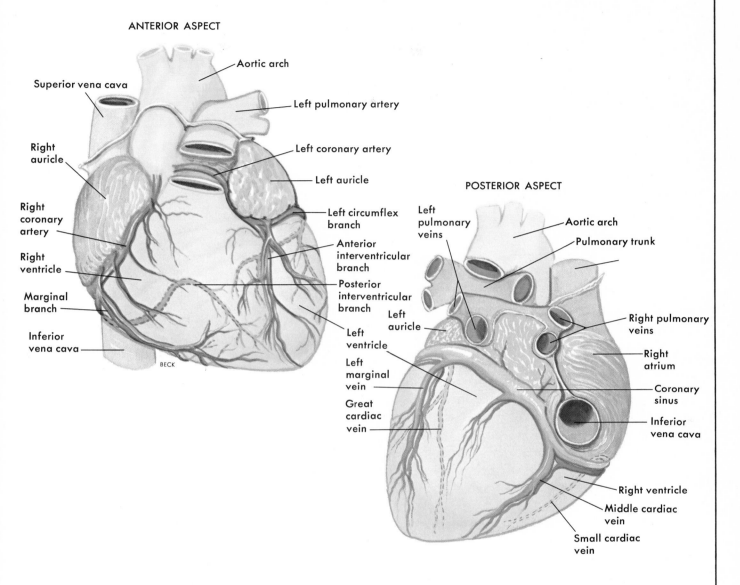

ANTERIOR ASPECT

Aortic arch

Superior vena cava

Left pulmonary artery

Left coronary artery

Right auricle

Left auricle

POSTERIOR ASPECT

Right coronary artery

Left circumflex branch

Left pulmonary veins

Aortic arch

Right ventricle

Anterior interventricular branch

Pulmonary trunk

Marginal branch

Posterior interventricular branch

Right pulmonary veins

Inferior vena cava

Left auricle

Right atrium

Left ventricle

Coronary sinus

Left marginal vein

Inferior vena cava

Great cardiac vein

Right ventricle

Middle cardiac vein

Small cardiac vein

BECK

affected area is replaced with scar tissue. Depending on the extent of damage, healing may require several months, but the scar shrinks greatly and the myocardium can recover normal function.

The so-called heart attack caused by coronary artery disease may result from any of the following conditions: (1) a hemorrhage into the walls of the coronary artery, causing the inner lining of the vessel to swell, thus preventing blood from flowing through it; (2) the interior of a segment of the vessel becoming blocked by the buildup of an atherosclerotic plaque; (3) the development of a clot (thrombus) that sticks to the inside of the vessel; or (4) the coronary artery going into spasm.

9|9

External cardiac compression

External cardiac compression is a method of mechanically causing the heart to contract and pump blood when it is arrested (the normal heartbeat has ceased). This technique should be learned through formal training, as it may be improperly or inadequately performed by an untrained rescuer.

The technique requires that proper identification of cardiac arrest be made before external cardiac compression is performed. The victim is placed supine on a hard surface and the hands are applied to a point measured two fingerwidths above the xiphoid process. The heel of one hand is placed over the lower half of the sternum above the xiphoid, and the other hand is placed over the first. Pressure exerted by the heel of the hand must push the sternum almost vertically downward about 5 cm (2 inches). Notice the relaxation and compression positions. During compression the blood is squeezed out of the heart; while the hands are relaxed, the heart fills with blood. The length of the relaxation and compression periods should be the same, and the number of compressions in the adult should be 60 per minute. The adequacy of the heart output during external cardiac compression can be checked by feeling the carotid pulse. Of course, artificial respiration is required along with cardiac compressions in order to maintain oxygenation of the blood.

The technique in infants and children is similar, except that less pressure is exerted so that the chest is not depressed more than 1.2 to 1.8 cm (½ to ¾ inch) in an infant and no more than 3.7 cm (1½ inches) in a child. For an infant, the tips of the middle and index fingers are used, and the number of compressions should be 80 to 100 per minute.

To reemphasize, cardiopulmonary resuscitation must be learned properly through a training program. The pictorial representation and text provided are not meant to substitute for such a program.

EXTERNAL CARDIAC COMPRESSION

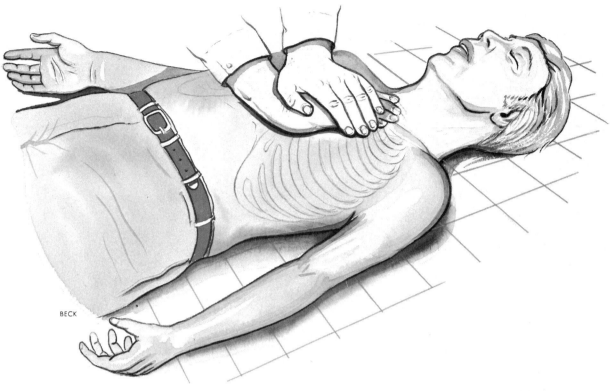

BECK

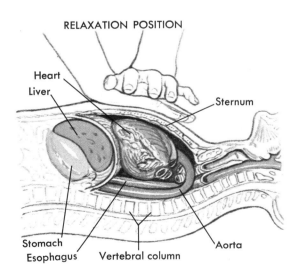

RELAXATION POSITION

Heart
Liver
Sternum
Stomach
Esophagus
Vertebral column
Aorta

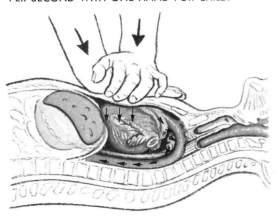

COMPRESSION POSITION (AT LEAST ONE
COMPRESSION PER SECOND FOR ADULT, TWO
PER SECOND WITH ONE HAND FOR CHILD)

9|10

Subdivisions of the mediastinum

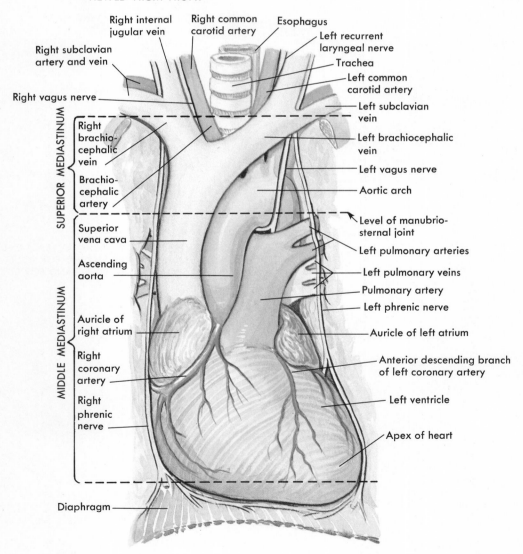

CONTENTS OF SUPERIOR AND MIDDLE MEDIASTINUM
VIEWED FROM FRONT

Right internal jugular vein
Right common carotid artery
Esophagus
Left recurrent laryngeal nerve
Right subclavian artery and vein
Trachea
Left common carotid artery
Right vagus nerve
Left subclavian vein
SUPERIOR MEDIASTINUM
Right brachio-cephalic vein
Left brachiocephalic vein
Left vagus nerve
Brachio-cephalic artery
Aortic arch
Level of manubrio-sternal joint
Superior vena cava
Left pulmonary arteries
Ascending aorta
Left pulmonary veins
Pulmonary artery
Left phrenic nerve
MIDDLE MEDIASTINUM
Auricle of right atrium
Auricle of left atrium
Right coronary artery
Anterior descending branch of left coronary artery
Left ventricle
Right phrenic nerve
Apex of heart
Diaphragm

186

The mediastinum is made up of thoracic structures located between the right and left pleural sacs. Contained within it are the heart and great vessels, the esophagus, the thymus and thyroid glands, the trachea and branching bronchi, and many nerves, arteries, veins, and lymphatic vessels. The mediastinum is commonly subdivided into a superior portion above a horizontal plane that passes through the top of the heart, an anterior portion between the sternum and the heart, a middle portion that consists of the heart and its pericardium, and a posterior portion between the heart and the bodies of the thoracic vertebrae.

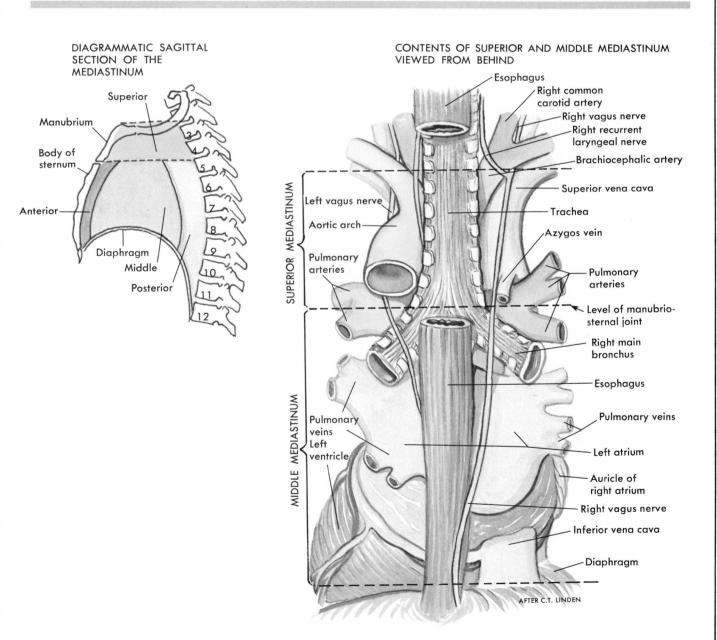

DIAGRAMMATIC SAGITTAL SECTION OF THE MEDIASTINUM

Superior
Manubrium
Body of sternum
Anterior
Diaphragm
Middle
Posterior

3
4
5
6
7
8
9
10
11
12

CONTENTS OF SUPERIOR AND MIDDLE MEDIASTINUM VIEWED FROM BEHIND

Esophagus
Right common carotid artery
Right vagus nerve
Right recurrent laryngeal nerve
Brachiocephalic artery
Superior vena cava
Trachea
Azygos vein
Pulmonary arteries
Level of manubrio-sternal joint
Right main bronchus
Esophagus
Pulmonary veins
Left atrium
Auricle of right atrium
Right vagus nerve
Inferior vena cava
Diaphragm

Left vagus nerve
Aortic arch
Pulmonary arteries

Pulmonary veins
Left ventricle

SUPERIOR MEDIASTINUM

MIDDLE MEDIASTINUM

AFTER C.T. LINDEN

187

9|11

Arterial aneurysm in brain as cause of CVA (stroke); vascular disease processes associated with hypertension

Cerebral vascular accidents, also known as CVAs, apoplexy, or strokes, are the most frequent of all causes of brain damage, occurring most commonly in the elderly. There are three main causes of CVAs. (1) Blockage of an artery can result from an arteriosclerotic plaque or thrombus. (2) Hemorrhage can be brought about by a leak or rupture of an artery within the brain; this may be caused by a ruptured arterial aneurysm (dilation of thinned arterial wall) or formation of an angioma (a tumor composed of blood vessels). The underside of the brain is illustrated with an aneurysm of the anterior cerebral artery. (3) An embolus or clot can break off from a major clot elsewhere in the arterial system, usually in the heart, and travel into the brain, where it lodges in a vessel and prevents blood flow through it. Cerebral thrombosis is the most common cause of CVA.

When brain tissue is suddenly deprived of its vital oxygen supply, it may cause neurological loss ranging from a slight weakness of a few muscle groups on one side of the body to almost complete hemiplegia (paralysis) of that side of the body. Many times a major CVA is preceded by one or more transient ischemic attacks (TIAs). These are episodes of sudden weakness, loss of consciousness, confusion, and speech problems. A CVA may often be avoided by proper medical care of the patient experiencing TIAs.

Once a CVA occurs, the potential for recovery is dependent on the degree of ischemia produced and the location of the blood vessels involved. If the left cerebral hemisphere is involved, the right side of the body experiences some degree of weakness, or hemiplegia. Speech and communication usually become problems, with difficulty in either language expression or in understanding of the spoken word. Both expressive and receptive aphasia can be present. The patient with right cerebral damage will experience left-sided hemiplegia but no aphasia. The ultimate potential for recovery, however, is greater in the patient with right-sided hemiplegia.

ARTERIAL ANEURYSM

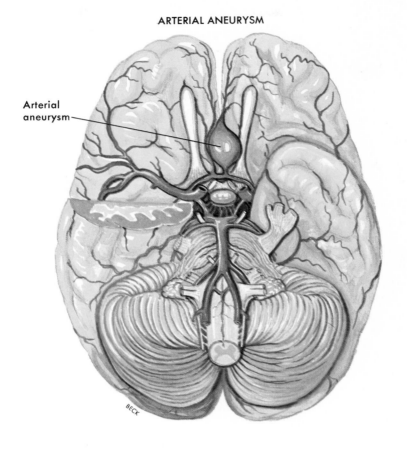

Arterial aneurysm

VASCULAR DISEASE PROCESSES

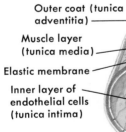

Outer coat (tunica adventitia)

Muscle layer (tunica media)

Elastic membrane

Inner layer of endothelial cells (tunica intima)

NORMAL ARTERY

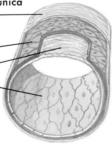

LUMEN NARROWED BECAUSE OF THICKENING OF MIDDLE LAYER

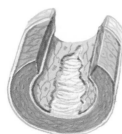

DETERIORATION OF INTIMA

RUPTURING ANEURYSM (HEMORRHAGE)

ARTERIOSCLEROTIC PLAQUE (THROMBUS)

10 | The lymphatic and reticuloendothelial system

10|1

The lymphatic system

The lymphatic system functions in close cooperation with the circulatory system. Lymph is the fluid that flows through the lymphatic vessels and eventually empties into the venous blood in the circulatory system. The right lymphatic trunk empties all of the lymph from the right upper quadrant of the body into the junction of the right subclavian and internal jugular veins. The thoracic duct drains lymph from the rest of the body into the left subclavian vein at its juncture with the left internal jugular vein. Notice the convergence of the lymphatic vessels to these main ducts. Lymph is formed from the capillary blood filtration within the tissue spaces and must continually be removed in order to recirculate fluid and protein that would otherwise be lost from the circulatory system. Lymphatic capillaries are pouchlike structures. Excess tissue fluid and protein enter these capillaries and are pushed along the lymphatic vessels by the action of surrounding skeletal muscle contraction, which results in pressure against the thin lymph vessel walls. Respiratory pressures also influence lymph flow. Lymphatics have one-way valves, like the veins, and therefore lymph flow occurs in only one direction.

Another function of the lymphatic system is body defense. Lymph nodes are located along the course of most of the larger lymphatic vessels. As the lymph moves through the lymph node, the vessels carrying the lymph drain into large sinuses lined with specialized cells. These cells are capable of recognizing and removing debris, foreign bodies, and microorganisms. Thus the lymph node filters and screens the tissue fluid before it reenters the circulatory system. The lymph nodes also produce lymphocytes, which are the "recognition" cells of the immune system.

Notice how the lymph nodes are arranged in groups. These can be palpated when enlarged, as usually occurs in infections. The major groups of lymph nodes are the submandibular, cervical, cubital, axillary, and inguinal. Infections of facial or head and neck structures cause enlargement of submandibular or cervical nodes.

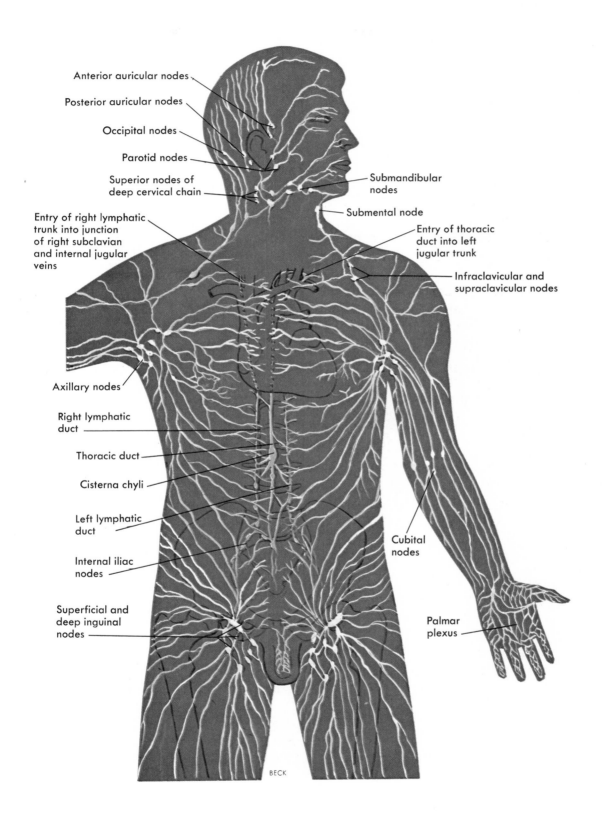

Anterior auricular nodes

Posterior auricular nodes

Occipital nodes

Parotid nodes

Superior nodes of deep cervical chain

Entry of right lymphatic trunk into junction of right subclavian and internal jugular veins

Axillary nodes

Right lymphatic duct

Thoracic duct

Cisterna chyli

Left lymphatic duct

Internal iliac nodes

Superficial and deep inguinal nodes

Submandibular nodes

Submental node

Entry of thoracic duct into left jugular trunk

Infraclavicular and supraclavicular nodes

Cubital nodes

Palmar plexus

BECK

10|2

A lymph node (diagrammatic view); lymphocytes

Afferent lymphatic vessels enter the lymph node, carrying lymph fluid that has been taken up from the tissue spaces. Within the lymph node this fluid flows slowly through sinuses that are lined with specialized phagocytic cells. These cells screen the lymph for foreign material, debris, dead cells, and microorganisms. Within the substance of the lymph node itself are germinal centers containing millions of lymphocytes. These are the major cells of the immune system and are produced in great number by the lymph nodes. The lymphoid progenitor, or stem cells, are initially produced in the bone marrow. The lymph nodes are involved in immunological defense as well, and evidence of hypertrophy (enlargement) in infections usually indicates that the lymph nodes are responding well to the foreign microorganisms.

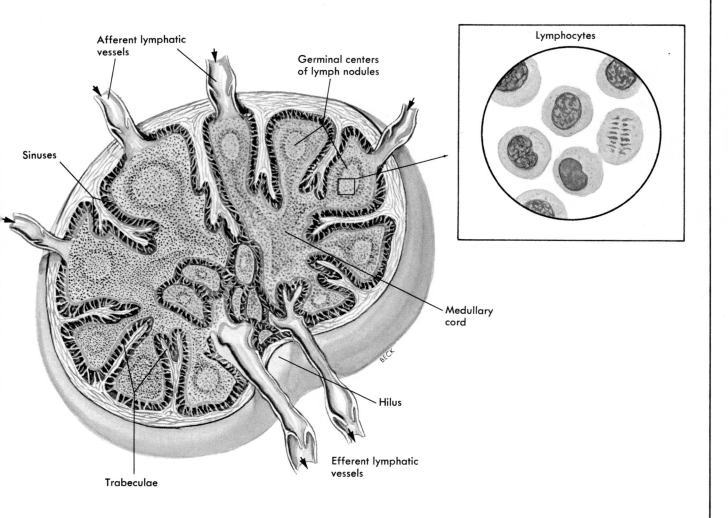

Afferent lymphatic vessels

Germinal centers of lymph nodules

Lymphocytes

Sinuses

Medullary cord

Hilus

Trabeculae

Efferent lymphatic vessels

BECK

10|3

Lymphatic drainage of the female breast

Extensive lymphatic drainage routes from the female breast are necessary for several reasons. First, the nipples provide a portal of entry for microorganisms, particularly during lactation. Thus effective defense must be provided through lymph node surveillance. Second, the glandular breast is an extremely vascular structure; when producing milk it requires an extraordinary amount of oxygenation and nutrition in order to function adequately. Lymph forms in the breast and must be drained quickly away to ensure continuous capillary filtration from the blood and, of course, milk production.

Breast cancer is the most common female cancer and causes its major damage through metastases. The cause of death in almost all malignant tumors, metastasis is the process by which single malignant cells or clusters of cells break off from the primary tumor and travel through body fluids to other sites. They set up new, secondary growths in different tissues that can then spread through metastasis even farther. Most metastatic cancer, including breast cancer, spreads via the lymphatic drainage of the tumorous tissue. The lymph nodes lining the vessels usually show evidence of response against the malignant cells, but in many cancers this defense is not adequate and tumorous growth actually occurs within the lymph nodes themselves.

One of the most important assessments to be made in diagnosing breast cancer and determining its seriousness is examination of the lymph nodes. Palpation of these nodes is part of routine breast examination. Furthermore, when a breast cancer is removed, the lymphatic drainage of the involved breast is also usually removed and examined microscopically. The number of nodes that are infiltrated with malignant cells is directly related to the prognosis for the patient with breast cancer. Lymph nodes are also removed and examined in many other types of cancer surgery.

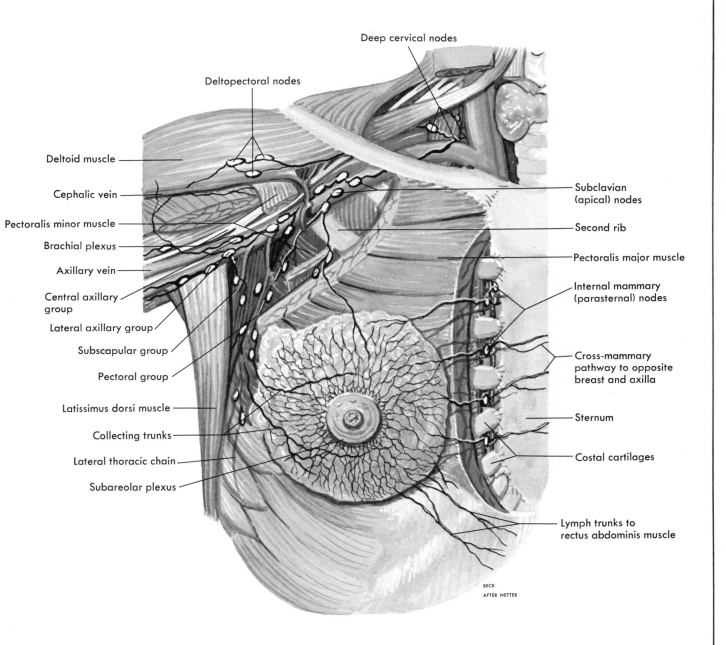

Deep cervical nodes

Deltopectoral nodes

Deltoid muscle

Cephalic vein

Pectoralis minor muscle

Brachial plexus

Axillary vein

Central axillary group

Lateral axillary group

Subscapular group

Pectoral group

Latissimus dorsi muscle

Collecting trunks

Lateral thoracic chain

Subareolar plexus

Subclavian (apical) nodes

Second rib

Pectoralis major muscle

Internal mammary (parasternal) nodes

Cross-mammary pathway to opposite breast and axilla

Sternum

Costal cartilages

Lymph trunks to rectus abdominis muscle

BECK
AFTER NETTER

10|4

The spleen

The spleen is an abdominal organ that receives a rich blood supply. It plays a central role in blood cell formation and destruction as well as in body defense. The spleen is a reticuloendothelial organ, that is, it is composed of cells and tissues that help maintain resistance and immunity to infection; its sinusoids are lined with phagocytic cells that can recognize and remove foreign cells, debris, microorganisms, and senescent erythrocytes. Other organs invested with reticuloendothelial cells include the lymph nodes, liver, bone marrow, and lungs.

The spleen functions in hematopoiesis during early life, but its role is eventually completely taken over by the bone marrow. However, if bone marrow function is severely compromised (as by radiation), the spleen will begin to once again produce blood cells. In some animals the spleen stores a significant volume of blood, which can be made available very quickly as a kind of autotransfusion when the animal undergoes stress. However, the human spleen does not store enough volume to have a significant effect.

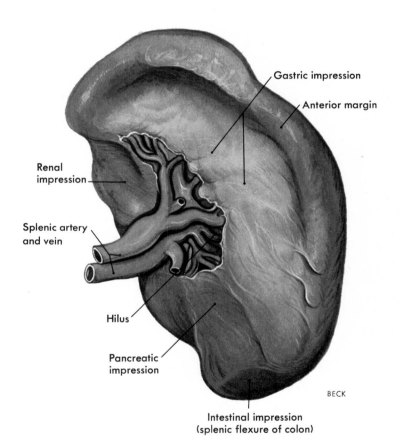

Gastric impression

Anterior margin

Renal
impression

Splenic artery
and vein

Hilus

Pancreatic
impression

BECK

Intestinal impression
(splenic flexure of colon)

11 | The digestive system

11|1

Oral cavity and pharynx (midsagittal section)

The oral cavity is continuous with the oropharynx, which extends to the nasopharynx above and to the laryngeal pharynx and esophagus below. The tongue occupies most of the space in the oral cavity. The epiglottis closes over the opening of the larynx and the trachea during swallowing, thus preventing aspiration into the bronchial tree. The pharynx is a mucous membrane–lined muscular tube containing largely voluntary (skeletal) muscle. Swallowing is a consciously initiated act rather than reflex. However, once begun, reflexive mechanisms propel the food down the esophagus to the stomach.

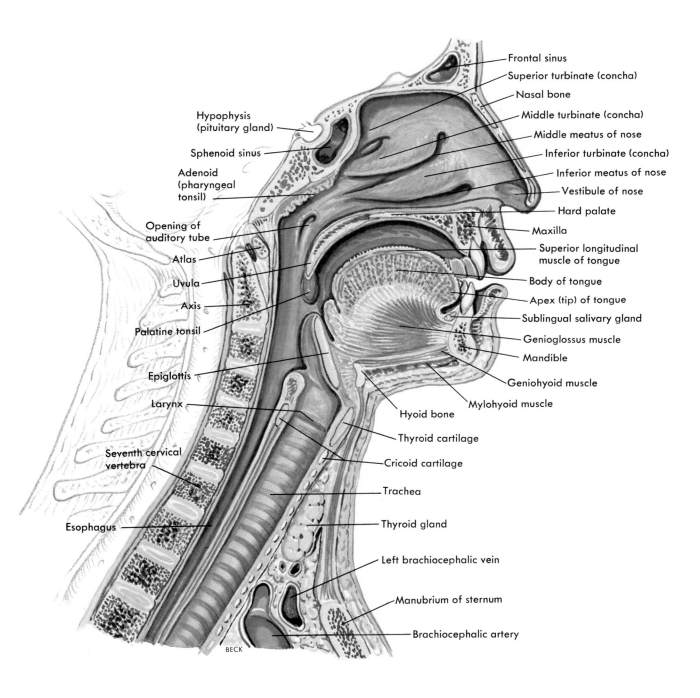

Frontal sinus

Superior turbinate (concha)

Nasal bone

Middle turbinate (concha)

Middle meatus of nose

Hypophysis
(pituitary gland)

Inferior turbinate (concha)

Sphenoid sinus

Inferior meatus of nose

Adenoid
(pharyngeal
tonsil)

Vestibule of nose

Hard palate

Maxilla

Superior longitudinal
muscle of tongue

Opening of
auditory tube

Body of tongue

Atlas

Apex (tip) of tongue

Uvula

Sublingual salivary gland

Axis

Genioglossus muscle

Palatine tonsil

Mandible

Geniohyoid muscle

Mylohyoid muscle

Epiglottis

Hyoid bone

Larynx

Thyroid cartilage

Cricoid cartilage

Seventh cervical
vertebra

Trachea

Thyroid gland

Esophagus

Left brachiocephalic vein

Manubrium of sternum

Brachiocephalic artery

BECK

203

11|2

The tongue

The tongue is a solid mass of muscle fibers coursing in three different directions (intrinsic muscles), which account for its extreme maneuverability. Extrinsic muscles attached to skull bones also insert into it. The genioglossus muscle protrudes the tongue; the styloglossus retracts it; the hyoglossus depresses it; and the palatoglossus elevates the root of the tongue. The tongue assists in speech and functions to mix saliva with food, aiding in chewing and swallowing.

The dorsal surface of the tongue is covered with numerous minute projections, or papillae, which vary in shape. The largest are the vallate, 7 to 12 in number, arranged in a V-shaped pattern at the root. Most numerous are the threadlike filiform papillae, dispersed over the entire dorsal surface and giving the anterior two thirds of the tongue a characteristic velvety appearance. The fungiform papillae derive their name from their mushroom shape and are most numerous at the tip of the tongue. The dorsal surface of the pharyngeal portion near the root is covered with lymphoid nodules called collectively the lingual tonsil.

The receptors of taste, the taste buds, are distributed on the dorsal surface of the tongue on the sides of the more rounded papillae and serve to distinguish four basic tastes—salt, sweet, sour, and bitter. The floor of the mouth includes the underside of the tongue, which has no papillae, the anterior lingual and sublingual glands and ducts, and the lingual vein, artery, and nerve. This region is extremely vascular, and the vessels are superficial, covered only by a thin layer of mucosa. Soluble drugs placed under the tongue are rapidly absorbed into the circulation.

DORSAL SURFACE

FLOOR OF THE MOUTH

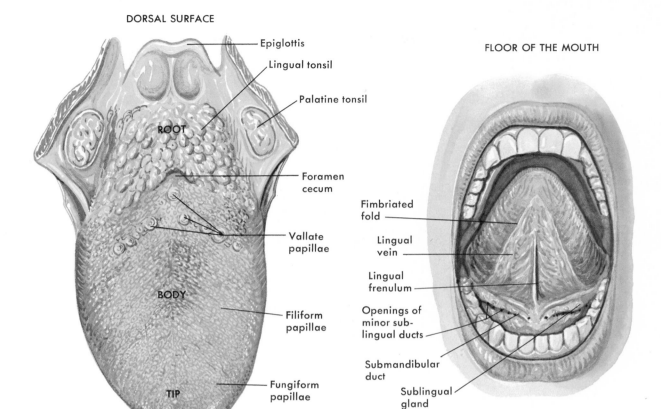

Epiglottis

Lingual tonsil

Palatine tonsil

ROOT

Foramen cecum

Vallate papillae

BODY

Filiform papillae

Fungiform papillae

TIP

Fimbriated fold

Lingual vein

Lingual frenulum

Openings of minor sublingual ducts

Submandibular duct

Sublingual gland

EXTRINSIC MUSCLES OF TONGUE   External acoustic meatus

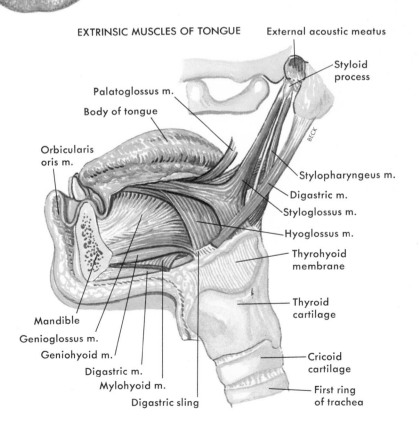

Palatoglossus m.

Body of tongue

Orbicularis oris m.

Styloid process

Stylopharyngeus m.

Digastric m.

Styloglossus m.

Hyoglossus m.

Thyrohyoid membrane

Thyroid cartilage

Mandible

Genioglossus m.

Geniohyoid m.

Digastric m.

Mylohyoid m.

Digastric sling

Cricoid cartilage

First ring of trachea

BECK

11|3

The salivary glands

Saliva is a liquid secretion of water, electrolytes, and the enzyme ptyalin. The salivary glands are exocrine glands with ducts draining into the mouth. The major glands are the parotid, submandibular, and sublingual; the minor glands include labial, lingual, buccal, and palatine. All of these structures are under the control of the autonomic nervous system, which stimulates salivation. Salivation occurs largely in response to food, odors, and taste, but mechanical, tactile, chemical, and thermal sensitivity may also be involved in a salivary response. Ptyalin begins the digestion of starch within the mouth and also acts as a lubricant, aiding in the grinding and mixing of the food in the mouth.

The salivary glands may become inflamed or infected. The most noteworthy condition involving these glands is mumps. This viral disease is also known as infectious parotitis, and the major structure involved is the parotid gland. The glands become enlarged, tender, and impaired in function. There may be peculiar or even painful tastes to certain foods and difficulty in swallowing.

MAJOR SALIVARY GLANDS

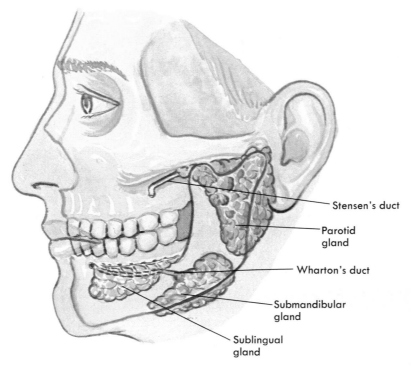

Stensen's duct

Parotid
gland

Wharton's duct

Submandibular
gland

Sublingual
gland

MINOR SALIVARY GLANDS

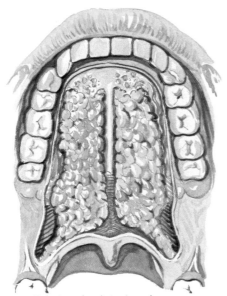

Palatine glands in the submucosa
of hard palate

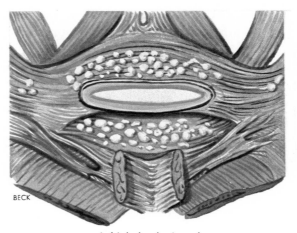

Labial glands viewed
from inside the mouth

11|4

Cleft lip; cleft palate

Cleft lip is a congenital anomaly that is relatively frequent in occurrence—1:1000 births. It occurs at a time in embryology when the face is rapidly developing, thus affecting not only the lip but also the inner and outer structure of the nose and the symmetry of the face in general. Even mild cleft lips are associated with sagging of the nostrils, deviations of the tip to the normal side, and flattening of the nostril on the affected side. Cleft lip may be associated with abnormalities in the number and position of the teeth. The anomaly is repaired surgically soon after birth, and the repair usually is quite successful. Cleft lip may be accompanied by cleft palate.

Cleft palate is also the result of a disturbance in normal development; it occurs in about 1:2500 births. There are several different varieties involving the soft palate alone or varying degrees of the hard palate along with the soft. The deformity leads to problems in feeding, since the infant can easily aspirate the liquid into the nasal cavity and the respiratory tract. Surgical repair of the cleft palate is generally delayed until 18 months of age, and several operations may be required. Children with cleft palate often develop swallowing and speech problems even when the palate is surgically repaired.

NORMAL AND CLEFT LIPS

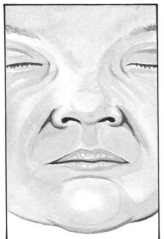 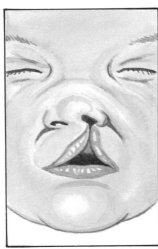 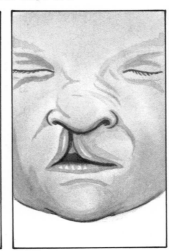 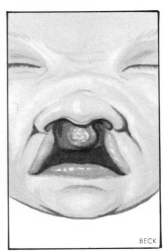

NORMAL AND CLEFT PALATES

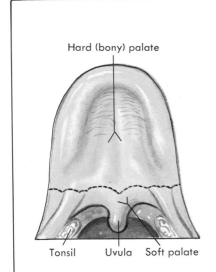

Hard (bony) palate

Tonsil Uvula Soft palate

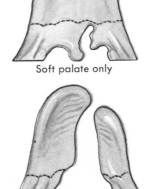

Soft palate only

Soft and all of hard palate

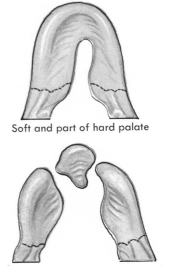

Soft and part of hard palate

Soft and hard palates on both sides

209

11|5

The stomach

The stomach is a food storage organ that is also required for normal digestion of food. It is capable of both secretion and motility. Notice the arrangement of muscle layers that allow for mixing, churning, and emptying. This is smooth muscle, innervated mainly by the vagus nerve, which is parasympathetic; sympathetic fibers innervate the blood vessels but not the muscles of the stomach. The stomach begins at the esophagus and ends at the duodenum. A true anatomical sphincter is present only at the pylorus, but the arrangement of muscle fibers gives the cardiac musculature sphincterlike properties. Both the cardiac and the pyloric sphincters are normally closed except when waves of peristalsis pass over them, before food enters or leaves the stomach.

The secretory function of the stomach is essential for normal absorption to take place in the small intestine. The stomach breaks down large food particles into tiny pieces that are then acted on enzymatically in the small intestine, before actual absorption of the food molecules can occur. Gastric glands secrete hydrochloric acid, pepsin (which begins protein breakdown), and "intrinsic factor," a substance needed for vitamin B_{12} absorption. The glands near the pylorus secrete the hormone gastrin in response to food distention and irritation. This hormone travels through the bloodstream and reaches the gastric glands, causing these glands to secrete hydrochloric acid.

Notice that the surface of the stomach itself is extensively folded into rugae and that at the microscopic level the glandular surface is also folded. This folding, which is characteristic of the entire gastrointestinal tract, allows for an expanded surface area that facilitates both digestion and absorption. The stomach is supplied with an intrinsic nerve network, Auerbach's plexus, which makes multiple connections with vagus nerve fibers and is also affected by biochemical secretions and biogenic amines.

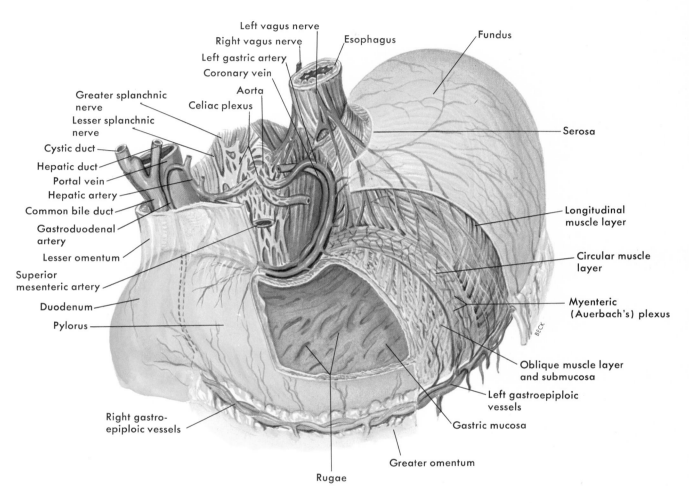

Left vagus nerve
Right vagus nerve
Esophagus
Left gastric artery
Coronary vein
Aorta
Celiac plexus
Fundus
Greater splanchnic nerve
Lesser splanchnic nerve
Cystic duct
Hepatic duct
Portal vein
Hepatic artery
Common bile duct
Gastroduodenal artery
Lesser omentum
Superior mesenteric artery
Duodenum
Pylorus
Serosa
Longitudinal muscle layer
Circular muscle layer
Myenteric (Auerbach's) plexus
Oblique muscle layer and submucosa
Left gastroepiploic vessels
Gastric mucosa
Right gastro-epiploic vessels
Rugae
Greater omentum

MUSCULATURE OF THE
PYLORIC SPHINCTER

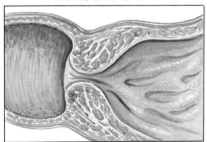

PYLORIC GLANDS   GASTRIC GLANDS

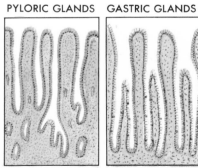

11|6

The small intestine

The small intestine is the part of the gastrointestinal system in which most of the absorption of food occurs. It consists of the duodenum, jejunum, and ileum and is about 600 cm (20 feet) in length. Notice the layers of the small intestinal wall, with the mucosal surface facing the lumen of the tract and the serosa being the exterior lining of the small intestinal tube. The musculature of this part of the intestine consists of a longitudinal as well as a circular layer throughout. This arrangement permits forward peristaltic action as well as a mixing action known as segmentation contractions. The latter action consists of rings of contractions that appear and disappear along the small intestine's length and cause the chyme present inside to be churned, mixed, and exposed to the large surface area of the mucosa. This surface area can be best appreciated by viewing the infoldings (plicae) of the jejunum. Examination of a single villus from the plicae shows even further folding. Finally, the individual mucosal cells are covered by a brush border of microvilli, further increasing surface area. The surface area of the entire small intestine is about 300 meters² (360 square yards).

The cell lining of the small intestine is shed completely, with an average turnover time of about 5 days. Thus the epithelium lining the intestinal tract is highly sensitive to any agents that act on rapidly dividing cells, such as chemotherapeutic drugs used for cancer and radiation. This is why gastrointestinal damage and bleeding are common side effects of such treatment.

Since the major function of the small intestine is food absorption into the bloodstream, it is highly vascular. Notice the blood vessels present in a single villus. Food molecules move through the brush border, the epithelial cells themselves, and perhaps between cells, and then diffuse into lymphatic capillaries and then to lacteals, or through vascular capillaries and into the venous blood draining the villus.

The mesentery holds the loops of intestines in place and provides support for the blood and lymph vessels of the intestinal tract.

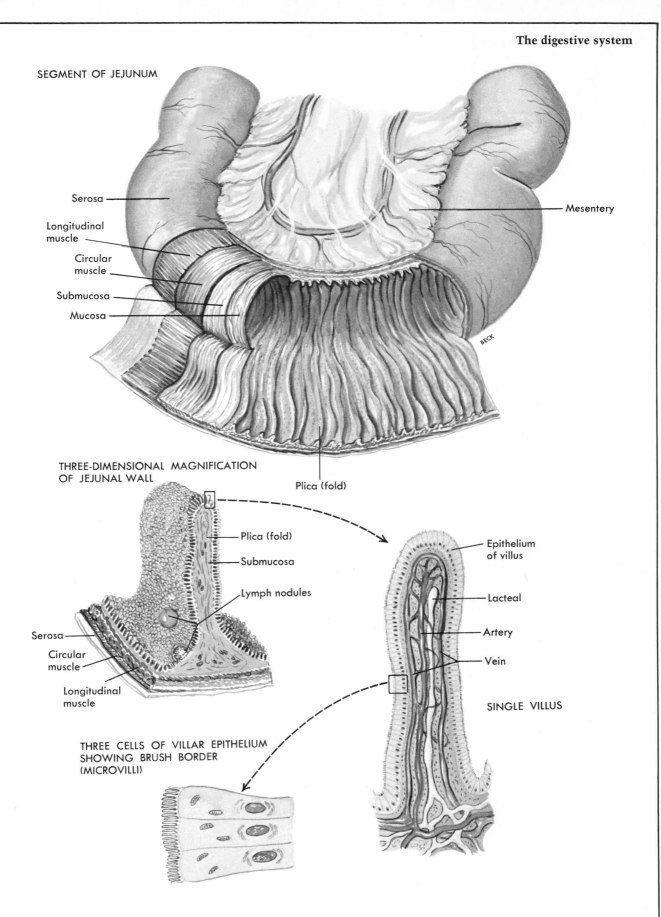

SEGMENT OF JEJUNUM

Serosa

Longitudinal muscle

Circular muscle

Submucosa

Mucosa

Mesentery

BECK

Plica (fold)

THREE-DIMENSIONAL MAGNIFICATION OF JEJUNAL WALL

Plica (fold)

Submucosa

Lymph nodules

Serosa

Circular muscle

Longitudinal muscle

Epithelium of villus

Lacteal

Artery

Vein

SINGLE VILLUS

THREE CELLS OF VILLAR EPITHELIUM SHOWING BRUSH BORDER (MICROVILLI)

213

11|7

Duodenal ulcer

The illustration depicts a deep ulceration in the duodenal wall extending as a crater through the entire mucosa and several muscle layers. The resultant exposure and destruction of nerves and blood vessels is also apparent. A duodenal ulcer usually results from excessive hydrochloric acid secretions from the stomach, which then reaches the pyloric area of the duodenum. The pH of this area is normally acidic, but the hydrochloric acid is quickly buffered by bicarbonate released from the pancreas in response to a duodenal hormone secretion. However, excessive acid can exceed the capacity of this buffering mechanism, and digestion of the duodenal mucosa can occur with eventual development of ulceration. Excessive acid secretion may be a response to stressful situations in some people, but many factors predispose to ulcer formation. Whereas most people think of ulcers as occurring in the stomach, the majority are actually duodenal.

The major problems associated with duodenal ulceration include pain, bleeding, and perforation. The pain is usually burning and can be relieved by eating. Bleeding occurs constantly, although it may be minimal, but there is the possibility that a massive hemorrhage can occur. The most devastating complication of a duodenal ulcer is actual perforation of the ulcer through the entire duodenal wall. This leads to massive bleeding, pain, intestinal obstruction, and shock in a very short time and is a surgical emergency.

There is considerable controversy about the treatment of ulcers. However, provision of six small, bland meals a day, drugs to decrease acid secretion, and reduction of stress are the usual modes of treatment.

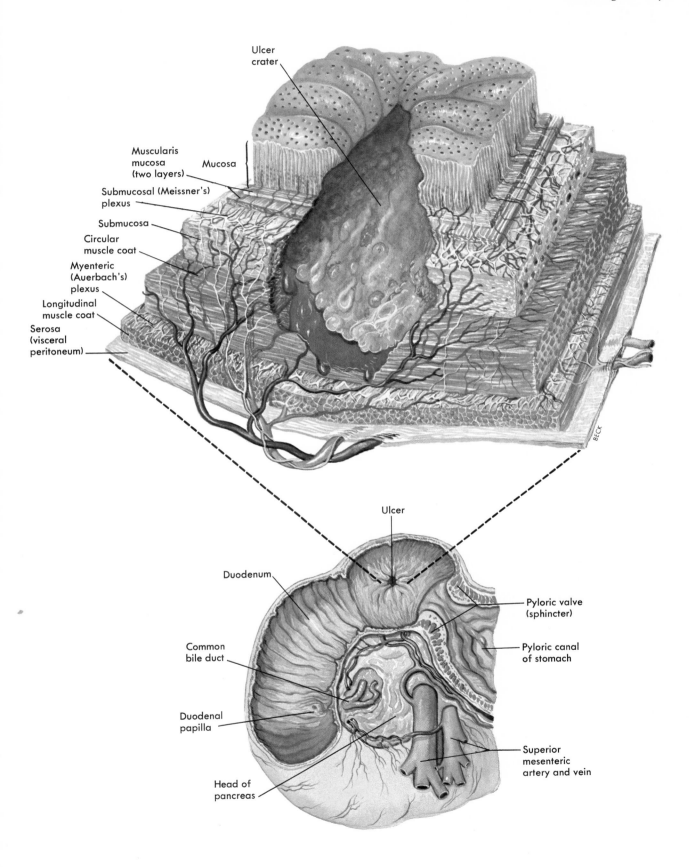

Ulcer crater

Muscularis mucosa (two layers)

Mucosa

Submucosal (Meissner's) plexus

Submucosa

Circular muscle coat

Myenteric (Auerbach's) plexus

Longitudinal muscle coat

Serosa (visceral peritoneum)

BECK

Ulcer

Duodenum

Common bile duct

Duodenal papilla

Head of pancreas

Pyloric valve (sphincter)

Pyloric canal of stomach

Superior mesenteric artery and vein

215

11|8

The large intestine

The large intestine is responsible for water and electrolyte reabsorption and for storage. The last part of the small intestine, the ileum, joins the large intestine at the ileocecal valve. Below the valve is a dilated segment of bowel, the cecum, from which the appendix emerges. The vermiform appendix is suspended by a fold of mesentery, the mesoappendix.

The lumen of the large intestine is considerably larger than that of the small intestine. The mucosal lining also differs significantly, reflecting functional variations of the intestine. The colon is marked by haustra, which are sacculations produced by infoldings of the muscular coat of the mucosa. Motility of the large intestine is characterized by "haustral churning," a to-and-fro mixing of colonic contents within the haustra. Peristaltic waves also occur in the colon; the most significant are mass movements that result from the defecation reflex. The colon consists of ascending, transverse, descending, and sigmoid sections; the sigmoid colon empties into the rectum. Important colonic landmarks are the hepatic and splenic flexures. Notice the relative position of the vermiform appendix to the posterolateral rectal wall. Because of this anatomical location, an acutely inflamed appendix can often be evaluated by a digital rectal examination.

Cancers of the large intestine are one of the most common malignancies of middle-aged Americans. The descending colon and rectum are the most common sites. Another frequent condition is rectal hemorrhoids, which are varicosities of the hemorrhoidal veins.

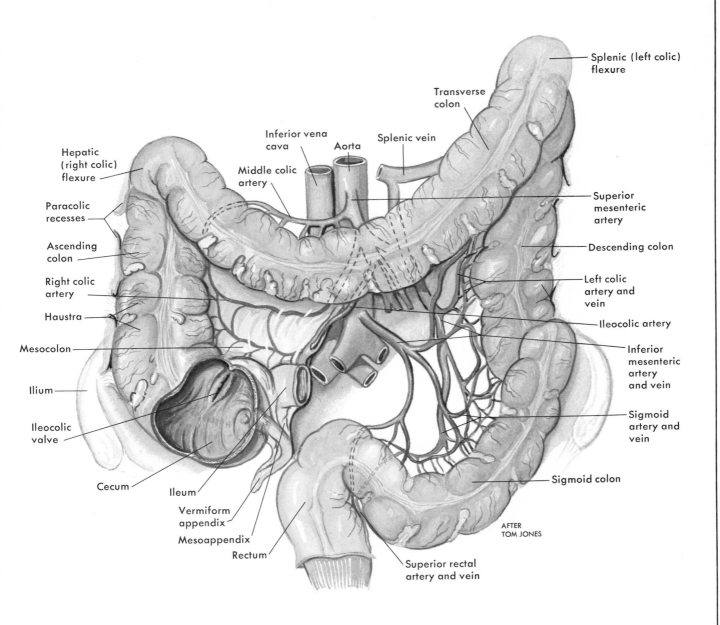

Splenic (left colic) flexure

Transverse colon

Inferior vena cava

Aorta

Splenic vein

Hepatic (right colic) flexure

Middle colic artery

Superior mesenteric artery

Paracolic recesses

Descending colon

Ascending colon

Left colic artery and vein

Right colic artery

Ileocolic artery

Haustra

Inferior mesenteric artery and vein

Mesocolon

Ilium

Sigmoid artery and vein

Ileocolic valve

Cecum

Sigmoid colon

Ileum

AFTER TOM JONES

Vermiform appendix

Mesoappendix

Rectum

Superior rectal artery and vein

217

11|9

The appendix

The vermiform appendix is a narrow, worm-shaped tube that joins the cecum where the three taenia (longitudinal muscles) of the cecum and large intestine meet. Its exact position and length (averaging 9 cm, or 3¾ inches) are highly variable; as many as one half are located in a retrocecal position. It may be twisted, coiled, or behind the cecum or ascending colon. The root or base of the appendix is generally constant. It lies on the transition of the outer to middle third of an imaginary line drawn from the anterior superior iliac spine to the umbilicus.

The appendix is a lymphoid structure that may play a role in immunological identity of cells during embryogenesis. Because it has a small lumen, obstructions from fecal matter, pinworms, or undigested foods such as small berry seeds may lodge in the lumen. Bacteria within the appendix are able to grow in the tissues when such blockage occurs, and an infection may begin. Without an adequate blood supply, the infection continues, proceeding to gangrene, and ultimately to perforation of the appendix with loss of infected material into the abdomen, leading to peritonitis. Surgery is imperative when the appendix is inflamed in order to prevent peritonitis.

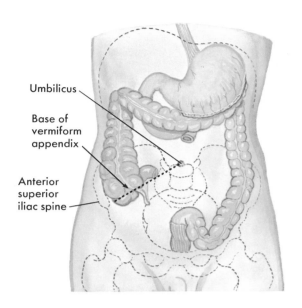

Umbilicus

Base of
vermiform
appendix

Anterior
superior
iliac spine

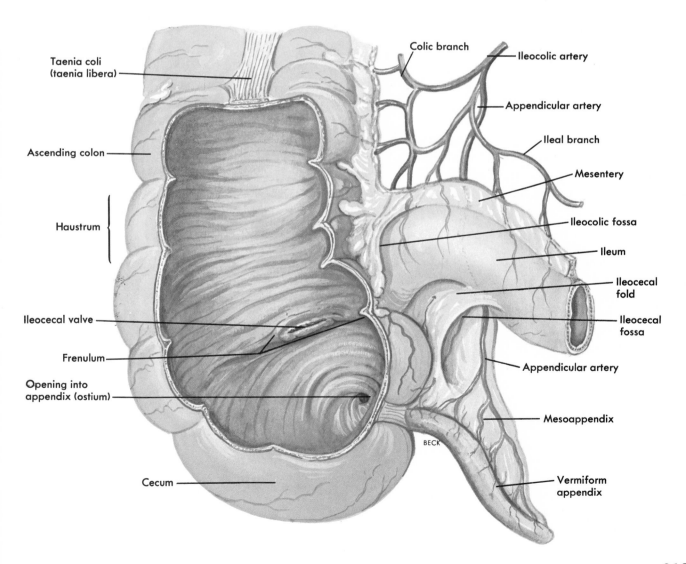

Taenia coli
(taenia libera)

Ascending colon

Haustrum

Ileocecal valve

Frenulum

Opening into
appendix (ostium)

Cecum

Colic branch

Ileocolic artery

Appendicular artery

Ileal branch

Mesentery

Ileocolic fossa

Ileum

Ileocecal
fold

Ileocecal
fossa

Appendicular artery

Mesoappendix

Vermiform
appendix

BECK

219

11|10

Appendectomy

An appendectomy is performed when acute appendicitis is suspected. However, the condition is difficult to diagnose, since there are many problems that can mimic the pain of acute appendicitis. The appendix base is located beneath McBurney's point, which is on the abdomen halfway between the iliac crest and the umbilicus. The wormlike structure may hang over the border of the ilium, or be entirely retrocecal, the position being highly variable. Because of this, the location of the pain and types of symptoms differ. The surgical procedures used for an appendectomy differ according to the preference of the surgeon and the position of the appendix. A popular technique used by many surgeons is illustrated. Removal of the appendix is usually not attempted if rupture and infection of the peritoneum are present.

Recovery from an appendectomy is rapid if there are no surgical or other complications. It is interesting that the incidence of appendicitis in the United States has decreased significantly over the past 15 to 20 years, although the reason is unknown.

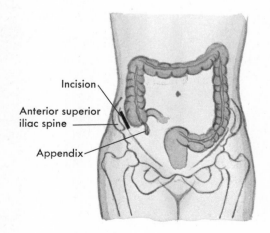

Incision

Anterior superior
iliac spine

Appendix

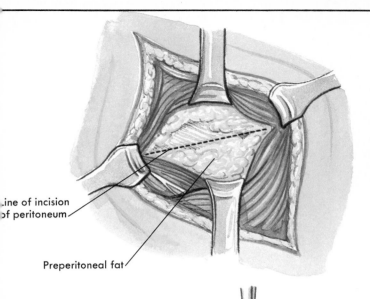

Line of incision of peritoneum

Preperitoneal fat

Successive layers of three abdominal muscles are separated in lines of direction of their fibers until peritoneum is reached. The peritoneal layer is cautiously incised while being held with two pairs of tissue forceps until cecum becomes visible.

Cecum is rotated up and out of peritoneal cavity. The mesoappendix is divided between several pairs of hemostats until base of appendix is free of mesentery. Vessels are ligated individually.

Some surgeons prefer to crush appendix at its base and tie a ligature in groove created by the crush. Amputation is done above ligature. In this technique (insets), stump is either allowed to lie free in peritoneal cavity or is inverted with or without crush. Ligatures are placed shallowly in taenia of the cecum.

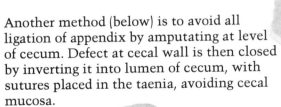

Another method (below) is to avoid all ligation of appendix by amputating at level of cecum. Defect at cecal wall is then closed by inverting it into lumen of cecum, with sutures placed in the taenia, avoiding cecal mucosa.

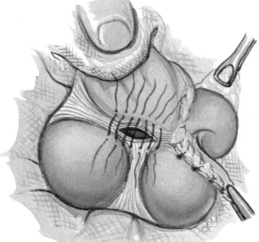

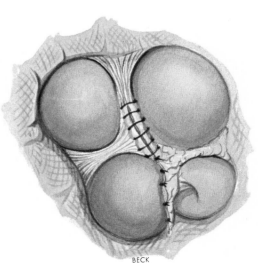

BECK

11|11

The liver

The liver is a highly vascular, abdominal organ serving the body in hundreds of ways, particularly in metabolism and defense. The anterior view of the liver shows its location directly beneath the diaphragm and the ligamentous attachments that bind it to adjacent structures. The liver has a larger right lobe and a left lobe. The drawing of the inferior surface of the liver depicts many of the vascular and biliary structures. The circulatory system of the liver involves both arterial blood received from the hepatic artery as well as a portal vein supply, which drains venous blood from the intestinal tract. The liver thus is a relatively hypoxic organ, which accounts for its dark red appearance. Leading from the liver are the hepatic veins, which carry blood from the liver into the inferior vena cava. A major function of the liver is to defend against microorganisms and toxins from the gastrointestinal tract. The portal blood is screened by specialized cells, as illustrated in Plate 11-12. Another function is detoxification by enzymatic pathways that convert drugs and chemicals into easily excretable harmless compounds. The liver is also a key metabolic organ participating in the regulation of glucose metabolism, lipid transport, and energy and protein metabolism. Additionally, during fetal life the liver is a blood-forming organ; it can revert to this function when the hematopoietic potential of the organ is severely threatened.

Another critical function of the liver is bile production. Bile is a detergent-like substance necessary for lipid and fat-soluble vitamin absorption from the small intestine. While it is synthesized continuously by the liver, it is only released into the duodenum when it is needed for fat digestion and absorption. Note the intimate relationship of the gallbladder to the liver. Bile, produced by the liver, enters the gallbladder, where it is stored. Bile can be released into the duodenum when signaled by the hormone cholecystokinin (CCK). The production of this hormone is particularly stimulated by a high fat content of the duodenal chyme. It also stimulates the pancreas to release fat-digesting enzymes.

ANTERIOR VIEW

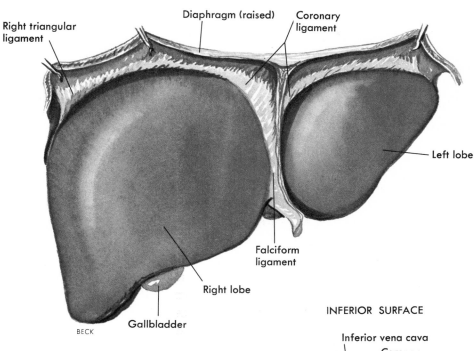

Right triangular
ligament

Diaphragm (raised)

Coronary
ligament

Left lobe

Falciform
ligament

Right lobe

Gallbladder

BECK

INFERIOR SURFACE

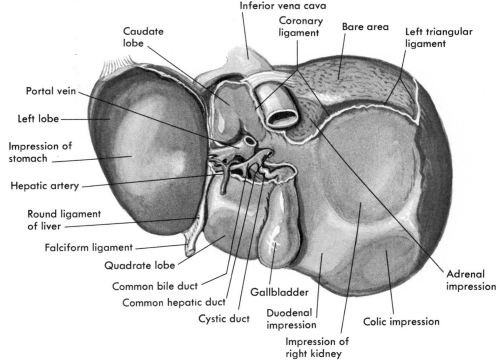

Caudate
lobe

Inferior vena cava

Coronary
ligament

Bare area

Left triangular
ligament

Portal vein

Left lobe

Impression of
stomach

Hepatic artery

Round ligament
of liver

Falciform ligament

Quadrate lobe

Common bile duct

Common hepatic duct

Cystic duct

Gallbladder

Duodenal
impression

Impression of
right kidney

Colic impression

Adrenal
impression

11|12

A liver lobule (three-dimensional scheme)

The liver lobule is the anatomical unit of the liver and is made up of thick, single-layer plates of hepatic cells surrounding the vessels and sinusoids. Each lobule has a separate vascular and biliary supply. The central vein, a branch of the hepatic vein, forms the center of each lobule. Branches of this vein form sublobular veins. The portal vein also sends off branches to the liver lobules around the periphery of the central vein, and these branches further subdivide into sinusoids. The sinusoids ultimately join with the central vein branches, providing an hepatic and portal interconnection between the two venous supplies of the liver. The sinusoidal endothelium is extremely permeable, permitting the venous blood in the sinusoids to be "screened" by the specialized phagocytic cells that line the sinusoids. It is here that the blood is efficiently cleaned of microorganisms, toxins, aged cells, and debris.

The peripheral portal triads contain not only a branch of the portal vein, but also an hepatic artery branch, a lymph vessel, and a biliary duct. The hepatic artery further subdivides into periportal arterioles that provide the liver cells with oxygen and nutrition. Bile formed by the liver cells is released from the cells into tiny bile capillaries (cholangioles), which eventually form bile ductules. From the ductules the newly synthesized bile empties into the bile duct. Hundreds of lobules make up the liver lobes and provide an extremely efficient configuration for facilitating the many functions of the liver.

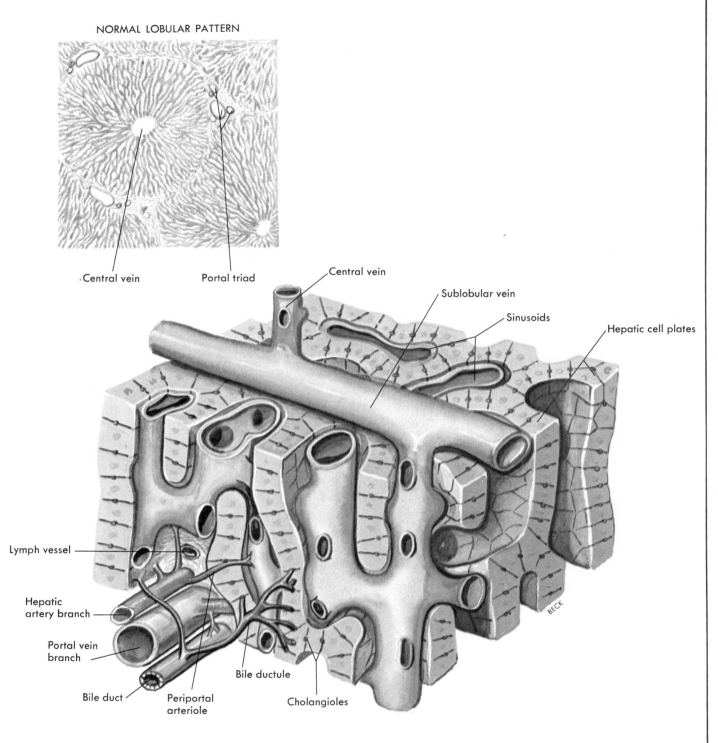

NORMAL LOBULAR PATTERN

Central vein

Portal triad

Central vein

Sublobular vein

Sinusoids

Hepatic cell plates

Lymph vessel

Hepatic artery branch

Portal vein branch

Bile duct

Periportal arteriole

Bile ductule

Cholangioles

BECK

(According to concept of Hans Elias)

11|13

Cirrhosis—clinical manifestations

Cirrhosis of the liver is usually caused by chronic alcoholism. The liver of the alcoholic passes through several stages in the cirrhotic process. Initially there is fatty infiltration and enlargement, and eventually the liver becomes hard, scarred, and nodular in appearance. The damage is extensive, and the many functions of the liver are impaired. As a result, the symptoms associated with cirrhosis are the result of interference with most of the organ systems of the body. Cardiovascular symptoms are often the most pronounced and serious. Portal hypertension is a major development of the cirrhotic process and results from increased pressure in the portal and splanchnic veins. The end result of portal hypertension is depicted in the illustration. Cirrhosis can also lead to accumulation of fluid from excessive filtration out of the blood vessels into the peritoneal cavity and esophageal varices (weakened areas in cardiac and esophageal veins from increased pressure); these are very susceptible to rupture and hemorrhage. Vascular engorgement of the spleen may occur, leading to splenic damage. There is usually an anemia caused in part by hyperactivity of the spleen (hypersplenism), as well as blood loss from the gastrointestinal tract. Patients often have ankle edema, and their skin is usually jaundiced. Because of impairment of liver synthesis of coagulation factors, there is a tendency toward bruising and bleeding. Another phenomenon results from a decreased ability of the liver to metabolize hormones. In males, estrogens are increased in blood concentration because of liver failure and exert a feminizing effect; there is altered fat distribution, changes in hair, increased breast tissue, and direct estrogen effects on blood vessels leading to palmar redness and spider nevi. If the cirrhosis progresses to end-stage disease, complete liver failure and hepatic coma result. At this point recovery is rare. However, even late in the cirrhotic process, abstinence from alcohol can result in recovery of significant liver function.

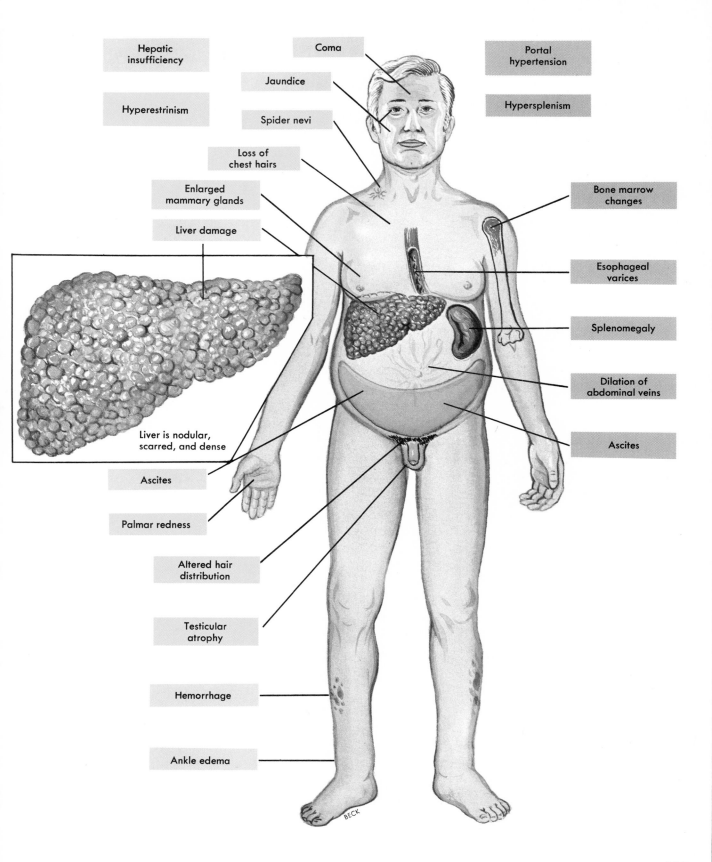

Hepatic insufficiency

Hyperestrinism

Coma

Jaundice

Spider nevi

Portal hypertension

Hypersplenism

Loss of chest hairs

Enlarged mammary glands

Liver damage

Bone marrow changes

Esophageal varices

Splenomegaly

Dilation of abdominal veins

Ascites

Liver is nodular, scarred, and dense

Ascites

Palmar redness

Altered hair distribution

Testicular atrophy

Hemorrhage

Ankle edema

BECK

11|14

The gallbladder

The pear-shaped gallbladder is a storage sac for bile produced by the liver, to which it is attached to the right and quadrate lobes by loose areolar tissue. Bile is conveyed from the liver by the right and left hepatic ducts, which unite to become the 2 to 3 cm (¾ to 1¼ inch) long common hepatic duct.

The cystic duct from the gallbladder joins the common hepatic duct immediately above and behind the pylorus of the stomach; the continuation of this combined duct forms the common bile duct, also known as the ductus choledochus. The latter, 10 to 15 cm (4 to 6 inches) long, courses through the free margin of the lesser omentum behind the junction of the stomach and duodenum at the papilla of Vater. Just before entering the duodenum, the common bile duct is joined by the main pancreatic duct, which empties pancreatic juice into the duodenum.

When food containing fat enters the small intestine, the gallbladder contracts, forcing bile into the cystic and common bile ducts and into the duodenum. The opening at the papilla is guarded by a ring of circular muscle fibers known as the sphincter of Oddi. When the sphincter is closed, bile flows down the hepatic duct and then through the cystic duct to reach the gallbladder for storage. Bile is concentrated five- to tenfold in the gallbladder. Bile is composed of bile salts, pigments, cholesterol, and phospholipids. The principal function of bile is to emulsify fats and prepare them for digestion by pancreatic lipases. Intestinal cells reprocess the lipids, forming chylomicrons, globules of lipid that are then absorbed into lacteals (lymphatics) in the villi of the small intestine.

Gallbladder disease is extremely common. Stones may form within the gallbladder itself or in the bile duct. A slight imbalance in the amount of bile salts or phospholipid contained in bile can result in precipitation of cholesterol and accretions can build up, resulting in gallstones.

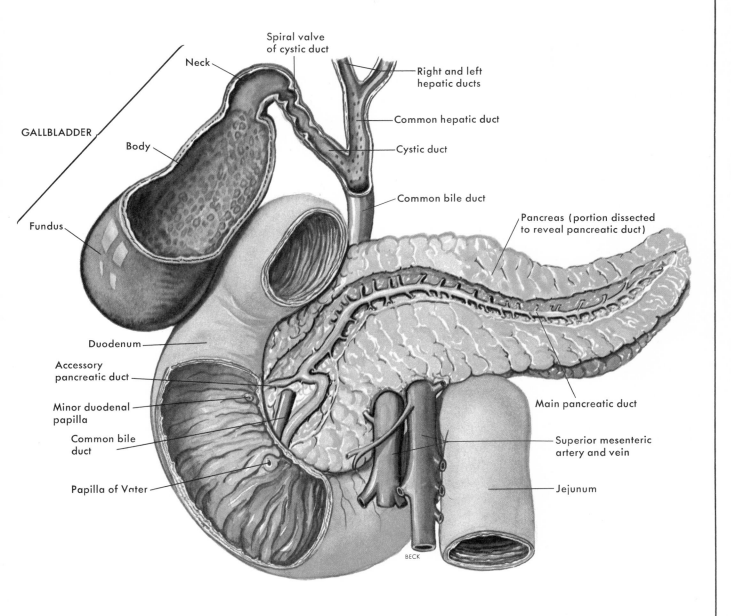

Spiral valve
of cystic duct

Neck

Right and left
hepatic ducts

Common hepatic duct

Cystic duct

GALLBLADDER

Body

Common bile duct

Pancreas (portion dissected
to reveal pancreatic duct)

Fundus

Duodenum

Accessory
pancreatic duct

Minor duodenal
papilla

Common bile
duct

Papilla of Vater

Main pancreatic duct

Superior mesenteric
artery and vein

Jejunum

BECK

11|15

Cholecystectomy

Surgical removal of the gallbladder is called cholecystectomy, which is usually performed for cholecystitis. This inflammation of the gallbladder is often associated with painful enlargement and gallstones. An attack of cholecystitis tends to follow a heavy or fatty meal, and the pain is acute and felt in the right upper quadrant. After the condition is diagnosed, the acute inflammation is allowed to subside and the gallbladder is removed as illustrated. Notice the anatomical connections of the gallbladder to the liver via the hepatic and cystic ducts and to the duodenum via the common bile duct. The pancreas is also anatomically near the gallbladder, emptying its secretions into the duodenum via the pancreatic duct. When gallbladder disease occurs, all of these structures may eventually become infected, inflamed, or obstructed. Digestive disturbances, jaundice and liver damage, and pancreatitis may develop.

People can easily adapt to life without a gallbladder. The hepatic duct dilates with time after a cholecystectomy and can serve as a storage area, functioning as a replacement for the gallbladder.

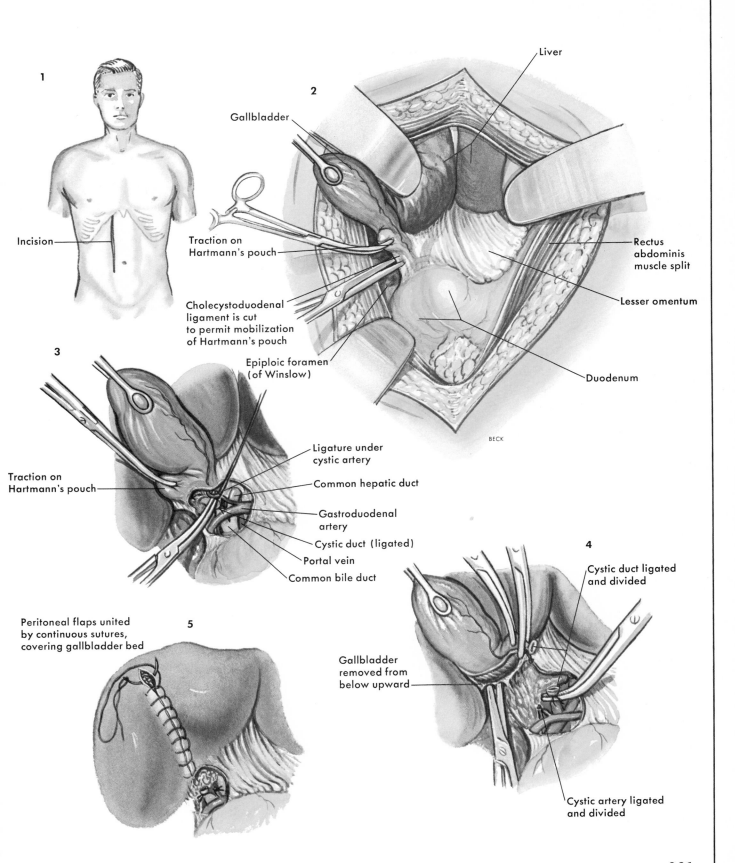

1

Incision

2

Liver

Gallbladder

Traction on
Hartmann's pouch

Cholecystoduodenal
ligament is cut
to permit mobilization
of Hartmann's pouch

Epiploic foramen
(of Winslow)

Rectus
abdominis
muscle split

Lesser omentum

Duodenum

BECK

3

Traction on
Hartmann's pouch

Ligature under
cystic artery

Common hepatic duct

Gastroduodenal
artery

Cystic duct (ligated)

Portal vein

Common bile duct

4

Cystic duct ligated
and divided

Gallbladder
removed from
below upward

Cystic artery ligated
and divided

Peritoneal flaps united
by continuous sutures,
covering gallbladder bed

5

231

11|16

The vomiting act

Vomiting is the expulsion of gastric and occasionally intestinal contents through the mouth. It occurs in response to many stimuli, such as noxious odors, contaminated food, distention, inflammation or irritation of the gastric mucosa, central nervous system dysfunctions, and some drugs. A central vomiting center is thought to exist in the hypothalamus, which regulates this highly integrated and chiefly autonomic act. The smooth muscle of the gastrointestinal tract is prepared for the efficient expulsion of the vomitus, but the actual propulsive force is supplied by skeletal muscles. The diaphragm contracts sharply, abdominal muscles contract, and the force provided causes an antiperistaltic movement through a flaccid stomach and esophagus.

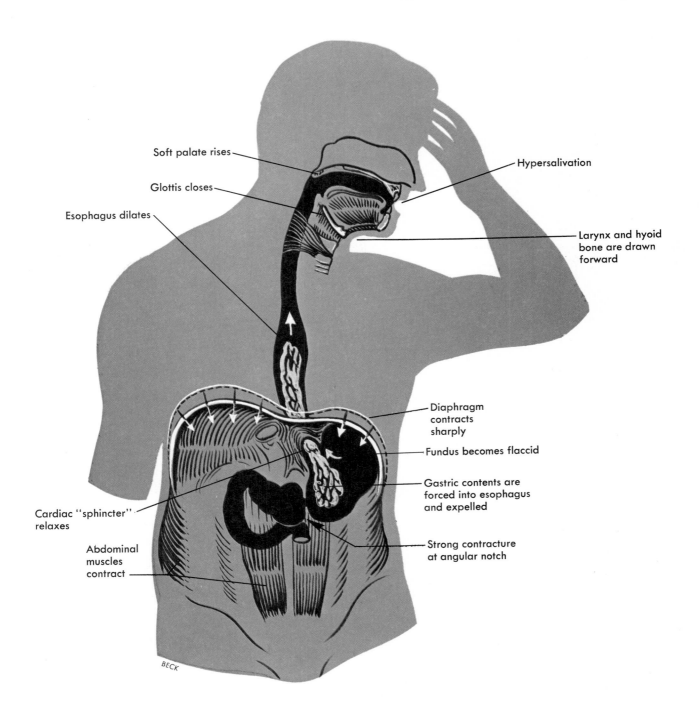

Soft palate rises

Glottis closes

Esophagus dilates

Hypersalivation

Larynx and hyoid bone are drawn forward

Diaphragm contracts sharply

Fundus becomes flaccid

Gastric contents are forced into esophagus and expelled

Cardiac "sphincter" relaxes

Abdominal muscles contract

Strong contracture at angular notch

BECK

12 | The urogenital system

Mitosis
Meiosis—female (oogenesis)
Meiosis—male (spermatogenesis)
The female pelvic organs
External female genitalia and perineum
Menstrual cycle
Ovulation, fertilization, and implantation of an ovum
Ovary and stages of ovum development
The lactating breast
Fertilization to implantation
Development of the embryo
Involution and puerperium
The male pelvic organs (midsagittal section)
Anterolateral abdominal wall and inguinal area in the male
Male genital duct system
The bladder—male and female
The kidneys
The nephron unit

12|1

Mitosis

Most living cells divide sometime during their existence. Cells that are constantly lost from the body, such as those of the skin, the linings of the respiratory and digestive tracts, and the male reproductive cells, are just as rapidly replaced during health. Mitosis is the process by which body cells divide to form new cells that are identical to parent cells. The cell cycle is marked by phases of growth, synthesis, and mitosis. For most cells the mitotic interval is very short, but during this phase a remarkable amount of complex intracellular activity takes place.

Chemical mediators appear to stimulate cells to divide when necessary. Furthermore, tissue density and cell-to-cell contact influence cell division in an inhibitory manner. Cancer is a disease characterized by uncontrolled cell mitosis, and abnormal mitosis is also observed. Because of this, malignant cells grow into tumors that invade normal tissue and reach a critical size after which abnormal cells are shed into the body fluids. New tumors arise from these cells at distant sites as a result of the uncontrolled mitotic activity of the cancer.

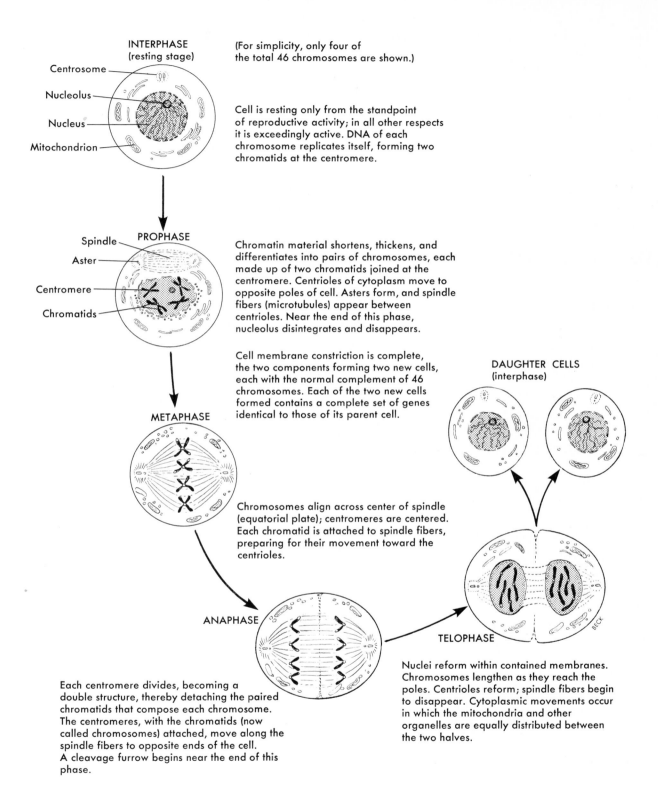

INTERPHASE
(resting stage)

Centrosome

Nucleolus

Nucleus

Mitochondrion

(For simplicity, only four of
the total 46 chromosomes are shown.)

Cell is resting only from the standpoint
of reproductive activity; in all other respects
it is exceedingly active. DNA of each
chromosome replicates itself, forming two
chromatids at the centromere.

PROPHASE

Spindle

Aster

Centromere

Chromatids

Chromatin material shortens, thickens, and
differentiates into pairs of chromosomes, each
made up of two chromatids joined at the
centromere. Centrioles of cytoplasm move to
opposite poles of cell. Asters form, and spindle
fibers (microtubules) appear between
centrioles. Near the end of this phase,
nucleolus disintegrates and disappears.

Cell membrane constriction is complete,
the two components forming two new cells,
each with the normal complement of 46
chromosomes. Each of the two new cells
formed contains a complete set of genes
identical to those of its parent cell.

DAUGHTER CELLS
(interphase)

METAPHASE

Chromosomes align across center of spindle
(equatorial plate); centromeres are centered.
Each chromatid is attached to spindle fibers,
preparing for their movement toward the
centrioles.

ANAPHASE

TELOPHASE

Nuclei reform within contained membranes.
Chromosomes lengthen as they reach the
poles. Centrioles reform; spindle fibers begin
to disappear. Cytoplasmic movements occur
in which the mitochondria and other
organelles are equally distributed between
the two halves.

Each centromere divides, becoming a
double structure, thereby detaching the paired
chromatids that compose each chromosome.
The centromeres, with the chromatids (now
called chromosomes) attached, move along the
spindle fibers to opposite ends of the cell.
A cleavage furrow begins near the end of this
phase.

237

12|2

Meiosis—female (oogenesis)

Meiosis is a cell division that produces the gametes, or sex cells, in males and females. This process is observed in oogenesis, the production of mature ova. In contrast to spermatogenesis in males (Plate 12-3), the meiotic process occurs cyclically in women. Furthermore, all ova that the woman possesses are already present at birth in the early prophase stage. Under the influence of follicle-stimulating hormone (FSH) and luteinizing hormone (LH) from the anterior pituitary gland, one follicle among many begins to develop and produces a mature ovum at about age 12. Although similar in most respects to spermatogenesis, oogenesis results in only one mature ootid and three nonfunctional polar bodies. Notice that a single sperm much smaller in comparison to the ovum is needed to fertilize the haploid ootid and produce a diploid zygote. The second maturation division does not take place until fertilization occurs; if the ovum is not fertilized within 18 hours after ovulation, it will degenerate.

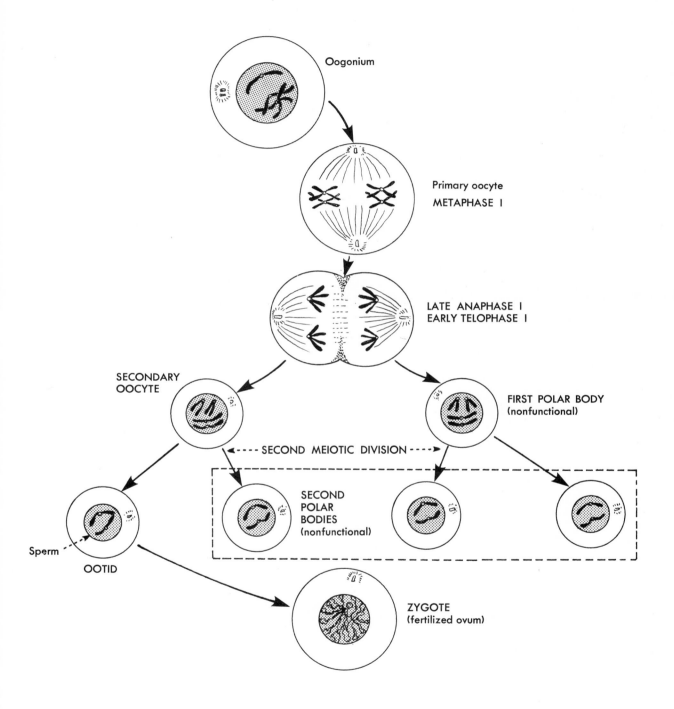

Oogonium

Primary oocyte
METAPHASE I

LATE ANAPHASE I
EARLY TELOPHASE I

SECONDARY
OOCYTE

FIRST POLAR BODY
(nonfunctional)

SECOND MEIOTIC DIVISION

SECOND
POLAR
BODIES
(nonfunctional)

Sperm

OOTID

ZYGOTE
(fertilized ovum)

12|3

Meiosis—male (spermatogenesis)

Spermatogenesis results in the production of mature spermatozoa, which have a haploid number of chromosomes. It involves a pattern of cell division in which the original diploid number of chromosomes (46 in human beings) is reduced to 23. In order for this to occur, during the first metaphase entire chromosomes are pulled apart into daughter cells. This contrasts with mitosis, in which whole chromosomes split into halves, and each half moves to a daughter cell. The first prophase is characterized by phases of leptotene, zygotene, pachytene, and diplotene. These phases are illustrated and depict condensation of chromosomes, pairing of homologous chromosomes, and eventual metaphase, anaphase, and telophase. Notice that the process allows for considerable heterogeneity of the sperm that are eventually produced. For example, crossing-over, although limited in human division, allows for mixing of genetic material between maternally and paternally derived pairs of chromosomes. Furthermore, at telophase I, there is a random assortment of maternal and paternal chromosomes lining up on the metaphasal plate, so that multiple combinations of maternal and paternal chromosomes in the sperm are possible. This, of course, allows for tremendous diversity of hereditary material.

The second meiotic division is a mitotic type of division—the sister chromatids, rather than whole chromosomes, move to the daughter cells. A key difference between meiosis and mitosis is that the centromeres (the point of attachment of the sister chromatids) do not split in meiosis. After the second meiotic division the chromatids present in the daughter cells will duplicate the sister chromatid that was lost to another cell during division; the end result is the formation of daughter cells identical to each other and to the secondary spermatocyte that was the cell of origin.

Spermatogenesis in the male occurs continuously within the testes and often until late in life. No cyclical pattern is apparent, and mature sperms are readily available any time.

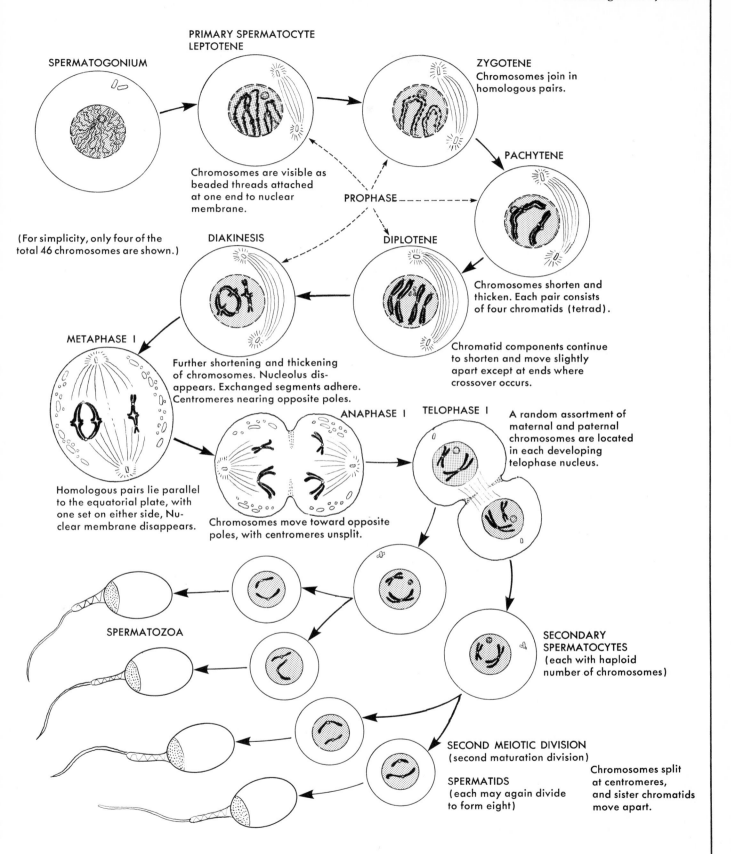

SPERMATOGONIUM

PRIMARY SPERMATOCYTE
LEPTOTENE

Chromosomes are visible as beaded threads attached at one end to nuclear membrane.

ZYGOTENE
Chromosomes join in homologous pairs.

PROPHASE

PACHYTENE

Chromosomes shorten and thicken. Each pair consists of four chromatids (tetrad).

(For simplicity, only four of the total 46 chromosomes are shown.)

DIAKINESIS

DIPLOTENE

Chromatid components continue to shorten and move slightly apart except at ends where crossover occurs.

METAPHASE I

Further shortening and thickening of chromosomes. Nucleolus disappears. Exchanged segments adhere. Centromeres nearing opposite poles.

ANAPHASE I

TELOPHASE I

A random assortment of maternal and paternal chromosomes are located in each developing telophase nucleus.

Homologous pairs lie parallel to the equatorial plate, with one set on either side, Nuclear membrane disappears.

Chromosomes move toward opposite poles, with centromeres unsplit.

SPERMATOZOA

SECONDARY SPERMATOCYTES (each with haploid number of chromosomes)

SECOND MEIOTIC DIVISION (second maturation division)

SPERMATIDS (each may again divide to form eight)

Chromosomes split at centromeres, and sister chromatids move apart.

241

12|4

The female pelvic organs

The female pelvic organs consist of the uterus, fallopian tubes, ovaries, and vagina. The uterus consists of the rounded body and the cervix, which opens into the vagina. The uterus is held in position by ligaments and bands of peritoneum and occupies a position between the urethra and rectum.

Projecting laterally on the superior surface of the uterine body are the fallopian tubes. These ducts, about 12 cm (4⅘ inches) long, are lined by a mucous membrane consisting of ciliated epithelium and smooth muscle which causes tubal contractions. The ends of the tubes are enlarged and have many fingerlike projections, which also contract in a valvelike manner. The endings of the tubes are loosely wrapped about the surfaces of the ovaries. The ovum must be transported through the fallopian tubes and into the uterus. Occasionally, an ovum will not be swept into the fallopian tube but will be lost in the peritoneal cavity. If such an ovum becomes fertilized, a peritoneal cavity pregnancy occurs.

The ovaries themselves are located in the upper part of the pelvic cavity and are held in place by ligaments and peritoneum. The ovaries appear smooth and white in young women but become wrinkled and scarred during the aging process.

The cervical os separates the cervix from the muscular vagina. It is seen in the drawing that the rounded, bulbous os can be digitally palpated through the vagina as well as through the rectum. The yearly physical examination of women usually includes this palpation, as the cervix is a common site of malignancy in females.

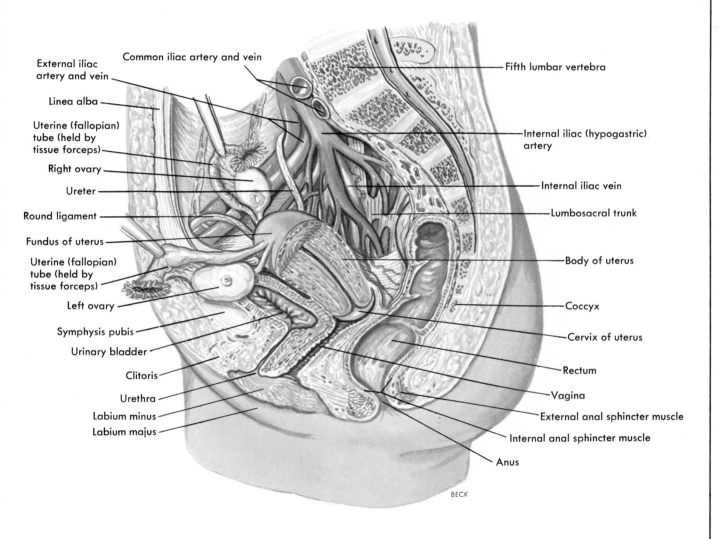

External iliac artery and vein

Common iliac artery and vein

Linea alba

Uterine (fallopian) tube (held by tissue forceps)

Right ovary

Ureter

Round ligament

Fundus of uterus

Uterine (fallopian) tube (held by tissue forceps)

Left ovary

Symphysis pubis

Urinary bladder

Clitoris

Urethra

Labium minus

Labium majus

Fifth lumbar vertebra

Internal iliac (hypogastric) artery

Internal iliac vein

Lumbosacral trunk

Body of uterus

Coccyx

Cervix of uterus

Rectum

Vagina

External anal sphincter muscle

Internal anal sphincter muscle

Anus

BECK

243

12|5

External female genitalia and perineum

The external female genitalia consist of external protective pads—the labia majora—that cover the more anterior clitoris, labia minora, vestibule, and vaginal opening. The interior is lined with moist mucous membrane and glands that produce the thin, acid vaginal secretions.

The perineum refers to a diamond-shaped area formed by drawing imaginary lines between the symphysis pubis, each ischial tuberosity, and the coccyx. The perineal body forms a tough, fibrous band of tissue between the vagina and rectum. This is part of the perineum usually incised during birth when performing an episiotomy.

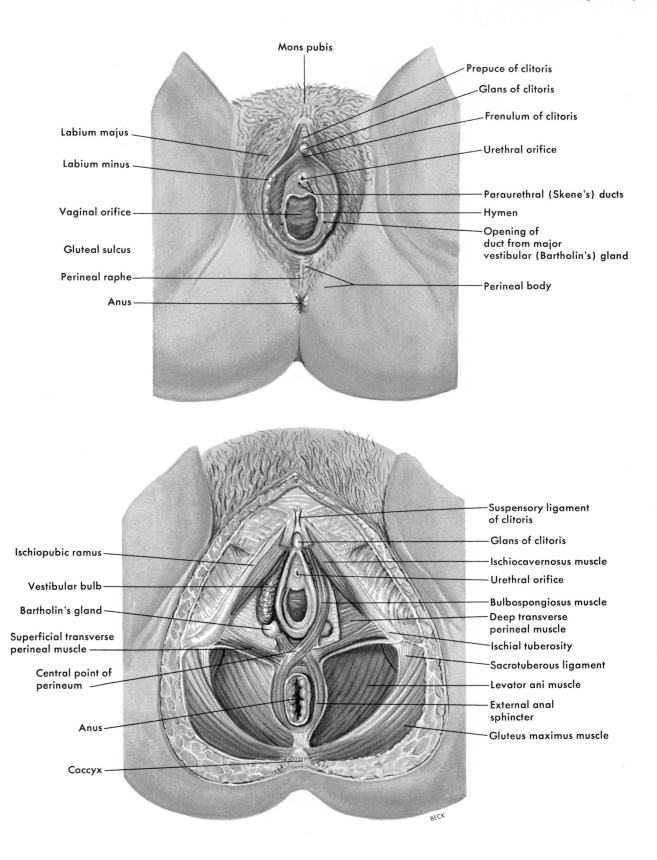

Mons pubis

Prepuce of clitoris

Glans of clitoris

Frenulum of clitoris

Labium majus

Urethral orifice

Labium minus

Paraurethral (Skene's) ducts

Vaginal orifice

Hymen

Gluteal sulcus

Opening of
duct from major
vestibular (Bartholin's) gland

Perineal raphe

Perineal body

Anus

Suspensory ligament
of clitoris

Glans of clitoris

Ischiopubic ramus

Ischiocavernosus muscle

Vestibular bulb

Urethral orifice

Bartholin's gland

Bulbospongiosus muscle

Deep transverse
perineal muscle

Superficial transverse
perineal muscle

Ischial tuberosity

Central point of
perineum

Sacrotuberous ligament

Levator ani muscle

Anus

External anal
sphincter

Coccyx

Gluteus maximus muscle

BECK

12|6

Menstrual cycle

The diagram shows the many separate and interacting factors involved in the normal 28-day menstrual cycle. Stimulating hormones from the anterior pituitary gland are released in a cyclical manner and affect the growth of the ovarian follicles. The biological 28-day "clock" regulating this process is believed to be neurological, but its precision is affected by many external stimuli. For example, psychological stress can completely disrupt the cycle, as can physiological factors, such as malnutrition or disease.

Follicle-stimulating hormone (FSH) from the pituitary gland enhances follicular growth and the production of estrogen by the ovaries. Luteinizing hormone (LH), also released by the pituitary, perhaps in response to the rising estrogen, causes the actual rupturing of the follicle (ovulation) at about day 14. Progesterone is then secreted by the corpus luteum under LH stimulation, and its concentration rises. Estrogen and progesterone stimulate the endometrial lining of the uterus to grow, thicken, and become rich in blood vessels. This prepares the uterus for the implantation of a fertilized ovum. If fertilization should occur, the corpus luteum enlarges and is maintained, releasing progesterone and estrogen to support the implanted embryo until the placenta can take over that function. When fertilization does not occur, the corpus luteum regresses and the pituitary stimulation ceases. The estrogen and progesterone blood concentrations rapidly fall, causing the death and sloughing off of the endometrial cell lining and bleeding; the result is menstruation. After the menstruation is completed, the uterus once again begins to prepare for possible pregnancy.

The basal temperatures are also indicated in the figure and show the typical rise that occurs at ovulation.

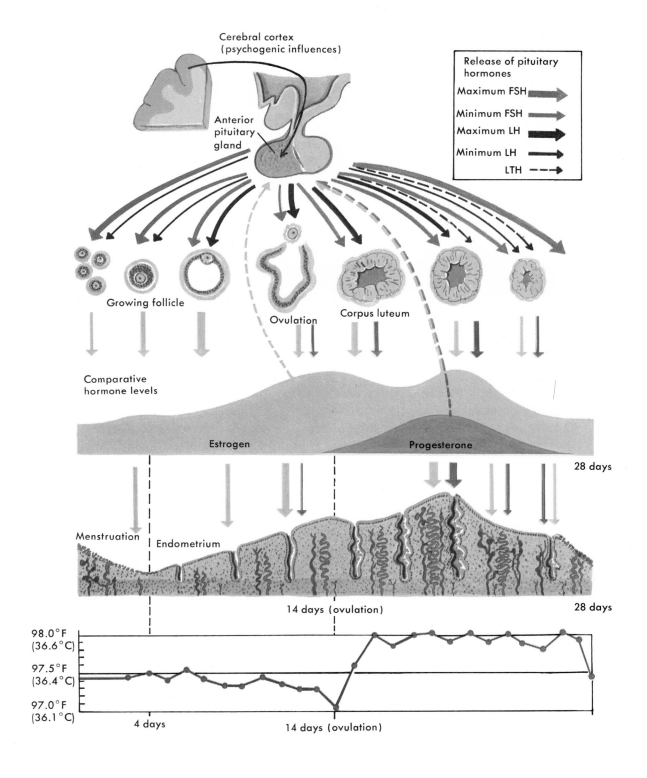

12|7

Ovulation, fertilization, and implantation of an ovum

Ovulation is a cyclical event in the human female occurring approximately every 28 days. It is the result of stimulation by the anterior pituitary hormones, FSH and LH, of developing follicles that contain ova. Once ovulation has occurred, the ovum is swept into the fallopian tube through its fingerlike ends close to the ovary. If fertilization of the ovum occurs within the fallopian tube, the zygote thus formed begins to divide and develop as it makes its way to the uterus. Implantation of a healthy zygote will take place about 10 days later if the endometrium (uterine lining) is sufficiently prepared by hormones to support a pregnancy.

There are many causes of infertility in the female. A common problem is reduced patency of the fallopian tubes, so that the ovum, even if fertilized, is not able to reach the uterus. Another cause is absence of ovulation, which may be a hormonal problem. Endometrial development also depends on a balanced hormonal environment and may not be adequate to support a pregnancy, even if fertilization has taken place.

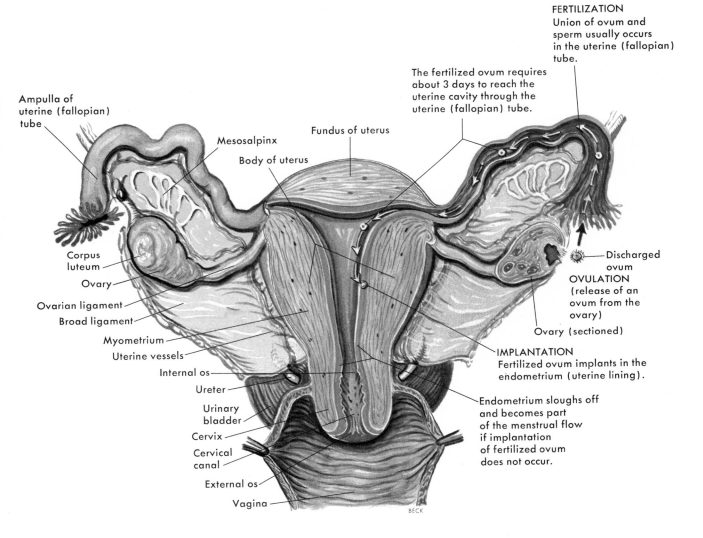

FERTILIZATION
Union of ovum and sperm usually occurs in the uterine (fallopian) tube.

The fertilized ovum requires about 3 days to reach the uterine cavity through the uterine (fallopian) tube.

Ampulla of uterine (fallopian) tube

Mesosalpinx

Fundus of uterus

Body of uterus

Discharged ovum

OVULATION (release of an ovum from the ovary)

Ovary (sectioned)

Corpus luteum

Ovary

Ovarian ligament

Broad ligament

Myometrium

Uterine vessels

Internal os

Ureter

Urinary bladder

Cervix

Cervical canal

External os

Vagina

IMPLANTATION
Fertilized ovum implants in the endometrium (uterine lining).

Endometrium sloughs off and becomes part of the menstrual flow if implantation of fertilized ovum does not occur.

BECK

249

12|8

Ovary and stages of ovum development

The schematic illustration shows the successive stages of ovarian follicle and ovum development. The first stage is poorly understood. It involves the selection and stimulation of a single primary follicle out of all the potential follicles present in the ovaries. This follicle begins to grow, and fluid accumulates in the antrum. At ovulation the mature follicle ruptures, releasing an ovum and a small amount of blood. The follicle becomes filled with lipid and appears yellow. This corpus luteum (yellow body) produces hormones and will grow and remain functional during a pregnancy, should it occur. If the ovum does not become fertilized, the corpus luteum recedes; the remnant is known as the corpus albicans. This eventually forms a tiny scar on the ovarian surface.

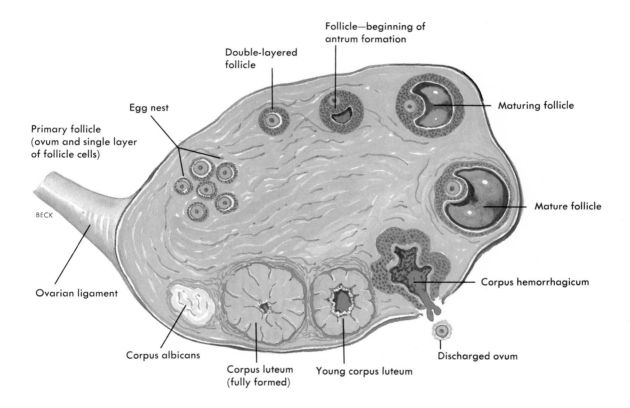

Follicle—beginning of
antrum formation

Double-layered
follicle

Egg nest

Maturing follicle

Primary follicle
(ovum and single layer
of follicle cells)

BECK

Mature follicle

Ovarian ligament

Corpus hemorrhagicum

Corpus albicans

Discharged ovum

Corpus luteum
(fully formed)

Young corpus luteum

12|9

The lactating breast

During pregnancy the levels of estradiol and progesterone in the mother's body are considerably increased. Estradiol causes the mammary glands to enlarge by deposition of fat and effects a proliferation of the duct system. Progesterone causes a development of the secretory cells that form the walls of the alveoli.

After the placenta is discharged and estradiol and progesterone levels fall, prolactin, a lactogenic hormone, helps prepare the secretory cells to produce milk. Normally, milk is not produced until about 3 days after parturition. The sucking action excites receptors within the nipple, causing impulses to be sent to the mother's hypothalamus and resulting in the release of oxytocin from the posterior pituitary. When oxytocin reaches the mammary glands, the cells surrounding the alveoli contract, forcing the liquid into the ducts, then into the sinuses behind the nipple.

Sucking reflexly stimulates the release of prolactin. If the infant is not breast-fed and if there is no sucking, the secretion of milk will halt. If sucking continues, milk production may continue for a year or longer.

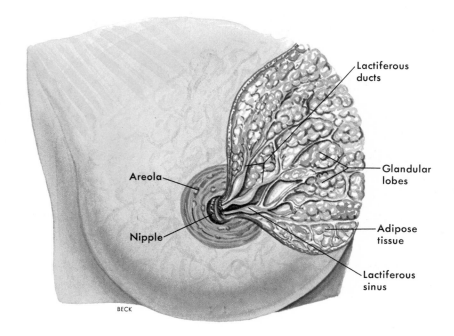

Fifteen to 20 sinuses (enlargements of the collecting ducts) lie just behind the areolar tissue. Each sinus receives milk from the corresponding lobe of the breast and each connects to a small duct that goes out through the nipple.

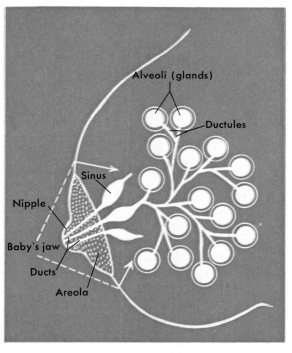

Proper method of compressing the sinuses to start milk flow

12|10

Fertilization to implantation

This plate shows the meiotic divisions and first few cleavages of the fertilized egg to the blastocyst stage. The blastocyst is a hollow ball of cells consisting of an outer layer of cells and an inner cell mass. Formation of the blastocyst occurs within 10 days of fertilization and completes the implantation in the uterine lining. The cells of the blastocyst continue to divide and form a structure with two cavities. The amniotic cavity becomes a fluid-filled, shock-absorbing sac in which the embryo floats. The yolk sac is formed by the cells of the lower cavity; it is a small vesicle attached to the belly of the embryo that breaks away during the second month of gestation. The chorion develops into an important fetal membrane that conducts exchange of nutrients between the mother and the fetus.

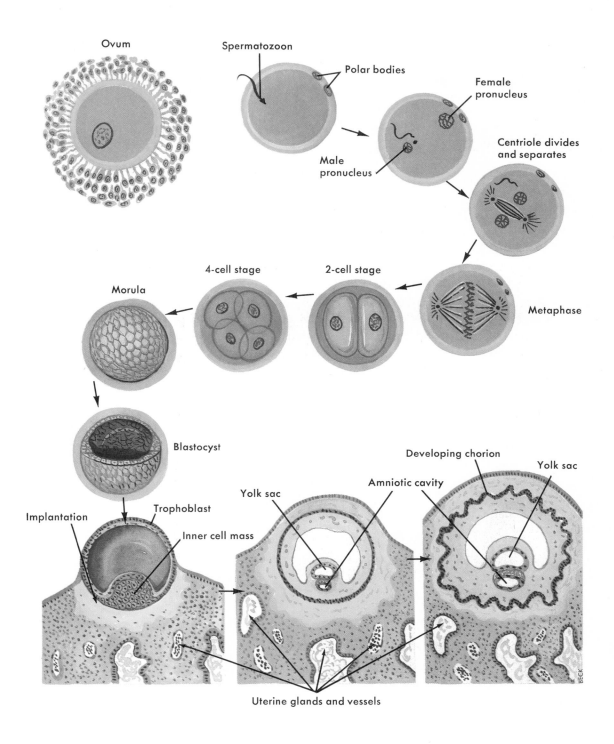

Ovum

Spermatozoon

Polar bodies

Female pronucleus

Male pronucleus

Centriole divides and separates

Metaphase

2-cell stage

4-cell stage

Morula

Blastocyst

Yolk sac

Developing chorion

Yolk sac

Amniotic cavity

Implantation

Trophoblast

Inner cell mass

Uterine glands and vessels

BECK

12|11

Development of the embryo

This illustration depicts the development of the embryo from the yolk sac stage to the fourth month of gestation. The placenta develops, taking over hormone production from the ovarian corpus luteum and providing the embryo with nutrition and oxygenation. The amnion produces amniotic fluid, which distributes any external pressure to the mother's abdomen and thus cushions the embryo. The yolk sac is separated from the amniotic cavity by the embryonic disk, which initially consists of two cell layers—the ectoderm and entoderm. The mesoderm forms between these two layers by the third week of gestation. These germ layers remain after the yolk sac has dropped off, and each forms the basis for definite fetal structures, such as skin, muscles, and nervous system. By the fifth week the heart is beating; the 8-mm (3/10-inch) embryo begins showing rapid development of all organ systems. An identifiably human form appears after 2 months, and the sex can be readily distinguished after another month. The organ systems are formed and functioning after 4 months; development then is primarily one of growth until term.

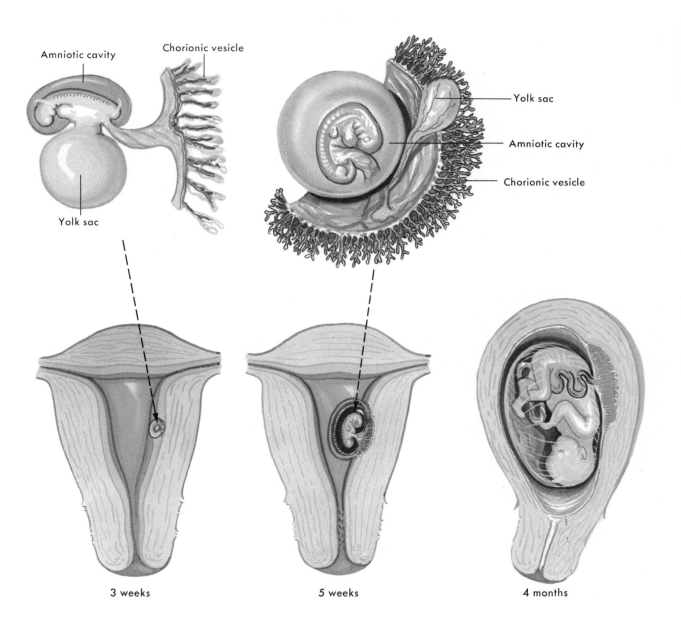

Amniotic cavity

Chorionic vesicle

Yolk sac

Yolk sac

Amniotic cavity

Chorionic vesicle

3 weeks

5 weeks

4 months

12|12

Involution and puerperium

After a pregnancy the enlarged uterus gradually undergoes a process of involution, or shrinkage, returning to its position as a pelvic organ from the abdominal position it occupied during pregnancy. Involution is accompanied by a decrease in vaginal discharge, a decrease in breast size and mass, and a resumption of the normal menstrual cycle.

The term puerperium refers to a 6-week period between the termination of labor and delivery and the return of the reproductive tract to a normal state. This includes both the preparation of glands of the breast for lactation, involution of the uterus and other retrogressive genital changes, and physiological adaptation to the nonpregnant state in many organ systems. Immediately following the delivery after the placenta is expelled, the muscular wall of the uterus (myometrium) contracts sharply and the uterus becomes an almost solid mass of tissue. The uterus at this stage of involution measures about 15 cm (6 inches) long and 12 cm (4⅘ inches) broad and 10 cm (4 inches) thick. It weighs about 1000 g (2¼ pounds).

Initially following delivery, the bladder fills and the uterus rises slightly. In the next 2 days the dome of the uterus sinks below the level of the navel, and gradually over the next 10 to 14 days, a steady decrease occurs in all its diameters. By the sixth to eighth week it has returned to normal size and location, weighing about 60 g (2 ounces). The shrinkage is slower in women who do not breast-feed.

During this 6-week period the placental site is gradually changing. By a process of exfoliation (shedding of cells) the placental site disappears without leaving a scar. Other puerperal changes include marked diuresis, leukocytosis, and cardiovascular changes resulting from a weight loss during the puerperium of about 2250 g (5 pounds) of fluid. Another striking phenomenon of the puerperium is the appearance of lochia, a bloody discharge that may last for several days, changing to a paler and finally white discharge that disappears in 3 to 6 weeks. Normal menstrual cycles become reestablished quite quickly, often by the second or third month postpartum, in the non-breast-feeding mother.

INVOLUTION

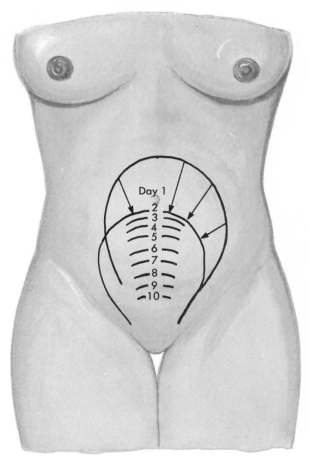

Day 1
2
3
4
5
6
7
8
9
10

UTERUS IMMEDIATELY AFTER DELIVERY

|← 12 cm (4 ¾ inches) →|

15 cm (6 inches)

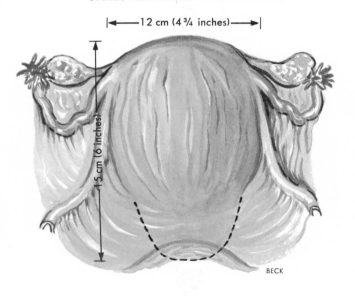

BECK

UTERUS 6 WEEKS AFTER DELIVERY

6.25 cm (2 ½ inches)

7.5 cm (3 inches)

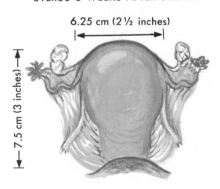

12|13

The male pelvic organs (midsagittal section)

This midsagittal view shows the various male pelvic organs that participate in urination, defecation, and reproduction. The penis is comprised mainly of the spongy corpus cavernosum and corpus spongiosum. These columns of tissue are extremely vascular; during erection muscular contractions restrict the return venous blood flow and the columns become engorged and rigid. The urethra conveys both urine and semen. Semen consists of fluid from the seminal vesicle, an alkaline fluid from the prostate gland, and mucus from the bulbourethral gland, as well as spermatozoa. The testes contain the seminiferous tubules that produce spermatozoa, which travel from testes to urethra during ejaculation (Plate 12-15).

The vas deferens can be surgically excised (vasectomy) to stop the flow of semen to the urethra, causing sterility. The testes continue to produce spermatozoa, which are merely reabsorbed into the system.

The size, shape, and location of the normal prostate gland should be especially noted in this illustration. This gland undergoes enlargement as part of the normal aging process, can become acutely inflamed, and is a common site for cancer. The prostate gland can be examined by digital palpation through the rectum, since it lies adjacent to the anterior rectal wall. As a result of excessive prostate enlargement the urethra is compressed with the result that urination becomes difficult to stop or start; frequency, dribbling, and dysuria are also symptoms.

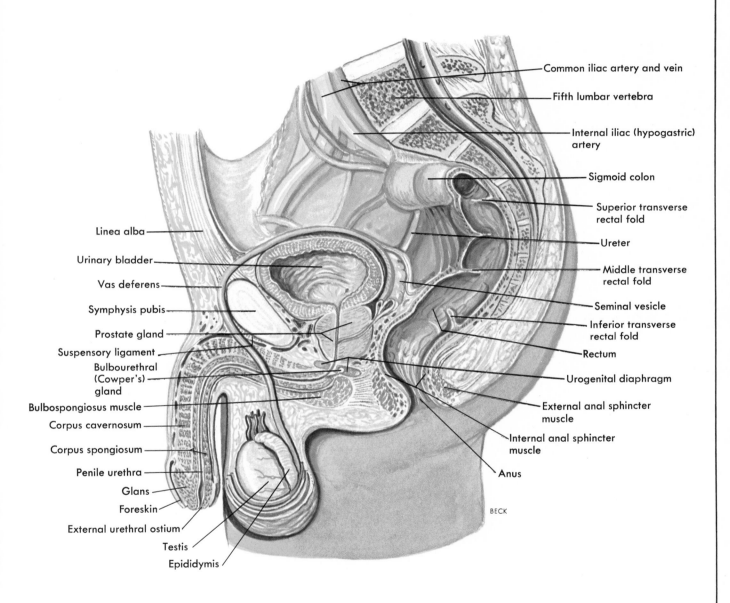

Common iliac artery and vein

Fifth lumbar vertebra

Internal iliac (hypogastric) artery

Sigmoid colon

Superior transverse rectal fold

Ureter

Middle transverse rectal fold

Seminal vesicle

Inferior transverse rectal fold

Rectum

Urogenital diaphragm

External anal sphincter muscle

Internal anal sphincter muscle

Anus

Linea alba

Urinary bladder

Vas deferens

Symphysis pubis

Prostate gland

Suspensory ligament

Bulbourethral (Cowper's) gland

Bulbospongiosus muscle

Corpus cavernosum

Corpus spongiosum

Penile urethra

Glans

Foreskin

External urethral ostium

Testis

Epididymis

BECK

12|14

Anterolateral abdominal wall and inguinal area in the male

The femoral ring is an opening in the musculature of the abdominal wall that is covered only by a thin membrane. This ring is the proximal end of the femoral canal, through which pass lymph vessels, and it is normally considered a rather weakened area in the abdominal wall. Occasionally, a segment of peritoneum and sometimes intestines can push through the femoral ring. This is often associated with straining or lifting of a heavy object, and the herniation of the intestine results in a visible bulge and often considerable pain. This type of hernia is quite susceptible to strangulation of the blood supply, leading to ischemia of the herniated segment and the symptoms of acute abdominal pain and intestinal obstruction.

Another common area for herniation is through the inguinal rings. A portion of the peritoneum and a loop in intestine can push through the inguinal canal. This form of hernia is more common in males because of a larger inguinal ring. An indirect inguinal hernia is the most common of all hernias and may be congenital or acquired. The hernia may be palpated through the scrotum and is felt as a bulge in the inguinal canal. The symptoms include pain, especially while straining or lifting, and a feeling of perineal pressure.

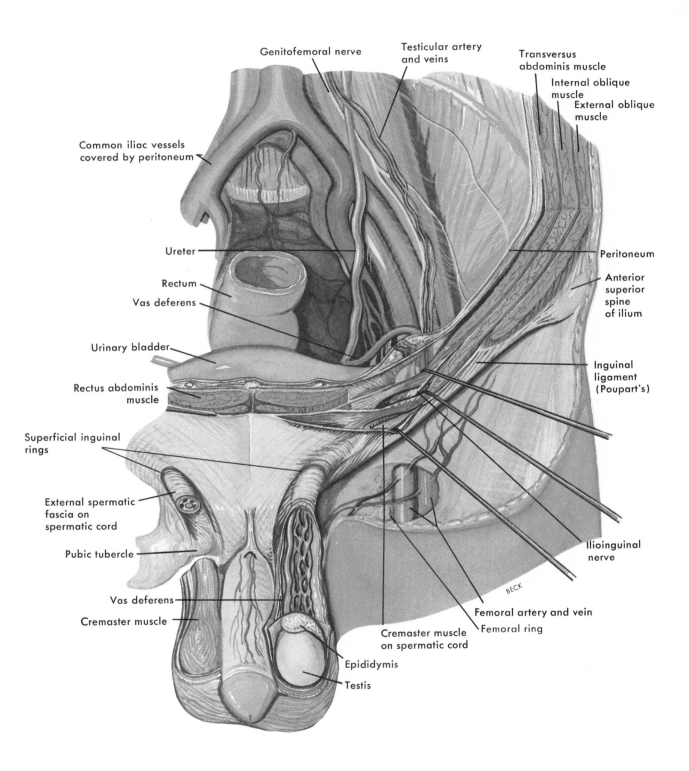

Genitofemoral nerve

Testicular artery and veins

Transversus abdominis muscle

Internal oblique muscle

External oblique muscle

Common iliac vessels covered by peritoneum

Ureter

Rectum

Vas deferens

Urinary bladder

Rectus abdominis muscle

Superficial inguinal rings

External spermatic fascia on spermatic cord

Pubic tubercle

Vas deferens

Cremaster muscle

Peritoneum

Anterior superior spine of ilium

Inguinal ligament (Poupart's)

Ilioinguinal nerve

BECK

Femoral artery and vein

Femoral ring

Cremaster muscle on spermatic cord

Epididymis

Testis

12|15

Male genital duct system

Formed during embryogenesis through the interaction of several different developing systems, the structure of the male genital duct system is quite complex.

Although spermatozoa are produced in the glandular testes, which are located outside the abdominal cavity in the scrotal sac, the actual delivery of sperm to the outside of the body involves a complicated transport system. During ejaculation sperm is transported through the following structures: testis, epididymis, vas deferens, ejaculatory duct, and urethra. The sperm is carried a considerable distance—high up into the pelvis through the vas deferens, down into the ejaculatory duct, and finally through the erect penis via the urethra. Along the way the fluid portion of the ejaculate is added to by secretions from the seminal vesicles, prostate gland, and bulbourethral glands. This fluid is alkaline, which allows for maximum motility of the sperm and neutralizes the acidity of the female vagina. The testes also produce the male androgenic hormones and thus function as endocrine glands under the stimulatory influence of hormones from the anterior pituitary gland.

The spermatozoon is a single, tiny, mobile cell consisting of four sections: head, neck, body, and tail. It is a unique cell perfectly designed for its function of travelling the comparatively enormous distance from the vagina to the fallopian tube to deliver its nuclear material to an ovum. Before fertilization can occur the sperm must be "capacitated" within the female reproductive tract, a process which involves removal of its acrosomal cap. This allows the sperm to penetrate the ovum.

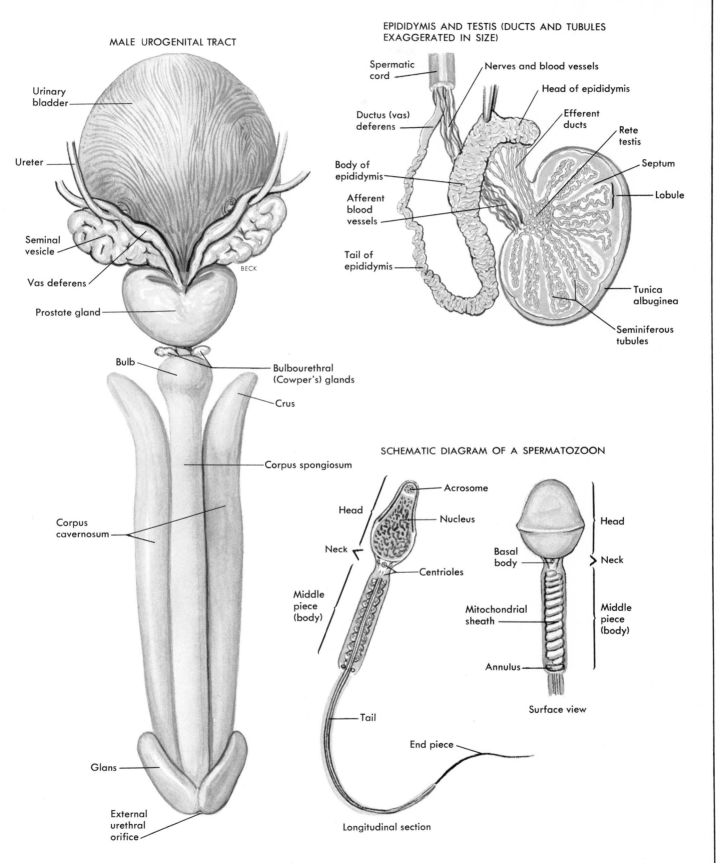

MALE UROGENITAL TRACT

Urinary bladder

Ureter

Seminal vesicle

Vas deferens

Prostate gland

BECK

Bulb

Bulbourethral (Cowper's) glands

Crus

Corpus spongiosum

Corpus cavernosum

Glans

External urethral orifice

EPIDIDYMIS AND TESTIS (DUCTS AND TUBULES EXAGGERATED IN SIZE)

Spermatic cord

Nerves and blood vessels

Head of epididymis

Ductus (vas) deferens

Efferent ducts

Rete testis

Septum

Body of epididymis

Lobule

Afferent blood vessels

Tail of epididymis

Tunica albuginea

Seminiferous tubules

SCHEMATIC DIAGRAM OF A SPERMATOZOON

Acrosome

Head

Nucleus

Neck

Centrioles

Middle piece (body)

Basal body

Head

Neck

Mitochondrial sheath

Middle piece (body)

Annulus

Tail

Surface view

End piece

Longitudinal section

265

12|16

The bladder—male and female

The bladder is a muscular organ that is capable of expansion as it fills with urine. Notice the extensive folding of the mucous membrane lining of the bladder. Smooth muscle innervated by the autonomic nervous system makes up the muscular wall. The trigone of the bladder is a triangular area formed by drawing an imaginary line between the openings of the ureters and the urethral orifice. The trigone is more broadly based in the female than the male, and the urethral opening is wider. In the male a fold of tissue, the uvula, extends down from the bladder trigone into the urethra. This folding is caused by the middle lobe of the prostate projecting forward. The prostate hypertrophies to a degree in normal aging and may project even farther into the urethral orifice. This causes urinary tract symptoms such as difficulty starting and stopping the stream, dribbling, and frequency of urination.

The female bladder's ligamentous attachments may be stretched during pregnancy, and eventually the ability of the bladder to hold urine is affected. The bladder may bulge forward, and coughing, straining, or laughing causes "stress incontinence."

The female urethra is much shorter than that of the male, and consequently there is a much greater likelihood for an ascending infection into the bladder. Urinary tract infections are much more common in females.

MALE BLADDER

Ureter

Urachus

Ureter

Peritoneum

Vas deferens

Urinary bladder

Ureteral orifice

Ureteral orifice

Trigone

Internal urethral orifice

Prostate gland

Seminal colliculus

Urogenital diaphragm

Prostatic urethra

Bulbourethral (Cowper's) gland

Bulb of penis

Corpus cavernosum

Penile urethra

FEMALE BLADDER

Urachus

Uterus (behind urinary bladder)

Uterine (fallopian) tube

Ovarian ligament

Round ligament

Urinary bladder

Ureteral orifice

Trigone

Vagina

Internal urethral orifice

Urethra

Sphincter muscle

External urethral orifice

Bulb

Crus of clitoris

Vaginal opening

Labium minus

BECK

Frenulum

12|17

The kidneys

The anatomical position of the kidneys is in the flank area, retroperitoneal, and between the twelfth thoracic and third lumbar vertebrae. The right kidney is lower than the left and may occasionally be palpated through the anterior abdominal wall. The arterial blood supply to the kidneys is through the renal arteries, which branch from the abdominal aorta. The renal veins drain deoxygenated blood from the kidney into the inferior vena cava. The kidney is illustrated in coronal section, and the calyces that drain the urine into the ureter are shown. Notice also the long ureters that carry the urine to the bladder. The ureters course downward on either side of the aorta, crossing in front of the right and left common iliac arteries before entering the bladder trigone. Normally, the ureters carry the urine downward by peristaltic contractions of their muscular walls.

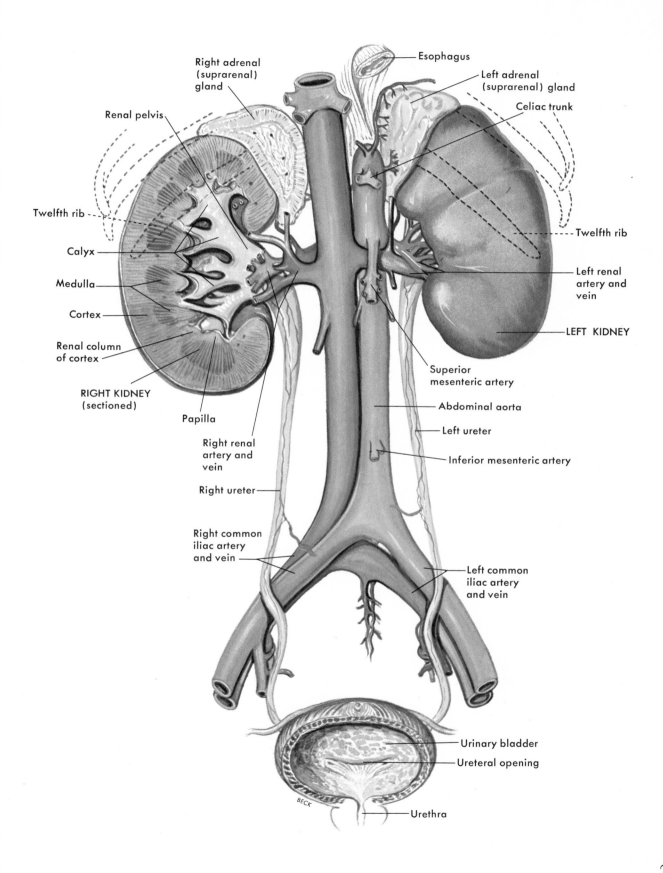

Esophagus

Right adrenal (suprarenal) gland

Left adrenal (suprarenal) gland

Celiac trunk

Renal pelvis

Twelfth rib

Twelfth rib

Calyx

Left renal artery and vein

Medulla

LEFT KIDNEY

Cortex

Renal column of cortex

Superior mesenteric artery

RIGHT KIDNEY (sectioned)

Abdominal aorta

Papilla

Left ureter

Right renal artery and vein

Inferior mesenteric artery

Right ureter

Right common iliac artery and vein

Left common iliac artery and vein

Urinary bladder

Ureteral opening

BECK

Urethra

12|18

The nephron unit

The nephron is the anatomical and physiological unit of the kidney. It consists of an epithelial tubule and a unique vasculature that permits blood to be filtered and urine to be formed. Thousands of nephrons are present in each kidney and function together to form urine at the rate of approximately 1 ml per minute.

Each nephron produces a filtrate that eventually drains through collecting ducts into the ureter, which transports urine from the kidney to the bladder. Urine is formed in the following manner. An afferent arteriole carries blood to the glomerulus, which is an extremely convoluted capillary. This blood vessel's origin is the renal artery. Filtration occurs across the glomerular capillary membrane, producing a protein and cell-free filtrate. The filtrate is collected by the cuplike Bowman's capsule. From here it drains into the system of tubules that is continuous with Bowman's capsule. The blood in the glomerulus exits via the efferent arteriole, which then forms a second capillary system. This peritubular capillary system is wrapped around the tubular loops of the nephron and eventually drains into veins, which carry blood away from the kidney. The peritubular capillaries provide a route by which substances within the tubular filtrate can be reabsorbed into the bloodstream and substances can be secreted from the blood into the tubular filtrate.

Urine is formed through a process of reabsorption of tubular filtrate substances needed by the body, a process that occurs at certain places along the nephron's tubules. Waste substances that the body excretes are secreted from the blood into the tubular filtrate as it passes through the tubules on its way to the collecting duct.

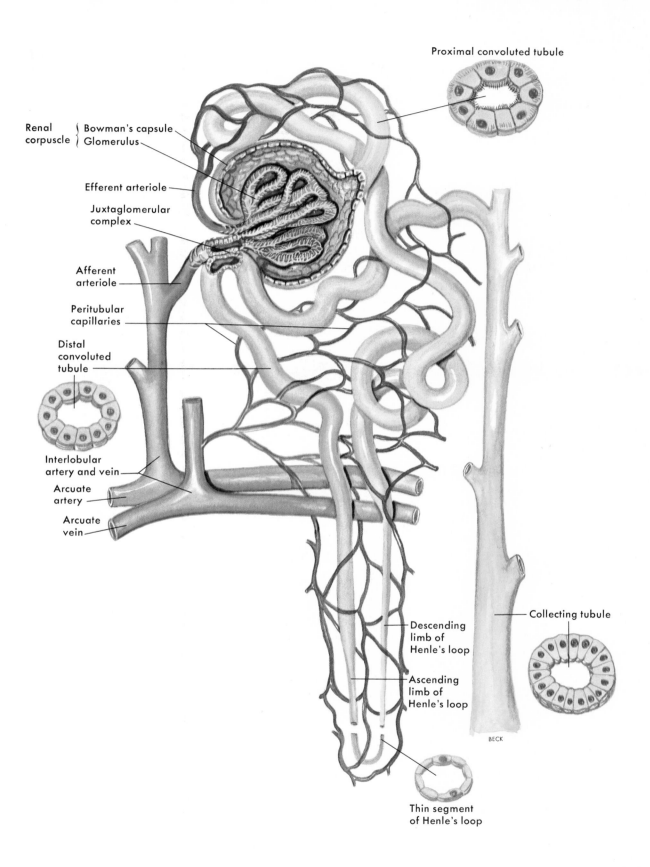

Proximal convoluted tubule

Renal corpuscle { Bowman's capsule Glomerulus

Efferent arteriole

Juxtaglomerular complex

Afferent arteriole

Peritubular capillaries

Distal convoluted tubule

Interlobular artery and vein

Arcuate artery

Arcuate vein

Descending limb of Henle's loop

Ascending limb of Henle's loop

Collecting tubule

Thin segment of Henle's loop

BECK

13 | Common surgical positions

Basic supine, Trendelenburg's, reverse Trendelenburg's, and
lithotomy positions
Modified Fowler's and sitting, basic prone, and jackknife
(Kraske's) positions
Knee-chest position and lateral positions for chest and kidney
procedures
Sims's, right kidney, and spinal tap positions

13|1

Basic supine, Trendelenburg's, reverse Trendelenburg's, and lithotomy positions

Basic supine position. The patient lies on his back with the head and spine anatomically aligned. Arms are at the side; legs are extended with feet slightly separated. All vulnerable pressure points are protected: occiput, scapulas, olecranons, sacrum, ischial tuberosities, and heels.
Indications: any anterior surgical approach.

Trendelenburg's position. The table is tilted at an angle so that the patient's head is lower than his legs. The sagittal plane is at right angles to the operating table. The knee strap is above the knees, and shoulder braces prevent sliding.
Indications: any anterior approach that is facilitated by the upward gravitation of the abdominal viscera; frequently used for suprapubic and colonic procedures. Pressure areas at the knee flexure should be avoided.

Reverse Trendelenburg's position. The entire table is tilted at a 45-degree angle, lowering the patient's feet and raising his head.
Indications: any anterior surgical approach that is facilitated by the downward gravitation of the abdominal viscera; frequently used for radical neck dissection, eye procedures, and gallbladder resection.

Lithotomy position. The patient's head and trunk are in the dorsal position, with legs elevated, abducted, and supported by stirrups. Lower portion of the table is fully lowered. The patient's hips are placed in line with the break in the table.
Indications: endoscopic examinations; rectal, vaginal, and perineal procedures.

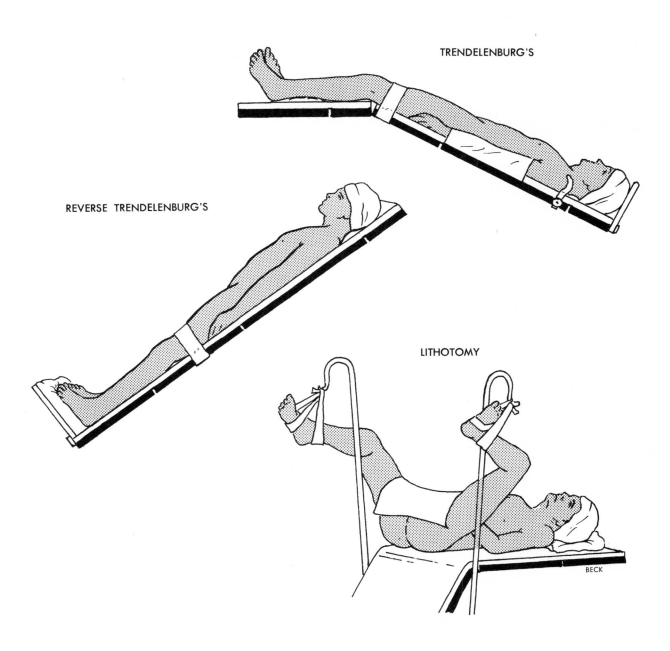

BASIC SUPINE

TRENDELENBURG'S

REVERSE TRENDELENBURG'S

LITHOTOMY

BECK

Modified Fowler's and sitting, basic prone, and jackknife (Kraske's) positions

Modified Fowler's and sitting position. The backrest is elevated to about 45 degrees; the patient's knees are flexed over the break in the table. The footboard supports the feet perpendicular to the legs; the knee straps are above the knees. A cranial headrest may be required for certain procedures. Indications: E.N.T. (ear, nose, throat) examinations, plastic repair (rhinoplasty, maxillofacial repair), tonsillectomy, adenoidectomy, laryngoscopy, bronchoscopy.

Basic prone position. The patient is lying face downward; arms are at his sides or on armboards. Leg straps are below the knees. Direct pressure on the female patient's breasts should be minimized. Special attention should be given to the patient's respiratory function, since the prone position causes a reduction of vital capacity. Chest rolls may be used to elevate the thorax. Pressure at bony prominences should be prevented.

Jackknife, or Kraske's, position. The patient's hips are positioned over the break in the table; table is flexed at a 90-degree angle. Both arms are on armboards; leg straps are below the knees. Adhesive straps may be applied to the buttocks and fastened to the sides of the table. Feet and toes should have soft support. If angle of lower portion of table is increased beyond 45 degrees, foot braces should be added.
Indications: rectal surgery; perineal and endoscopic procedures.

MODIFIED FOWLER'S AND SITTING

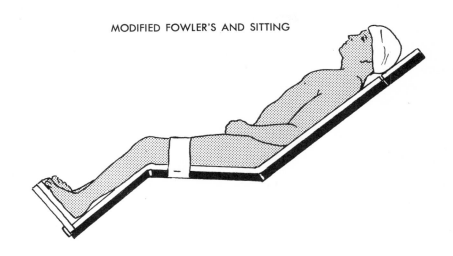

BASIC PRONE

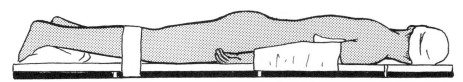

JACKKNIFE, OR KRASKE'S

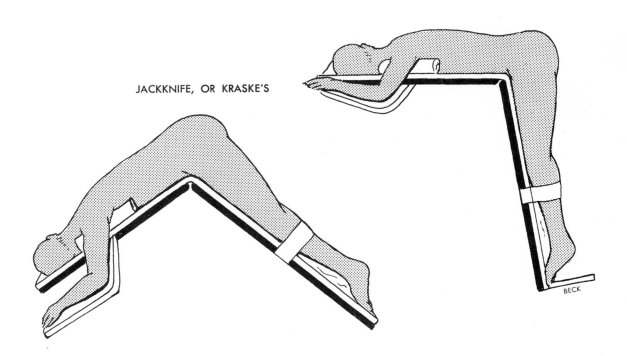

BECK

Knee-chest position and lateral positions for chest and kidney procedures

Knee-chest position. The patient's arms are extended and the elbows flexed; hands are pronated on the table superior to the head. The leg-thigh angle is adjusted as required.
Indications: for any procedure that is facilitated by enhancing the gravitational effect on the sigmoid flexure (culdoscopy, proctoscopy, sigmoidoscopy).

Lateral position for chest procedures. The patient is positioned on the unaffected side; his hips and shoulders are aligned. The lower arm is positioned in front of him on an armboard, and the upper arm is positioned over the table to draw the scapula superior to the operating site. The lower leg is flexed. A pad is placed between the patient's legs to prevent direct contact between the skin surfaces. A body strap or adhesive strip is placed over the hips.

Lateral position for kidney procedures. The patient's arms are on boards away from the body. Kidney rests are used to stabilize and maintain the position. A pad is placed between the patient's legs, and a body strap or adhesive strip is placed over the hips.

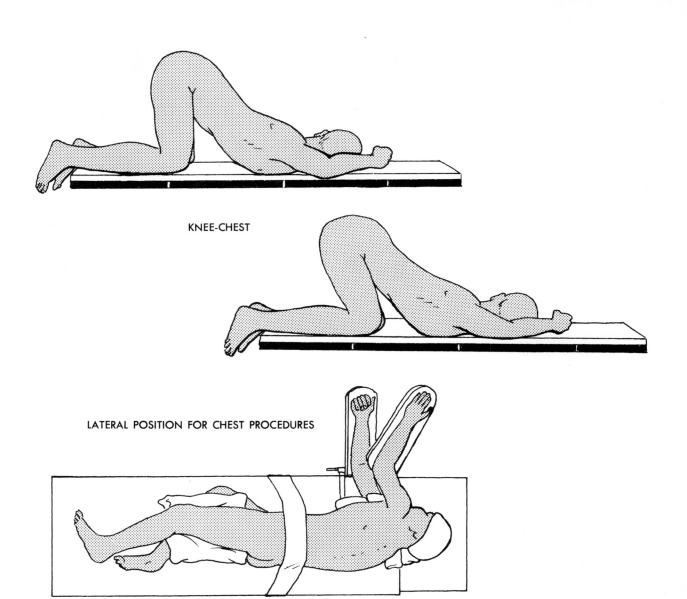

KNEE-CHEST

LATERAL POSITION FOR CHEST PROCEDURES

LATERAL POSITION FOR KIDNEY PROCEDURES

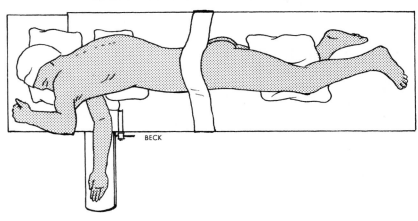

BECK

13|4

Sims's, right kidney, and spinal tap positions

Sims's position. The patient's left side and buttocks are positioned at the edge of the table. The left arm is behind the patient, the right arm in front. The left leg may be straight or slightly flexed. The right knee is flexed over the left. The lower leg is supported on the table. A pad is placed between the patient's legs.
Indications: for some perineal surgery.

Right kidney position. The patient is in a lateral position with the kidney region over the break in the table. The patient's side is horizontal from shoulder to hip. A sandbag or kidney elevator is placed at the break for hyperextending the operative area.

Spinal tap position. The patient is in a lateral position with both legs flexed, spine arched, and head on chest. Support is given at the head and hips.

SIMS'S

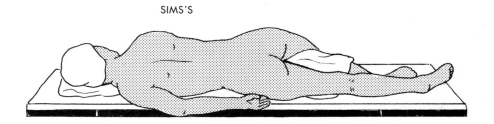

RIGHT KIDNEY

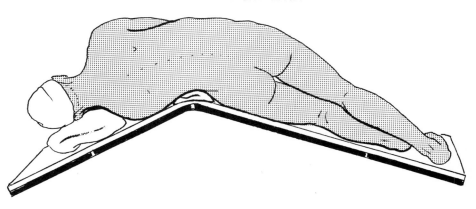

SPINAL TAP

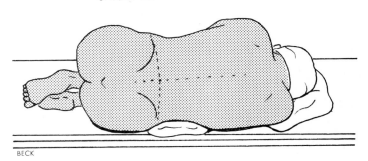

BECK

Index